TACTICS OF SCIENTIFIC RESEARCH

TACTICS OF

SCIENTIFIC RESEARCH

Evaluating Experimental Data in Psychology

MURRAY SIDMAN

Authors Cooperative, Inc., Publishers
BOSTON

Authors Cooperative, Inc.

Reprinted 1988

Library of Congress Catalog Card Number: 60-13278

MANUFACTURED IN THE UNITED STATES OF AMERICA

Preface

ALTHOUGH THIS BOOK IS NOT, in the usual sense, a textbook, I offer it to the student; in particular, to the experimental psychology student. In it I have gathered together some of the methodological problems he will face in evaluating his own and others' data. Evaluation will remain an ever-present concern to the student throughout his career. He will find it continually necessary to monitor his own standards of adequacy and excellence. Furthermore, to the extent that science is cumulative and integrative, his ability to evaluate and thus to *appreciate* the data of other investigators will have an important bearing upon the value of his own contribution.

Preface

The procedures employed in evaluating experimental data cannot properly be described without recourse to specific cases, and even to case histories; for evaluation is an empirical, not a philosophical, problem. It can be separated neither from the data themselves nor from the techniques that made the data possible. I have found it necessary, therefore, in many instances to make fairly detailed presentations of particular data, of experimental procedures, and of technical problem areas. The examples I have selected come either from my own experience or from areas close to my own competences. I hope the reader will not infer that I therefore consider these to be the only, or even the best, sources that are available. Divorced from experience, evaluative exercises would lack their most essential ingredient.

During the past thirty years experimental psychology has developed its problem areas and its technical requirements to a level demanding a high degree of methodological competence of its practitioners. The kinds of problems that I discuss in this book can no longer be considered the province solely of the advanced investigator. The beginning student, if he is to meet the challenge of his subject matter with the respect that challenge both demands and deserves, must take yesterday's advanced problems as his lesson for today. What was formerly out on the frontiers is now basic.

The conception of experimental methodology that I advance here is neither revolutionary nor new. But I must caution the student not to expect a set of rules of experimental procedure, to be memorized in classic textbook fashion. The pursuit of science is an intensely personal affair. Experimenters cannot always tell us how or why they do what they do, and the fact that their conclusions are sound so much of the time remains a puzzle even to the many philosophers, logicians, and scientists who have devoted a major portion of their time and effort to this problem. I do not claim to be either a systematizer or even a classifier of the rules of experimental practice. Nor do I claim to be a spokesman for any unified group. Even those who find their activities most accurately described here would feel uncomfortably restricted if they had to proceed solely as I have outlined. Neither the practice of experimentation nor the evaluation of its products can be bounded by any specific rules—a qualification that lends a certain note of irony to any book on experimental methodology.

There are many individuals who have contributed to the making of this book. My debt to B. F. Skinner will be evident to the reader, but I am pleased to acknowledge it specifically at this point. Many portions of the book have profited from my stimulating association, personal and professional, with such men as Charles B. Ferster, Joseph V. Brady, David McK. Rioch, Richard J. Herrnstein, Arthur J. Bachrach, and Richard L. Sidman. The latter two also made significant contributions through their comments on early versions of the manuscript. Special thanks are owed to Martha Crossen, who edited the manuscript with a degree of affection and competence such that only the author, who saw the book both before and after, can really appreciate. And I owe profound gratitude to Lillian Howell and Katherine Moyes, whose devotion and labor led to the production of a readable manuscript.

None of the above can in any way be held responsible for the contents of this book. There are two, however, of whom I cannot say this. Fred S. Keller and William N. Schoenfeld were my teachers, in the best sense of that word, and they are responsible for everything I have written here, even where they disagree. I can only hope that they will be pleased to accept the responsibility, for it is to them that I dedicate the book.

MURRAY SIDMAN

Contents

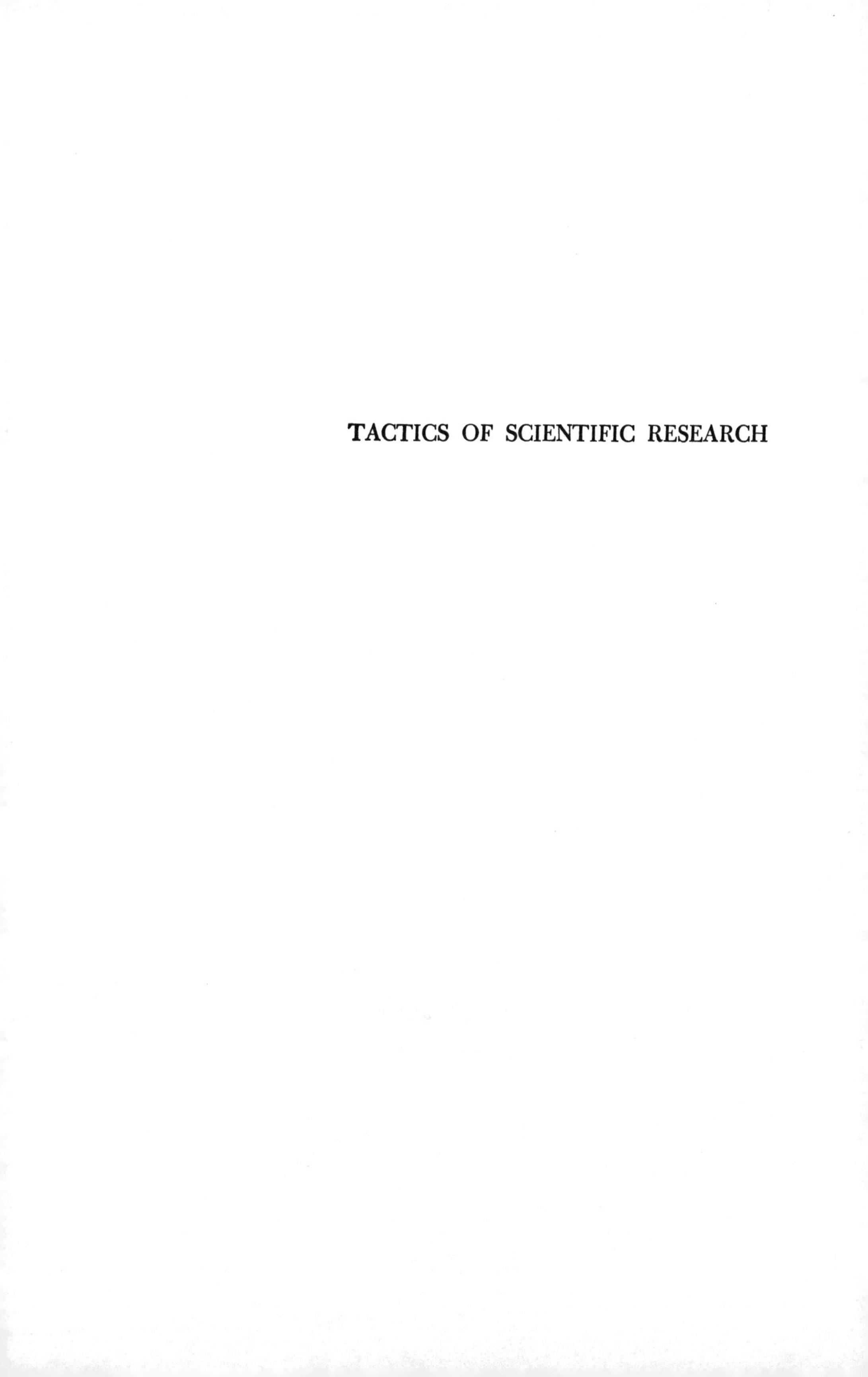

TACTICS OF SCIENTIFIC RESEARCH

Part I

Guideposts for Evaluation

THERE ARE THREE QUESTIONS of paramount concern in evaluating experimental findings: (*a*) the scientific importance of the data; (*b*) their reliability; and (*c*) their generality. These considerations are by no means independent of each other, but for the sake of convenience I shall treat them here as though they were separable.

Specialized though they may seem to the outsider, most sciences cover broad territories. Few scientists are familiar with all facets even of their own particular area of research. Most of us have neither the time, the energy, nor the intellectual scope to permit free range to all our interests. With such limitations in mind, it must be recognized that we each have, and are entitled to, our own prejudices as to the importance of particular data.

It is necessary, therefore, to be wary about using the presumed importance of data as a criterion for evaluating them. Science, like fashion, has its fads and cycles. A discovery that lies outside the current stream of interest may be unrecognized and eventually forgotten, perhaps to be rediscovered at some later date. On the other side of the coin, we often find experiments acclaimed as significant because they resolve a problem of great contemporary concern, but of little lasting interest. It is characteristic of science that we are seldom able to predict its future course of development. Many of the exciting issues of today will be forgotten tomorrow as the stream of scientific progress shifts into new channels.

That is not to say that today's experiments are worthless. At their best they will themselves determine the new directions; at their worst they will prove fruitless. But many will serve the function of clearing away the dead wood of pseudo-problems, minor controversies, and methodological fallacies that encumber every stage of scientific advance. It is never easy to determine whether contemporary enthusiasm (or apathy) represents a sound judgment. That verdict will develop concurrently with the particular science.

Chapter 1

The Scientific Importance of Experimental Data

WHEN EVALUATING the *reliability* and *generality* of data, it is often important to know the aims of the experimenter. When evaluating the *importance* of experimental results, however, science has a trick of disregarding the experimenter's rationale and finding a more appropriate context for the data than the one he proposed. Problems arise, however, when scientists make value judgments about the reasons for performing experiments and then use such judgments as a basis for accepting or rejecting the data. Good data are always separable, with respect to their scientific importance, from the purposes for which they were obtained. There are many reasons for the making of experiments. All of them have influenced and all continue to influence experimenters. All of them are legitimate.

WHY PERFORM EXPERIMENTS?

It is probably not possible to list all the purposes of experiments. I shall confine myself, therefore, to a discussion of some of the more common reasons that are advanced for the making of experiments. The order in which they are presented implies no priority. For each investigator his own reasons are the most appropriate.

Experiments performed to evaluate hypotheses. Philosophies of science which hold hypothesis testing to be an essential step in experimental procedure have been frequently and ably expounded, and require no further elaboration here. In psychology, the hypothesis-testing school of experimentation is undoubtedly dominant today. Many of those who organize their research in this manner have made significant contributions. But I caution the student not to fall into the error of insisting that all experimentation *must* derive from the testing of hypotheses. For this position can also indicate an inability to separate data from the author's purpose in collecting the data. Psychologists must recognize, as do other scientists, that advances in knowledge come from many unexpected quarters. A man may have a guess about nature, and the proof or disproof of his guess may indeed mark an important contribution. On the other hand, as Skinner has noted, "There are doubtless many men whose curiosity about nature is less than their curiosity about the accuracy of their guesses . . ." (81, p. 44). Such experimental activities can result in the piling up of trivia upon trivia.

Hypotheses may be formulated at many levels. Although the *psychology* of scientific hypothesizing is not very advanced, the *philosophy* of theory construction is an active field. Most experimental psychology students will be exposed to a course in this area and I need not go deeply into the topic. But let me describe two extreme examples in order to make some points relevant to the evaluation of data.

First, let us take the type of hypothesis that is so trivial as hardly to be called a hypothesis at all. For example, I once set up an experimental procedure to determine whether a stimulus which was followed by unavoidable shock would alter the probability of occurrence of ongoing avoidance behavior. A monkey had been trained to press a lever, thereby postponing the occurrence of brief electric shocks. After the monkey's lever pressing had reached a stable frequency, an auditory stimulus (in this case, a buzzer) was occasionally turned on for five minutes, and at the termination of the stimulus, an *unavoidable* electric shock was administered to the animal. (In other words, the environment had been changed: although the monkey could still avoid most of the shocks by pressing the lever, there were now periods at the end of which his lever-pressing activity would no longer serve the same function. Whenever the buzzer had sounded for five minutes, the monkey received an *unavoidable* shock.)

A colleague asked me what I expected would happen to the ongoing avoidance behavior as a result of the pairing of stimulus and unavoidable shock. After some consideration I replied that I could not conceive of there being no change in the behavior, because the experimental operation represented a radical alteration of the subject's environment. We did not usually find organisms unresponsive to this kind of manipulation. Also, I could not conceive that the probability of the avoidance response would decline, because if such a reaction were to occur under analogous conditions outside the laboratory the species would never have survived to become subjects for my experiments. This left only one more possibility. The probability of the behavior would have to increase.

The subsequent confirmation of my hypothesis gave me no satisfaction. Nor would many other psychologists have greeted my experiment as a theoretical triumph. The reasoning was obviously unsound. Although the subject's environment was radically altered, the effects might have shown up elsewhere than in the measures I employed. Also, it is not uncommon to find subjects in the laboratory behaving in a less than optimally adaptive fashion. And, finally, the effect did not have to be *either* an increase or decrease in probability, but could have been some complex cyclical process that included both.

Fortunately, I had performed the experiment without any prior commitment to this hypothesis. I was able, therefore, to follow up the phenomenon for its own sake and eventually to arrive at a relatively firm explanation of the findings. There is, of course, nothing intrinsic to hypothesis testing which will prevent data from being followed up. But when the chain of reasoning between hypothesis and data is weak, the follow-up may bear no real relation to the original findings.

The hypotheses tested by psychologists are not always so naive and simple-minded as the one cited above. They sometimes consist of an elaborate series of assumptions concerning both behavior and the techniques for measuring behavior. In some cases, the argument is reduced to a mathematical statement. The motivation for this kind of theorizing cannot be criticized. Those who practice their science in this way are trying to place psychology on an equal footing with other highly developed theoretical sciences. Whether this is possible, or even reasonable, is not my concern at this point, for its discussion would carry us far afield.

Experiments that test the adequacy of mathematical models and other types of deductive theory currently carry great prestige, and their importance is generally taken for granted. I wish to point out, however, that the importance of data is not affected by the sophistication of the hypotheses that may have generated the experiments. With the exception of those who *define* the importance of data in terms of their amenability to theoretical integration, there are few psychologists who would deny that the most interesting behavioral phenomena have not even been touched by the most rigorous present-day theories. The investigator is thus faced with a dilemma. Shall he follow the lead of sophisticated theoreticians and design experiments whose data may be of interest only in reference to the theory in question? Or shall he perform experiments that he believes will yield data of general interest, irrespective of whether current theories have been designed to handle them? The answer to such a question cannot be legislated. The student, however, should be aware that there is a question, and he should answer it specifically for himself, keeping in mind the scientific truism that good data are notoriously fickle. They change their allegiance from theory to theory, and even maintain their importance in the presence of no theory at all.

Experiments performed to indulge the investigator's curiosity about nature. At some time or other, everybody asks the questions, "Why? What? How?" The child asks, "Where do babies come from?" Parents ask, "Why does he behave like that?" Samuel Johnson remarked that curiosity is one of the permanent and certain characteristics of a vigorous intellect. The scientist might be defined as a person whose indulgence of his curiosity is also the means by which he earns his living.

What are the consequences of placing one's curiosity under the discipline of science? There are differences between everyday and scientific curiosity. A child, for example, notices a large number of bees flying about the rose garden. He asks his father, "Why are all those bees there?" The father replies, "They are gathering pollen from the roses so that they can make honey from it."

The nonscientific child will stop here, his curiosity satisfied. The boy with a slightly greater scientific potential is likely to continue his questioning. "What is pollen? How do they make honey out of it? Isn't there any pollen in grass? Why do roses have pollen?" If the father hasn't yet lost patience, the budding scientist will come out with a real back-breaker: "How do you know?" Here then, is the first distinction between scientific and everyday curiosity. Scientific curiosity is concerned with the methods by which the answers to its questions are obtained. The curiosity is not satisfied simply by a demonstration that flowers are always present when bees congregate, and that flowers bear pollen. Perhaps the bees are attracted by certain colors. Or perhaps the shape of the petals is important. Perhaps the pollen that sticks to the bees' legs is only incidental to their search for some substance that makes them attractive to bees of the opposite sex. These possibilities can be resolved only by controlled observation and experiment.

Another difference between everyday and scientific curiosity lies in the consequences that follow upon the answers to the initial questions. Everyday curiosity will subside once a direct answer to its first question is obtained. Scientific curiosity, on the other hand, is characterized by a chain reaction. Instead of quieting it, the answer to a question only arouses scientific curiosity further. It has been said that any experiment worth its salt will raise more questions than it answers. The investigator who is really curious about nature will not be satisfied to demonstrate the simple relationship between bees, flowers, and pollen. He will go on to ask other questions: How do the bees find their way to the flowers and then back to their hives? Does the pollen from different types of flowers produce different kinds of honey? What function does the pollen serve for the flower itself? What happens to the bees in the winter when there are no flowers? And in the course of answering these questions, the investigator will make observations which may, in turn, lead to information about the social structure of the bee colony, the language of bees, the reproductive cycles of flowers, and eventually to broader ecological problems of the interactions among the seemingly separate worlds of plants, insects, and people. At the end of a lifetime of work, the scientist may well look back upon his career not only with pride but with astonishment at the results of innocent inquiries begun many years before.

Curiosity may, of course, be guided by hypothesis and by theory, but the history of science reveals many discoveries that resulted from the inquiry, "I wonder what will happen if. . . ." Great experiments have been performed without the experimenter having the slightest inkling as to the probable results. In testing a hypothesis in which he believes, a scientist is surprised only if the data *do not* support his guess. A scientist hostile to a hypothesis is surprised only if it *does* receive support from the data. When an investigator performs an experiment to test *no* hypothesis, his life is full of surprises.

There is a distinction to be made here between having a hypothesis and performing an experiment to test that hypothesis. We often make guesses about the outcome of our experiments—even those who feel themselves to be bedrock empiricists. But often the experiment may be planned and begun before the guess is formulated. The experiment is performed for other reasons than to test the adequacy of the hypothesis. Nor will the outcome of the experiment be judged a success or failure in terms of its agreement or disagreement with the prediction. This point emphasizes an important property of experiments that are designed to answer the "I wonder what will happen if . . ." type of question. Such experiments, if they meet adequate criteria of reliability and generality, *never produce negative results.* Data can be negative only in terms of a prediction. When one simply asks a question of nature, the answer is always positive. Even an experimental manipulation that produces no change in the dependent variable can provide useful and often important information.

Scientific psychology is in a developmental stage in which negative experimental results should be the exception rather than the rule. Behavior is a rich subject-matter, and thus far we have observed only a small sample in the laboratory. The variables of which behavior is a function have hardly begun to be explored. It is a worthwhile aim to strive for an eventual theoretical integration of the facts of behavior. But so far we have not even approached agreement as to what the significant data are that such a theory must handle. One thing is certain. All the significant data have not yet turned up in the laboratory. There is a wealth of behavioral phenomena still to be brought under experimental control for more precise study and analysis. That is, perhaps, why negative results seem wasteful.

It is precisely because behavior is such a wide open field that B. F. Skinner paid his respects to apparatus failures as a source of new discoveries (85). With a subject matter so complex, so sensitive to environmental change, and so little explored, it is possible for the apparatus to perform an experiment on its own. In my own laboratory, for example, an experiment on avoidance behavior was in progress in which an animal was scheduled to receive only 20 per cent of all the shocks that became due when it failed to make the avoidance response in time. A relay failure in the automatic programing circuit altered the procedure one day in such a way that every fifth shock was delivered *regardless* of whether or not the animal had made an avoidance response. The apparatus failure was discovered when the animal's usually stable rate of lever pressing began to accelerate, and continued to increase throughout the experimental period. The increased rate of avoidance responding in the face of unavoidable shocks was so unexpected that a new research program was immediately launched, a program which has been productive for three years and is still continuing.

But it takes a human experimenter to evaluate the results of a relay breakdown, just as it does when everything functions smoothly. And there is nothing to guarantee that a scientist will appreciate an accidental discovery. Unless the experimenter's attitude is one of interest in anything that turns up, he is likely to overlook a chance finding. When a hypothesis-bound investigator, after carefully designing his apparatus and experimental procedure to answer a specific question, finds that his equipment has broken down in the midst of the investigation, he is likely to consider the experiment a failure. He may shed a few tears of frustration, but will probably roll up his sleeves, rebuild the apparatus, and start all over again, knowing that science is made by martyrs like himself. On the other hand, the simple-minded curiosity tester is likely to look closely at the data produced by the apparatus breakdown. Since he has little personal investment in his own guesswork, he may find the accidental experiment more interesting than the one he started to do—and without tears he is off on a new track.

Here, perhaps, is the greatest virtue of the curiosity-testing school of experimentation. Those who have no hypothesis or who hold their hypotheses lightly are likely to be alert to the accidental discovery of new phenomena. The student should not underrate the role of accident in scientific progress. Important discoveries have been made in the course of investigations designed for another purpose. That distinguished and productive physiologist, Walter Cannon, coined the by now well-known word "serendipity" to refer to such accidental discoveries (21).

In this connection, the student may find some valuable lessons in the behind-the-scenes story of a series of experiments that came to be known in the Walter Reed laboratories as the "ulcer project." It started with some work that was being carried out in the behavior laboratories by Joseph Brady. Some long-term experiments were being run in which monkeys were exposed to a wide variety of conditioning procedures, including a number of different food-reinforcement, shock-avoidance, punishment, and brain-stimulation schedules and several combinations of each of these.* An annoying

* Wishing not to interrupt the major discourse, I have introduced some technical terms in the early chapters without adequate definition. Although I do not believe that precise definition of all these terms is necessary for an understanding of the major points at this stage, some readers may justifiably

feature of these experiments was the unusually large number of deaths that occurred among the subjects. The experimenters might have continued to treat the attrition rate simply as an unavoidable evil were it not for a fortunate accident. This was the assignment of R. W. Porter to the Walter Reed laboratories during his mandatory period of military service. Porter had done a considerable amount of research on ulcers and, when he heard about the attrition rate among Brady's subjects, asked if he could perform a postmortem examination upon the next few animals that became available. As Brady tells the story, "During the next few months, Porter would occasionally appear in my office bearing in his rubber-gloved hands a piece of freshly excised monkey gut. Somewhere in the tissue there would be a clean round hole which, as Porter carefully explained, was a perforated ulcer. 'Too bad,' I would murmur, and Porter would leave without saying anything more. Eventually, it began to get through to me that Porter was carrying a message in his hands. That message finally burst out in neon lights when he remarked that out of several hundred monkeys which he had had occasion to examine in the past, not one had shown any sign of a normally occurring ulcer."

Because of the raw coincidence of a high mortality rate among his subjects and the wholly unrelated presence of a pathologist who was interested in ulcers, the course of Brady's research was changed. But serendipity had only just begun. The next fortunate accident was the selection of the avoidance procedure, out of all those to which the monkeys had been exposed, as the most likely candidate for further investigation. An experiment was set up in which a monkey had to press a lever to avoid shock for six-hour periods, each avoidance period alternating with six hours of rest. The alternating six-hour cycles continued around the clock, day in and day out. When the monkeys were finally sacrificed, there were the ulcers, while control animals which had received exactly the same

---

find the practice disconcerting, and for them I have prepared a terminological appendix (p. 393) which can be read independently of the rest of the book. I must caution the reader that the Appendix is not an index to the book's content, but contains only definitions, largely ostensive, of some of the technical terms I have found it convenient to use.

shocks, but without the opportunity to avoid them, showed no unusual pathology.

One might ask how the six-hours-on, six-hours-off program was selected. This schedule turned out to be nearly optimal for the production of ulcers, as was first discovered when the investigators tried to speed up the process by lengthening the avoidance periods and shortening the rest periods—thereby producing no ulcers at all. Subsequent measurement by Edwin Polish of acid secretion in the stomach (via gastric fistulas) revealed that there was little or no secretion during the avoidance periods, but that copious acid secretion began about three hours after the end of a six-hour avoidance cycle. Another fortunate accident. It resulted directly from the fact that the initial experiments had to be carried out in Dr. Porter's office, because of space limitations. By programing six-hour cycles, with a rest period scheduled during the day, Dr. Porter's office could be maintained relatively free of distracting apparatus noises during his regular working hours.

To the credit of those involved in the ulcer project, they did not yield to the temptation, in reporting their work, of retrospectively forcing their procedure into the triple mold of hypothesis, test, and confirmation. This could have been done very nicely, with Polish's data on gastric secretion providing the hypothesis, variations in the periodicity of the on-off cycle providing the test, and the appearance of ulcers only during the six-hour alternating cycle providing the confirmation. Fortunately, however, the investigators had no stake in forcing their procedure into any predetermined conception of scientific methodology, and their honestly told story can stand as an inspiration both to the student and to the philosopher of science (16).

Theoreticians sometimes tend to minimize the importance of experiments that are performed with the aim of gratifying the experimenter's curiosity. They hold that experiments without a theoretical orientation lead, not to a systematic body of knowledge of the sort that science seeks to achieve, but only to the haphazard collection of unrelated facts. This, if true, would be a serious criticism. Science should not and does not consist of the simple cataloguing of facts and miscellaneous bits of information. Experimental observations must be brought into some kind of order before they can be said to contribute to a science of behavior.

The Scientific Importance of Experimental Data

What constitutes an orderly arrangement of experimental findings? Is theory the only method of organizing data? Theories themselves are subject to criteria of inclusiveness, consistency, accuracy, relevance, fruitfulness, and simplicity. They are accepted or rejected according to the number and type of phenomena they encompass, their consistency of formulation when applied to various data, the correctness of their predictions, the logical adequacy of the connections between theoretical statements and data, the number of new and interesting phenomena to which they direct attention, and the number of assumptions that are required relative to the amount of data that can be handled. It is obvious, from this list, that theory construction, while it may provide intellectual stimulation, is a hazardous occupation. This is particularly true in psychology, where the phenomena are diverse, complex, and relatively unexplored. In the face of this complexity, the current trend in psychological theorizing is toward a limited coverage of a small amount of relatively simple data.

But where does this leave the experimenter, who is supposed to coordinate his data gathering with theory? He, too, is faced with the rich complexity of behavior. Is he to give up his search for experimental control over and systematic exploration of the fascinating, but theoretically untouched, behavioral phenomena which he uncovers in his laboratory and sees in the world about him?

A prominent psychological theoretician once complained to me that he had been unable to lay his hands on a certain type of data that are generated in an elementary animal conditioning experiment. He was interested in examining a polygraph-type record of lever-pressing responses taken during the period when the subject was initially learning that it would receive a food pellet each time it pressed the lever. He did not want the record "contaminated" by any deliberate shaping procedure instituted by the experimenter to hasten the learning. In order to develop his theoretical formulation, he had requested such data from a number of investigators, but they had never been made available to him. He attributed this situation to the spirit of noncooperativeness induced by the antitheoretical bias of the experimenters who used this particular conditioning technique. I had to explain to him that those who use the technique in question had long since passed to the study of more complex and interesting phenomena. It was simply a case of the theoretician being too far behind the experimenter. The bias was not so much against theory as it was against turning back the experimental clock.

What other kinds of systematization are there, beyond the mere cataloguing of data? There are two broad and diametrically opposed schools of thought concerning the most effective methods for integrating diverse data. The difference between the two schools lies, not in the presence or absence of theory, but in the way theory is brought into the picture. In one case, the theories are formulated first and then tested deductively by means of experiment. The other method is to experiment first and let the theories emerge inductively from the data.

Those who espouse data-before-theory often argue that the data are not yet sufficiently complete for a worthwhile theory to emerge. Those who prefer theory-before-data reply, "How do you know whether an adequate theory is possible until you try?" The resolution of the argument must come from an evaluation of current theories. For this I refer the student to other sources (e.g., 28). My task at present is to point out the techniques by which data may be systematized even though a tenable theory may not yet be available. Familiarity with these techniques will also provide an answer to the problem of how a nontheoretical curiosity can still be selective with respect to the specific experiments to be performed.

In practice, there are a number of techniques for organizing data outside of a theoretical framework. All of these methods, however, have the same beginning. The experimenter first selects an area of research and determines to investigate the area thoroughly. Many experimental psychologists are more accustomed to a "leapfrog" plan of experimentation. They jump from area to area, uncovering a fact here, performing a "crucial" experiment there, "opening up" a new field somewhere else. But what constitutes an area of research? This, itself, is a question that can be answered only by the data and by the degree of systematization possible. The experimenter may find that the area he has defined is too broad and that he must restrict his sphere of operations if he is to produce a systematic body of data. On the other hand—and this is the more exciting eventuality—he may find that his data reveal interconnections with phenomena that he originally considered far removed from his selected area.

Intensive cultivation of an area of research by an alert observer will inevitably bring out interrelations among the phenomena comprising that area. The interrelations will take the form of similarities among the variables that are relevant to the different phenomena. It may be discovered that apparently different types of behavior result from quantitative variations in a single determining factor. Or it may be found that a complex behavioral effect can be produced by an appropriate combination of two, or several, simpler behavioral processes. Sometimes a series of seemingly irreconcilable experiments will suddenly fall into line upon the discovery of a previously unrecognized behavioral process which is common to all and serves as the connecting link. The highest form of integration occurs when one recognizes similarities in the relevant variables between one's own experiments in a restricted field and other experiments in an apparently remote area of research.

Systematization of data by exposing the similarities among their determining variables may seem an uninspiring pursuit to the ambitious student. As a young graduate student, for example, I felt that my work had to be different, that it had to produce something new that would startle the world. Along these lines I once wrote a paper, describing some of my work, in which I emphasized how different my experiments were from anything else that had ever been done. One of my teachers, W. N. Schoenfeld, agreed that the data were very interesting. But he went on to add that I had written the paper from a peculiar point of view. I had emphasized the *differences* between my work and everyone else's. But science does not ordinarily advance that way. It is the job of science to find orderly relations among phenomena, not differences. It would have been more useful if I could have pointed out the similarities between my work and previous experiments. Although the task he set for me was not an easy one, I reached a higher level of scientific maturity when I finally accepted his advice.

For those who look forward eventually to an empirically sound and rational theory of behavior, systematization in terms of common variables—perceiving similarities—is a vital prerequisite. No theory will take account of all possible observations. As I pointed out before, psychologists have not yet been able to agree upon the behavioral phenomena that a theory—even a restricted theory—should encompass. Only the discovery of variables and processes that are common to many phenomena will resolve this problem. Before such discoveries can occur, we will have to increase our experimental control over our subject matter, and we will have to perform a large number of experiments with no other hypothesis than the simple faith that order will emerge. It is a rash scientist who will dare to predict the form that orderliness will take, or to insist that others make such predictions.

EXPERIMENTS PERFORMED TO TRY OUT A NEW METHOD OR TECHNIQUE. Experiments are often carried out to test the fruitfulness of a new technique. Sometimes the technique is developed deliberately in order to obtain information that could not be gained by standard methods; sometimes the technique is tried simply out of curiosity as to the kind of data it will yield. All experimenters recognize the desirability of technical advance. Disagreements arise, however, when judgments are made as to what constitutes an advance. It is, in fact, sometimes difficult, if not impossible, to secure agreement among psychologists as to what constitutes a technique. Since evaluation of the importance of a technique depends first of all upon its recognition as such, it is relevant to inquire into the question, "What constitutes a technique in experimental psychology?"

As in other sciences, technical developments in experimental psychology may include improvements in measuring instruments, advanced methods of recording data, sophisticated data analysis, the design of specialized apparatus to do a particular job or generalized apparatus to perform many functions, and the extension of old techniques to new areas. There is, however, one type of technical development that is uniquely appropriate to experimental psychology. This is the development of *behavioral control techniques*. I noted earlier that there are many behavioral phenomena yet to be brought under experimental control. There are also many phenomena we are able to study in the laboratory only under the most primitive conditions. Whenever, for example, we are forced to use groups of subjects or large behavior samples from an individual subject in order to smooth the data, we are demonstrating a lack of experimental control over our subject matter. Technical improvements that permit us to bring new behavior into the laboratory, or that permit refined experimental control over behavior, are among the most important contributions that we can make.

But psychologists differ with respect to the phenomena they consider important. Their evaluation, therefore, of a new behavioral control technique will be colored by the importance they attribute to the phenomenon over which the improved control is demonstrated. The student should be cautious about such judgments. Seemingly useless techniques, like seemingly esoteric data, have a way of becoming important in the most unpredictable fashions.

The development of behavioral control techniques is, strangely enough, seldom cited as one of the prime goals of psychological research. Students hear that their research should be oriented toward theoretical development, or that what we need are more data, more functional relations. Techniques are held to be secondary to these goals. But behavioral control techniques are not secondary; they are primary to both theory and data. Without behavioral control techniques a science of behavior would be impossible. Those who stress the artificiality of the boundaries between the various areas of science are at least partially correct when they refer to theory and data. One science is distinguished from another neither by theory nor by data. Different techniques of experimental control over the various subject matters provide the defining characteristics. The phenomena of interest to science are accessible only by means of a variety of technical approaches, although the resulting data may well turn out to be amenable to integration which cuts across the technically defined areas. The experimental psychologist can contribute to such integration only to the extent that he discovers and applies behavioral control techniques. We must consider our science immeasurably enriched each time someone brings another sample of behavior under precise experimental control.

The failure to recognize the importance of such demonstrations is reflected in the shallow textbook classification of behavioral control techniques. Laboratory methods of controlling behavior are often not analyzed beyond a description of the space in which the subject is placed for observation. Thus we find descriptions of mazes, runways, Skinner boxes, shuttle-boxes, Wisconsin General Test Apparatus, etc. Often there is included a brief mention of the particular response that is selected for measurement. Here the student learns about running responses, left and right turns, lever pressing, hurdle jumping, or lid-flipping. Such details are obviously important, but not as descriptions of the kinds of behavior over which psychologists have achieved experimental control. Behavioral control techniques are properly characterized not in terms of the apparatus employed but rather in terms of the variables that are manipulated and the behavioral consequences that follow upon such manipulation. The adequacy of a technique should be assessed in terms of the precision and reliability of the control it achieves.

Of general interest is the methodology Ferster and Skinner have worked out for studying the phenomenon of conditioned reinforcement. The problem is one of central importance in psychology. Reinforcement—the control of behavior through its consequences—is generally recognized to be a key variable in determining the characteristics of behavior. But it is obvious that some consequences of behavior which cannot by any stretch of the imagination be termed "natural" or "primary" reinforcers (e.g., food, water, oxygen, etc.) are responsible for the emergence and maintenance of much, if not most, of the behavior of higher organisms. This difficulty has been handled by the notion of "conditioned" reinforcement. Events paired somehow in time with primary reinforcers are held to acquire a reinforcing function. Thus a stimulus which immediately precedes the delivery of food to a hungry organism is said to acquire the ability to control behavior in much the same way as does food itself. Unfortunately, the experimental demonstration of this phenomenon has until recently been far from satisfactory. Where the effect has been achieved, it has been slight and short-lived. There have been many actual failures to demonstrate conditioned reinforcement, and when it has been demonstrated, it has been necessary to use statistical techniques in order to tease the desired effect from the data. In contrast, Ferster and Skinner have developed techniques by means of which complex patterns of behavior can be developed and maintained indefinitely by means of conditioned reinforcement (34, pp. 658-702). The phenomenon is reliably demonstrable in the individual organism and has been obtained with pigeon, rat, monkey, and chimpanzee.

Their technique is not merely the so-called Skinner box. The student who is satisfied with a specification of technique in terms of the type of enclosure in which the subject is placed, or in terms of the form of the recorded response, will never learn how to control conditioned reinforcers with the precision and rigor required to make their study profitable. Ferster and Skinner developed their technique only after long experimental analysis of reinforcement schedules and chaining.

The following is a relatively simple example: A hungry pigeon can obtain brief access to food by pecking a disk, or key, on the wall of its experimental space. However, it produces the food only with every fiftieth peck. Furthermore, it never produces food unless the key is illuminated by a green light. Sometimes the green light changes to red, but when it has been red for five minutes the pigeon can then peck the key and return it to green. We have, then, a chained sequence of events: The red light must be on for at least five minutes. After five minutes have elapsed, the next peck at the key will produce the green light. In the presence of the green light the bird can produce a small amount of food by pecking the key fifty times. After it receives the food, the key changes back to red and the cycle starts again.

The green light is a conditioned reinforcer. Its appearance is responsible for the bird's behavior of pecking the key when it is red. The green light acquires its reinforcing function by virtue of the primary reinforcement, food, which is available to the animal in its presence.

Ferster and Skinner demonstrated that a stimulus like the green key light can maintain its effectiveness as a conditioned reinforcer indefinitely if the subject can produce the terminal reinforcement (food, in this case) according to an appropriate schedule. The effectiveness of the conditioned reinforcer in maintaining prior behavior is in large part a function of the schedule according to which terminal reinforcement is produced. The chaining of responses and stimuli, leading eventually to terminal reinforcement, is central to the technique. Their refinements of the chaining procedure permitted Ferster and Skinner to replicate, with conditioned reinforcement, many of the effects of primary reinforcement, and to uncover variables unique to behavior controlled by conditioned reinforcers. The student who insists that techniques be specified in terms of the variables employed and the behavior observed will, regardless of the type of apparatus he uses, be able to bring conditioned reinforcement under experimental control.

The behavioral control techniques utilized in the study of conditioned reinforcement may be used in many ways, to generate either high or low response probabilities, cyclic response patterns, discrete responses, or long chains of behavior. Sometimes, however, a control technique is valuable because it generates a specific pattern of behavior. It may be of interest, for example, to examine behavior while it is being emitted at an extremely high frequency or at an extremely low frequency. There is a strong likelihood that behaviors differing widely with respect to their frequency of occurrence may differ also in other ways, quantitatively and/or qualitatively. Thus, techniques have been developed for maintaining behavior at rates of over 10,000 responses per hour for many hours. On the other hand, it is also possible to maintain steady response rates as low as one response every two minutes over a period of several hours, or even several days. Such a degree of experimental control constitutes a technique. It makes possible the experimental study, in the individual organism, of behavioral phenomena that have never before been subject to laboratory control.

In addition to their importance in the demonstration of behavioral principles, or in the generation and maintenance of particular types of behavior, control techniques are also valuable in the production of behavioral baselines for use in studying related phenomena. For example, there is wide interest in the relations between behavior and the action of pharmacologic agents. One important aspect of a drug is its time course of action. To illustrate, let us establish a baseline of avoidance behavior with the white rat as subject. The animal is given a brief electric shock every 20 seconds if it does not press a lever. Each time it presses the lever it postpones the next shock for 20 seconds. Under these circumstances the rat will learn to press the lever, and will do so at a rate sufficiently high to avoid most of the shocks. After some experience, the animal will settle down to a steady rate of lever pressing which remains constant for periods of six hours or longer. Once the avoidance behavior has reached this stable state we can then administer a drug, e.g., amphetamine sulfate (commonly known as Benzedrine), to the animal. Our record of the subject's rate of lever pressing will then display a sequence of departures from its usual appearance. A short while after the drug has been administered, the rat will begin to press the lever more and more rapidly, and the record will show a smooth acceleration from its baseline rate. The rate will reach some limiting value, say three to four times higher than usual, and will remain at this level for two to three hours. Then it will begin to decline, and the record will show a smooth return to its baseline level. But the animal will not simply return to its former rate of lever pressing. The rate will actually decline below its baseline level, and it will remain depressed for several hours.

In order to follow temporal relations between a drug and behavior, it is necessary to maintain the behavior at a stable level over long periods of time. In addition, the measures employed to characterize the behavior must be potentially variable in either direction. That is to say, the measure, in addition to being stable in time, must also be able to increase or decrease over a wide range in order to provide a sensitive test of the drug action. A behavioral control technique that possesses these properties will permit the moment-to-moment recording of the temporal course of the drug action. In addition, if physiological and behavioral measures of the drug's activity are recorded concurrently, it may be possible to pick out those particular physiological effects that are most likely to be related to the behavioral effects. The value of such behavioral techniques is attested to by the large number of behavior laboratories that have been set up in pharmaceutical houses. These industrial concerns have not classified their behavioral techniques in terms of the Skinner box or the bar-pressing response. They have been impressed not by the experimental chamber but by the precision of control and the sensitivity of individual behavior to pharmacologic manipulation under the influence of many diverse variables. It has become evident that when profits are at stake behavioral control techniques are evaluated in terms of their success in controlling behavior, and not in terms of an outmoded architectural classificatory scheme. The "pure" scientist may well take this lesson to heart.

What constitutes a *new* behavioral technique? It is possible to invent an apparently new technique which, in reality, is no improvement over older methods. This is especially true of new apparatus designs. An editor of a psychological journal once remarked that it was the policy of his journal to publish new techniques, but he stated emphatically that he would never again publish a description of a new tachistoscope. I am certain, however, that he would be happy to publish a new method of utilizing a tachistoscope. One of the criteria of a new technique is its success in producing data that have never been seen before. The new data may be produced by a tachistoscope, by a projective test, by a maze, a runway, or a Skinner box, but if these instruments are utilized in a novel fashion to yield new data, then a new behavioral technique has been born. As the method is more intensively used in the laboratory, it may even open up areas of research that were not conceived of during its initial applications.

For example, the combination of reinforcement scheduling methods with an adaptation of the Békésy Audiometer technique has resulted in the development of a new area of animal psychophysics. In the Békésy technique (6), the subject is instructed to press a key whenever he hears a tone, and to release the key whenever the tone becomes inaudible. A continuously driven attenuator gradually decreases the intensity of the tone whenever the subject is pressing the key. When the subject no longer hears the tone and releases the key, the attenuator reverses direction and brings the intensity back above threshold. By recording the position of the attenuator as it moves up and down across the lowest audible intensity of the tone, a continuous measure of the auditory threshold is obtained.

The Békésy technique was modified by Blough, who used it to measure visual intensity thresholds in pigeons (9). Pigeons, of course, cannot be instructed verbally, and Blough had to employ other techniques to bring their behavior under stimulus control. The situation he devised was one in which the bird had two keys available. By the use of appropriate reinforcement scheduling techniques, he trained the pigeon to peck one key when a stimulus patch was visible and the other key when the stimulus was dark. Pecks on the first key, however, drove the stimulus intensity down, while pecks on the second key increased the intensity. A record of the oscillations in stimulus intensity describes the visual threshold continuously in time.

As Blough pointed out, "The novelty of Békésy's method lies in the way that the subject's responses govern the stimulus intensity. Equally important, however, is the control exerted in the opposite direction: the stimulus intensity controls the subject's responses" (9, p. 31). The contribution of behavioral control techniques lay in the establishment of this feedback link. If the student gives a little thought to this problem, he will realize that it is a remarkable feat to teach a pigeon to indicate the precise point in time when it no longer sees a spot of light, especially when its threshold is changing during dark adaptation and it is required to make its judgments continuously in time. The details of Blough's procedure are too intricate to describe here, but I strongly recommend that the student go to the literature for a complete description of the manner in which precise stimulus control was developed and maintained. Out of this marriage of two apparently unrelated sets of techniques is emerging a new conception of the problem of "subjective sensation."

Thus a new technique may involve new or improved instrumentation, or it may simply be the result of novel uses or combinations of older methods. In evaluating the importance of the new technique, the chief criterion is the resulting data.

EXPERIMENTS PERFORMED TO ESTABLISH THE EXISTENCE OF A BEHAVIORAL PHENOMENON. The introduction of a new control technique may result in the demonstration of a previously unobserved, unmeasured, or uncontrolled type of behavior. Very often, however, experiments are carried out for the specific purpose of demonstrating a particular behavioral effect.

Experiments that simply demonstrate a new behavioral phenomenon are sometimes dismissed as "exploratory." Science, it is argued, proceeds by manipulating variables in a systematic fashion, and by unifying the results of such manipulation within a conceptual framework. The simple demonstration of a behavioral effect is held to be only the prelude to systematic investigation. There is some justification for this attitude. It can be a frustrating experience to follow the publications of some scientists who seem to have devoted their careers to demonstrating new phenomena without ever following even one of them through with a systematic study. It is, however, a weak policy to allow such feelings to influence our evaluation of the reported phenomena. Our frustrations will die with us, but the experimental findings will remain. If the discoverer of a phenomenon does not follow it up, someone else will, when the importance of the discovery is recognized. It is true that its importance is less likely to be appreciated if the discovery is not immediately elaborated experimentally. But it is just this fact which should make us wary of dismissing a new phenomenon as trivial.

It sometimes seems that a brilliantly creative experimenter does not possess the qualities of patience and plodding thoroughness that most of us feel are vital for scientific progress. While it would, of course, be desirable for all investigators to be simultaneously brilliant and plodding, such a combination is, in fact, rare. Most of us are elaborators of other workers' discoveries; a few of us are creators; only a handful are both. We are all necessary, for even the most creative scientist builds upon an established foundation. A scorn for the everyday scientific laborer will blind the student to the immensely valuable and *necessary* contributions that can come only from hard and often uninspired "pick and shovel" work. On the other hand, if the student is taught, as many are, that pick and shovel labor *is Science*, then he will inevitably fail to appreciate the results of important, but unelaborated, discoveries.

The discovery of new phenomena is, above all, a creative enterprise (although the role of accident cannot be ignored here any more than in other kinds of experimentation). Some well-developed sciences implicitly acknowledge this fact by christening a new phenomenon with the name of its discoverer. But one rarely hears of a behavioral process that is named for the man who discovered it. Many experimental psychologists seem to be preoccupied with data gathering or theory construction or statistical methodology or many other problems, some worth while, some trivial. But when an intelligent outsider looks in on their activities, he may ask, in bewilderment, "Where is thinking? What are you doing about neurosis, about psychosis? Have you forgotten that behavior occurs in the temporal as well as the spatial dimension?

What have you found out about behavior that is multiple-determined? Do you know anything about the deep apathy developed by American POW's in the Chinese prison camps?" The questions could be multiplied indefinitely. The sorry answer to most of them is that we have not yet been able to reproduce the necessary phenomena, or their equivalents, in the laboratory. It is not enough to excuse ourselves on the grounds that we are trying to develop a *science* of behavior, that science necessarily involves the investigation of much that is important only with respect to its own internal consistency, that we must start with the narrow and simple in order to lay a solid groundwork for the more significant research to be accomplished later. Such concerns are valid, but as a reply to our hypothetical visitor their sincerity is doubtful unless we can demonstrate to him that we display a great receptivity toward new behavioral phenomena. In fact, receptivity is not enough. We must actively seek new behavioral processes in the laboratory by training our students toward this end and by providing appropriate professional rewards. We will then speed up the process by which our science can be made to cope with behavior as it actually proceeds in the world about us.

How does one go about finding new behavioral processes to bring into the laboratory? There are no formulae to follow. The source of new phenomena may arise from one's own systematic experimentation, from casual observation of behavior outside the laboratory, from predictions generated by a theory, or from practical problems that arise in such areas as education, equipment design, therapy, or traffic control. New processes that emerge from experimental data possess one advantage over those derived from other sources—their immediate availability for experimental manipulation. Since the phenomena have been generated by specifiable procedures, their elaboration in the form of systematic investigation can be accomplished with a minimum of trial and error.

When one attempts to establish experimental control over a behavioral phenomenon observed outside the laboratory, a difficult creative problem arises. Guesses have to be made concerning the relevant variables. Are the suspected variables similar to any that have previously been studied experimentally? If not, how can we contrive to bring them under control? How broadly can the behavior in question be conceptualized? Must we, for example, duplicate precisely the hysterical paralysis of a hospitalized patient, or can we deal with the same phenomenon in terms of a monkey's lever-pressing activity? Are the behavioral processes well enough understood so that we can reproduce them elsewhere than in their original setting?

I have posed these questions somewhat differently from the way they are commonly asked. An often discussed problem in psychology is the question of whether laboratory data can be extrapolated to everyday life. But we are now asking whether the behavior of everyday life can be brought into the laboratory. This question brings us close to one aspect of the problem of the generality of experimental data, a problem with which I shall be concerned at some length in later chapters. My concern at this point is how the answer will affect our judgments of the *importance* of data.

Psychologists are often criticized on the grounds that their experiments are too far from real life to provide useful information about human behavior outside the laboratory. Behavior, it seems, is one of the last subject matters to be accepted as an experimental science. Similar objections have been leveled at all sciences in the past. But no one now expects the physicist to study gravity by observing falling autumn leaves, or the physiologist to investigate the speed of nerve transmission by means of reaction times. The laws of behavior, too, may be expected to hold true inside the laboratory. And insofar as there is biological continuity from lower to higher organisms, we may expect this to encompass their behavior also.

Unfortunately, psychologists themselves are split on this question. Some of them simply do not care whether their work is relevant to human behavior. They may be interested in the behavior of lower animals, or they may simply like to putter around with any kind of behavior that catches their fancy. There can be no real objection to this point of view. Knowledge of nature for its own sake is a legitimate pursuit, and can provide much satisfaction.

There are some psychologists, however, who feel that relevance to human behavior is a prime objective of their experimental studies, yet who claim a special relevance for one type of experimentation and no relevance for others. Thus we have the man who uses white rats as his experimental subjects claiming that the study of paramecia is a waste of time. Another experimenter strongly champions the monkey over the rat as a representative of the human species. He disowns any resemblance between his own behavior and that of a rat. A more fastidious psychologist argues that the college freshman is the only one who can provide data worth having. Then we find the college freshman discarded in favor of the military trainee seated in front of an instrument panel, or "display." Finally, realistic research is sometimes held to be possible only in the mental hospital.

Such points of view are, in reality, no more sophisticated than are those which claim that all laboratory investigations are irrelevant to a proper understanding of human behavior. They have in common the mistaken notion that we must somehow contrive experimental *analogues* of the behavior we observe in our fellows. "In order to study psychosis in animals we must learn how to make animals psychotic." But why should we expect a rat's psychosis to bear any surface resemblance to that of a human being? While a particular constellation of variables experienced by a man may lead him to retire to a cave and eat excrement, the same class of factors may lead a rat to continue pressing a lever at a high speed long after we have withdrawn any visible reinforcement. Our problem is not one of analogizing, but of obtaining sufficient understanding of both rats and men to be able to recognize resemblances in *behavioral processes.* We must be able to classify our variables in such a manner that we can recognize similarities in their *principles of operation*, in spite of the fact that their physical specifications may be quite different.

Suppose we are interested in the problem of human depression following the death of a loved one, and we feel that the investigation could profitably be carried out in the animal laboratory. Our task is not simply to find a monkey who will go into a depression when its mate dies. Our course of action will be, rather, to apply to the monkey those behavioral principles that we suspect are operative in the human case. We must create the appropriate conditions in the laboratory so that we may then manipulate them and examine their respective contributions. Perhaps our preliminary analysis of the problem leads us to suspect that the type of behavioral depression in question results from the withdrawal of a strong generalized reinforcer. We might then, by means of all the technical skills at our disposal, establish a generalized conditioned reinforcer for our experimental monkey. Perhaps this generalized reinforcer could even be another monkey. In that case, the second monkey would be associated with as many of the experimental animal's reinforcements as possible, and with a large number of different responses. The association would be accomplished in accordance with those principles of chaining and conditioned reinforcement that have proven to be most effective in other laboratory experiments. Once the desired relationship has been established between the two monkeys, the second monkey could be removed, leaving the first one bereft of the source of many of its reinforcements. We could then observe any subsequent changes in the behavior of the experimental animal. We might even use a warning stimulus to signal the impending withdrawal of the generalized reinforcer and note the behavior of our monkey in the presence of this stimulus.

Will the behavioral changes in the laboratory monkey be similar in principle to the type of human depression in which we are interested? We are certainly dealing with variables similar to those in the human case. We may not have the whole story, but we shall have made a start toward the identification and investigation of critical factors. Carrying out such an experiment with a monkey does not, of course, guarantee an increased understanding of the human behavior. The monkey may prove to be an unsuitable organism for the problem at hand, or, even if this is not the case, our technical and systematic know-how may not be adequate for the job.

An even more serious bar to extrapolation, however, will be the scarcity of objective data on the human side. While the monkey's behavior can be investigated extensively and thoroughly, our control and observational techniques on the human side are likely to lag far behind. Extrapolation from the monkey will be difficult because the case to which extrapolation is to be made will in many instances be poorly defined. Nonetheless, the possibility of obtaining the desired clarity of definition is one of the chief values of experimentation designed to establish a behavioral phenomenon in the laboratory. It is likely that our understanding of human behavior will increase, through experimentation and accumulated clinical observations, to the point where a connection can be established with the laboratory findings. Even more to the point, the laboratory data may actually suggest new angles from which to view human behavior. Suggestions of this sort will not often be self-evident in the data. Like any act of induction, they will be the product of careful experimentation, creative imagination, and a host of factors that would require a more thorough analysis than is possible here. Analogizing may or may not play a part, but it is certainly not a necessary, nor even always a desirable, component.

Sometimes, when a commonly observed type of behavior is demonstrated in the laboratory, we hear the remarks, "So what! Everybody knows people behave like that. Who cares if rats or monkeys or college freshmen can do it too?" Such a statement assumes beforehand that common observation is an adequate substitute for controlled observation. The two may, at times, be in agreement, but there is no predicting this before experimental studies are undertaken. Everyday observation of human behavior is notoriously unreliable. In our impressions and interpretations of behavior as it goes on around us, we tend to overlook many properties of the behavior and of its controlling variables. We read into our descriptions of behavior much that is not actually there, and assume on too little evidence that two or more types of behavior are the same simply because they look the same. The very language of our everyday discourse often serves to obscure the critical data. We "explain" behavior by using terms that refer to some hypothetical condition of the organism. As Skinner has pointed out:

> An organism possesses a "habit" to the extent that a certain form of behavior is observed with a special frequency—attributable to events in the history of the individual. It possesses an "instinct" to the extent that a certain form of behavior is observed with a special frequency—in this case because of membership in a given species. An "attitude" expresses a special frequency of a number of forms of behavior. These frequencies are the observable facts and may be studied as such . . . (84, p. 69).

For reasons such as these, the straight confirmation, in a laboratory study, of our everyday impressions of behavior is likely to be relatively rare. We are almost certain to observe variables that were not sharply enough delineated in the give-and-take of the behavioral world outside the laboratory, and to discover that seemingly important factors are actually irrelevant or are, at best, unnecessary concomitants of the behavior in question.

In addition to its advantages of manipulative and analytic precision, laboratory control in lower animal subjects is useful in studying phenomena that are not amenable to human experimentation because of our cultural and ethical traditions. It is recognized, for example, that punishment, mild and severe, is a common form of behavioral control in almost all societies, including our own. But we do not acknowledge this fact to the point where we admit strong punishment into the laboratory, except with subhuman subjects. Punishment and various types of "stress" phenomena are, therefore, key areas in which it is extremely important to gain laboratory control over relevant phenomena. If we are to get the insights of controlled investigation in these areas, we must bring all our ingenuity to bear upon the problem of reproducing the behavioral processes involved in aversive control.

The inspiration for the experimental discovery of new behavioral phenomena does not necessarily come directly from a concern with human problems as they are perceived in everyday life or on the psychoanalyst's couch. Walter Hunter, for example, deliberately developed his well-known delayed-response technique (48) out of a desire to investigate symbolic processes. But another useful delayed-response technique, introduced by B. F. Skinner, developed simply as an experimental by-product (81, pp. 306-307). In his studies of fixed-ratio reinforcement schedules, in which the subject must respond a fixed number of times for each reinforcement, Skinner performed a control experiment to demonstrate the part played by the correlation between reinforcement and rate of response. He simply arranged a condition in which a given response was never reinforced if it had been preceded within fifteen seconds by another similar response. The behavior generated by this technique, a low rate of temporally spaced responses, has since become one of the experimental psychologist's most interesting and useful baselines.

A consistent and integrated experimental program, then, can

provide a fertile source for the discovery of new behavioral phenomena. If the program is sufficiently intensive, a point will be reached at which old conceptions begin to crumble and new techniques become necessary for the investigation of variables that were previously unrecognized. Such a point, whenever it is reached, constitutes a crisis in experimental progress. Some investigators fail to recognize when they have reached it, and simply continue to make experiments along the lines they laid out at the start of their program. Other scientists recognize the crisis when they meet it but, lacking the inspiration to take up the challenge, turn in other directions. Science makes its greatest leaps forward, however, when a researcher is able to grow with his data; when he is prepared to discard or drastically modify his old techniques and conceptions in favor of the new and unorthodox. A science that cannot turn up new phenomena by what we might call "the technique of intensive investigation" is on its way down hill. Psychology can hardly be said to have reached this stage.

Impetus for the experimental demonstration of new behavioral phenomena may come from yet another direction. Not only the psychologist but also the physiologist, the functional anatomist, the psychiatrist, the sociologist, the anthropologist, the ecologist, the pharmacologist, the geneticist, and the representatives of other scientific disciplines are concerned with behavioral phenomena. These other disciplines are, however, generally concerned with behavior as a tool for investigation of something else, such as the nervous system, drugs, culture, population movements, or heredity. They have ingenious techniques for investigating their own spheres of interest, but when they want to relate their observations to behavior they often turn to the psychologist for the appropriate behavioral techniques. The experimental psychologist should meet the challenge of these requests even if they impose a strain on his experimental facilities. He may be able to make important contributions in areas wider than psychology's particular sphere of competence; more than that, he may find an opportunity for bringing new behavioral phenomena under experimental control.

Many scientists not directly concerned with behavior for its own sake are nonetheless keen observers of behavior. Furthermore, their techniques can produce or reveal behavioral changes that are of direct interest to the psychologist. Sometimes these changes are subtle and difficult to define. It is important to bring them under as rigorous experimental control as possible. Let me cite an example in which, unfortunately, experimental psychology has not yet distinguished itself by any remarkable contributions.

I was once introduced by a neurologist to a patient whose diagnosis was that of Korsakoff's psychosis. The symptoms were classical for this syndrome. When asked where he was (in a hospital), he would often reply with the name of a hotel at which he had stayed some time in the past. When asked about his family, he might reply that he had none, or name a deceased member of the family. When the neurologist asked the patient for his (the neurologist's) name, the patient could not answer. The neurologist told him his name and warned that he would ask for it again in a few minutes. When asked again, the patient replied with other names, including those of the other physicians in the hospital who frequently interviewed him. When these physicians were present, however, the patient could not come up with their names. During this interview the patient seemed to be trying hard, and appeared embarrassed at his own replies to the questions. The patient was able to carry on a game of checkers, but if a momentary interruption occurred he was unable to resume play in the same game.

The neurologist asked me a simple question. "How," he asked, "do I classify this man's behavioral defect? Is it a memory failure, a temporal and geographical disorientation, a failure of concentration or discrimination? Or is it a motivational problem? Is he deliberately lying? Does he care?" There was, of course, no ready answer. The point I wish to make is that the phenomenon was there, waiting for the techniques of behavioral analysis. The problem did not even require that we reproduce the phenomenon in the laboratory. The neurologist had done a fine job of observation with the skills at his disposal. He was simply asking the psychologist to contribute, if possible, to a more refined analysis of the behavioral processes involved. If this could have been accomplished, it might have been possible to return to the laboratory and produce a similar behavioral process for more precise study, with a continuing interchange between the laboratory and the clinic contributing to the progress of both. Experimental psychology is barely at the threshold of this kind of collaboration.

EXPERIMENTS PERFORMED TO EXPLORE THE CONDITIONS UNDER WHICH A PHENOMENON OCCURS. Once a new technique has been introduced or a new phenomenon brought into the laboratory, a theory formulated or curiosity aroused by some data, new tasks are set for the investigator. A new experimental finding or a promising theory remains a challenge so long as it stands alone, unrelated to other findings and other theories. The process of discovering the conditions under which a phenomenon occurs constitutes the first step of integration. Most of the data of science are by-products of this process, and this is the reason why many experimental findings are of little or no interest to the nonscientific observer. The layman often asks, "What are you trying to prove?" When the investigator replies, for example, that he is simply trying to find out whether primary and conditioned reinforcements obey the same laws, the inquirer may wonder why such an esoteric problem should command so great an expenditure of energy, time, and money. A psychiatrist of my acquaintance had a ready answer to the question: "mental masturbation" was his characterization.

What is not easily apparent, even to the educated and sympathetic nonscientist, is that the scientist is, primarily, seeking order in nature. Only the rare discovery turns out to be useful in a practical way. But the rare discoveries are usually built upon a foundation of small findings, none of them world-shaking in themselves, without which the final step could never have been taken. A major concern of science is the soundness of the basic edifice. Thus, many experiments are performed solely to establish a sound and rational system within a particular area of interest. No one pretends that such experiments will yield immediate findings of practical interest. Often, data are important only as they establish—or refute—the soundness of other data or of some conceptualization of natural phenomena. They serve to strengthen the internal consistency of the science; in this role they are fundamental to the advance of knowledge. It is rarely possible to predict the point in the chain of evidence at which the data will spill over into the world outside the laboratory.

In the search for the controlling variables relevant to a given behavioral phenomenon, there are several considerations that influence the directions of experimentation. Often the initial impetus comes from a desire to achieve a finer degree of experimental control. The experimenter may trust to luck in designing an experiment to produce a given behavioral effect, and if the variables with which he is accustomed to work are sufficiently powerful, his luck may hold. But it can be a frustrating experience to find, for example, that only a certain percentage of the experimental subjects yield the particular type of baseline data necessary for a successful experiment.

In such cases, the experimenter, if he is interested in experimental rather than statistical control, will take a step backward. He will temporarily give up his immediate goal and instead begin an investigation of the variables that influence his baseline conditions. For example, he will search for a diet formula that is optimally effective as a reinforcer, in the sense that it will maintain behavior in a steady state over a long period of time. Or he will search for the conditions that will maintain a particular form of behavior at an intermediate level, so that he will have a more sensitive measure, capable of change in either direction when he finally applies the variables in which he is most interested. Such investigations may occasionally yield data that are of greater interest than the original problem; their usual function, however, is to establish a reliable methodology for the pursuit of more general problems. This function seldom produces spectacular experiments; nevertheless, their importance should not be underestimated.

These experiments, designed to find the optimal combination of variables to be used for some other purpose, can be dismissed as "exploratory" because they are not usually followed up for their own sake. The variables themselves may not be of intrinsic interest; they may serve no additional function once the necessary information is obtained. Even so, they should be reported to one's colleagues. Although the data may not fill any important gap in the systematic factual content of the science, they supply vital methodological information. For example, the optimal size of the response key in a pigeon experiment, the lighting conditions in a maze, the instructions in a psychophysical experiment, all pose problems that any experimenter using such devices has to work out. If the problem has already been solved and the solutions have been made generally available, it will save time and effort for other laboratories.

Experimentation designed to explore the conditions under which a phenomenon occurs can also have more general implications for methodology. One may, for example, be interested in steady-state behavior, behavior whose characteristics do not change for long periods of time. In the course of determining the variables responsible for maintaining a particular type of behavior in the steady state, one may arrive at general principles that will also apply to other behavior.

Usually the definition of a steady state involves some sort of criterion. How long must the behavior be maintained and what magnitude of variability can be permitted before one can be satisfied that a steady state has been achieved? The criterion may be determined in terms of convenience, or by visual inspection of curves or by elaborate mathematical procedures, depending upon the precision demanded by the problem under consideration (see Chapter 9). In the course of determining the suitability of a criterion, observations may be made whose importance transcends the immediate problem. Such observations must be recognized as important and be placed in the public domain for the general uses of science. For example, the variable-interval reinforcement schedule, in which the time between reinforcements is irregular, has become a relatively common technique for establishing a stable level of baseline behavior in both animal and human experiments. This schedule has the virtue of generating a stable response rate, consistent for a given subject over long periods of time. But few investigators using this technique are aware that behavior under the control of variable-interval reinforcement schedules often displays long-term cyclic fluctuations. The behavior may be consistent over the time covered by most experiments; but long-term investigations will require more intensive study of this cyclic phenomenon not only for data of immediate methodological importance but also for basic systematic information relevant to the larger general problem of steady-state behavior.

Another type of problem often encountered is that of the reversibility of a behavioral process (Chapter 8). After observing a behavioral change as a function of some experimental manipulation, is it possible to recover the original baseline behavior? Irreversibility is a major behavioral phenomenon; what variables are responsible in those instances in which it appears? In any particular case the solution of the problem will have, in addition to its systematic importance, an effect upon experimental methodology in the study of behavior. If a subject's behavior can be manipulated first in one direction, then in another, with a return to its original state always possible, much of the intersubject variability that has plagued experimental psychology can be side-stepped (when it is not, in itself, the object of study).

These examples constitute only a negligible fraction of the methodological problems that demand exploration of possibly relevant variables. They are only a few of the problems that are of current interest. There is no foreseeing the nature of the demands that will be made by the methodologies of the future. If history teaches us that we cannot predict, with any long-term accuracy, the directions of future research, it also teaches us that the seeds of future advance are being sown now. For this reason, we cannot afford to overlook *any* demonstration of a relevant variable. Even if the variable seems of little current systematic or methodological importance, it is, nonetheless, a fact about behavior. As such, it is important.

Thorough exploration of the conditions under which a phenomenon occurs often accomplishes more than a demonstration of internal consistency within a given area. The quantitative evaluation of relevant variables may establish connections between hitherto unrelated phenomena, made by way of variables common to the phenomena. Systematization does not necessarily require that many observations be subsumed under a single set of principles, although such unification is probably the highest form of systematization. There are many phenomena which do not actually overlap and yet are related. Systematization occurs not only when one phenomenon "swallows up" another but also when two or more phenomena are found to possess boundary points in common. The systematic integration of two experimental findings does not require that we be able to deduce one from the other. When it is possible to make such a deduction without additional assumptions, we are dealing not with two phenomena but with one. A successful deduction means that the statement of phenomenon A actually includes phenomenon B, but that the complexities of the statement require logical analysis to reveal its content.

Data can be integrated in other ways, in which the deductive process is not involved. Two sets of phenomena may be completely unrelated, except that at some value of a variable common to both, the two phenomena are found to merge into one. Take, for example, the analysis of reinforcement schedules proposed by Schoenfeld, Cumming, and Hearst, although its adequacy has not yet been firmly established (67). In this analysis there is no attempt to deduce the behavioral consequences of one reinforcement schedule from those of another schedule. These writers attempt instead, to demonstrate that at limiting values of certain empirical variables the behavior generated by several schedules is identical. It does not matter that, at other quantitative values of the critical variables, the schedules produce markedly different patterns of behavior. Nor is there any problem posed by the fact that, as the critical variables diverge more and more from their limiting values, the behaviors under the different schedules display markedly different effects when exposed to similar experimental manipulations. For systematization is not necessarily synonymous with reduction. Certain phenomena simply are not derivable from each other. But a demonstration that they meet at some point and then diverge systematically is a major accomplishment in integration. This technique of integrating experimental data may be termed the "method of quantitative contiguity."

A second technique of systematization may be termed the "method of functional contiguity." By means of this method, contiguity—in the form of functional similarities—between two phenomena might be established even though the crucial variables are quantitatively and qualitatively different in the two cases.

For example, take an experimental situation in which an animal receives food reinforcement for a certain response—say lever pressing. However, during a given stimulus—perhaps the sounding of a buzzer—the animal *never* receives food reinforcement. We find that the stimulus may serve either to increase or to decrease the probability of the response that preceded it. Whether the stimulus functions positively or negatively is determined by the relative duration of two critical time intervals: one, the duration of the stimulus itself; the other, the mean time interval between food reinforcements received in the absence of the stimulus (42). Let us call this phenomenon A.

Phenomenon B is seen in a shock-avoidance experiment in which an animal receives shock *only* in the presence of a given stimulus. Again, the stimulus may either increase or decrease the probability of a response that precedes it, with its positive or negative function determined by the relative duration of two critical time intervals. In this case, the first is the length of the time interval by which each avoidance response emitted in the stimulus postpones the shock. The second is the length of the time interval by which each avoidance response emitted in the absence of the stimulus postpones the onset of the stimulus (73).

The critical variables involved in the two experiments are markedly different. In phenomenon A we are dealing with schedules that determine how frequently a response can produce food reinforcement. In phenomenon B we are dealing with schedules that determine the length of time a response may postpone shock. But in each case, the controlling variable had to be specified as a *relation* between two temporal intervals. The function of the stimulus could be explained only by taking into account *both* the schedule in the presence of the stimulus and the schedule in its absence. Thus, even though the variables were quantitatively and qualitatively different, functional analysis revealed that a relational process was involved in two cases, each dealing with quite distinctive phenomena.

Both the method of quantitative contiguity and that of functional contiguity depend, for their success, upon the selection of appropriate dependent and independent variables. Behavioral phenomena may be examined from many points of view, each of which emphasizes different variables. The first requirement for adequate systematization, however, demands that we select, as our dependent variable, some aspect of behavior that will prove to be sufficiently basic to serve as a focus for integrative efforts. Although several dependent variables have been suggested, psychologists are not as yet in substantial agreement with respect to any of them. Are we to concentrate on the temporal aspects of behavior or on its spatial characteristics or on its intensive properties, to name but a few of the alternatives? The independent variables of which behavior is a function pose similar problems. Which ones of the multitude of variables that affect behavior will prove to be most efficient as a framework for systematization?

The answers to these problems are critical for a science of behavior, as they have been for other sciences. Chemistry could not emerge as a modern science before the recognition that weight, rather than color, was the critical variable. Physics was revolutionized when, by means of the equivalence of mass and energy, the number of basic variables was reduced by one.

In order to systematize by means of a demonstrated communality of variables in diverse situations, it will be necessary to design experiments aimed at exploring the range of variables that are relevant to a given phenomenon. Theoretical considerations may dictate the specific direction of such experimentation, but the student should take care not to permit his theory to imprison him. It may be possible to solve the theoretical problem by a "two-point" experiment; nevertheless, the student should, as a matter of general practice, test a wide range of values of the variables in question. Then, even if the theory is not supported, the data will be complete enough to reveal other integrative possibilities. If the student is an alert practitioner of the methods of induction, it is safe to predict that some degree of systematization will result from experiments that yield a series of complete functional relations within a relatively circumscribed area.

The demonstration of the relevance of a variable in a particular situation may not be recognized as a major discovery until other variables and different experimental situations have been explored. Frequently such data remain relatively isolated until later discoveries place them properly in the larger systematic scheme. Skinner's paper "Superstition in the Pigeon" (82) offers a striking example of late recognition (see page 348). For several years, the data he reported were regarded only as an interesting curiosity. But in recent years the variables described in this paper have proved of central importance in a wide variety of experimental and clinical situations. Some theorists now assert that most human behavior is under the control of "spurious" contingencies similar to those described by Skinner. Behavioral phenomena traceable to adventitious reinforcement contingencies have been observed in experimental situations ranging from dark-adaptation studies to investigations of punishment. Such contingencies are beginning to play a unifying role in the systematization of a wide variety of data.

If one wishes to explore the conditions under which a phenomenon occurs, how does one determine the variables with which to work? There is no pat answer to this question. One may select those variables relevant to a given theory; or proceed on the basis of analogues from similar phenomena about which more is known; or select a variable for some reason of which one is completely unaware and cannot verbalize adequately. *Neither these nor any other methods of selection have any bearing upon the importance of the resulting data.* A variable may turn out to be relevant in contexts never suspected by the experimenter, or it may turn out to be minor and of minimal systematic importance. Since the directions of future progress are always uncertain, the student should not try to make a final decision on the importance of any demonstrated variable.

HOW TO EVALUATE THE IMPORTANCE OF DATA?

IN DISCUSSING the importance of experimental data, I have considered many facets of science. I may seem to have wandered far from the topic under consideration, but this is because of the nature of the beast. The problem of evaluating the importance of experimental data cannot be solved by a neat little argument. It is a problem as big as science itself, and the experienced scientific practitioner will recognize that my discussion, far from being too comprehensive, has been too circumscribed. But of more immediate concern to the student, after reading the foregoing pages, will be his feeling that he has received no definitive answers. A problem has been raised, but no solutions have been forthcoming. I have discussed several types of data and several reasons for experimentation. The importance of data is usually judged on these bases, but I have tried (despite my undoubtedly apparent prejudices) to make the point that these bases are not in fact adequate foundations for judgment.

What then, are we to substitute? Science is supposed to be an orderly, logical process, not subject to the whims of prejudice and other human frailties of its participants. If science is to use the importance of data as a criterion for accepting or rejecting an experiment, it must have a set of impartial rules within which the scientist can operate when he has to make his evaluation. Do such rules actually exist? The answer is no.

If I have led the student out on the end of a limb and left him to shift for himself, I have done so on purpose. For I cannot take him any further. Whether he likes it or not, he will be on that limb for the rest of his scientific lifetime. If he has gone into science with the illusion that he would find a way of life in which a fixed set of rules would provide security and safety from error, it is well that he learn the realities of the situation as quickly as possible. Some scientists either never realize at all that they are sitting on a shaky limb, or they deny that realization and claim that *their* feet are firmly on the ground. They do not hesitate to condemn a colleague's work as unimportant, for to them importance is, by definition, circumscribed by their own set of rules. The position provides security, but it does so at the expense of the objectivity that is the first requisite for effective science.

I do not, however, recommend that the student permit himself to be buffeted about by all the data that come to his attention, hopelessly accepting it all in an attempt to be the Universal Man. As Bachrach has noted, "To be eclectic may . . . mean that he has his feet firmly planted in mid-air" (4, p. 43). The student should have some convictions as to what kinds of data are most needed by his science. This will give direction to his research, and will provide it with an over-all unity that will permit him to make a sounder contribution. But he should never be so self-centered in his convictions that he ignores methodologically sound data that arise from other points of view. And, as his science progresses, he must be able to change the directions of his research with new developments.

The cumulative development of a science provides the only final answer as to the importance of any particular data; sometimes it is the younger scientists, who enter the field unencumbered by the prejudices of past controversies, who pick out the threads of continuity from the tangle of theory, data, and pseudo-problems that form a part of every stage of scientific progress.

Chapter 2

The Reliability and Generality of Data

SCIENTIFIC IMPORTANCE is only one of the criteria by which data are evaluated. I have pointed out that this is, at best, a shaky basis upon which to accept or reject data. The remainder of the book will be devoted to two other criteria, *reliability* and *generality*, with this chapter constituting a rather general introduction.

As was the case with the importance of data, the assessment of reliability and generality requires maturity of judgment. There are, however, many psychologists who *insist* that reliability and generality be evaluated on a purely impersonal basis. The popularity of this point of view is possibly due to the psychologist's recognition, by virtue of the nature of his subject matter, of the frailties of human judgment. He does not like to trust important decisions to the whims of personal judgment. But individual judgment is by no means synonymous with individual whim. Although it may have no foundation in logic, and its result cannot be expressed as a number, it nonetheless deals with tangibles and has been found to work. Mistakes are possible, but there are means for detecting and correcting them. The objectivity of science consists not so much in set rules of procedure as in the self-corrective nature of the scientific process.

The exercise of mature judgment in evaluating the reliability and generality of experimental data is seldom discussed in textbooks on experimental method. Yet it plays a basic role in the evaluation of data. A thorough awareness of this general fact will prove more valuable than any of the individual evaluative techniques that are described in the following chapters.

RELIABILITY

When we ask whether data are reliable, we usually mean: "Will the experiment, if repeated, yield the same results?" In psychology, this question is usually answered by means of an elaborate set of statistical assumptions and arithmetical computations.

The chief antagonist of statistical reliability is "Chance." Modern psychology has set Chance up as its devil. All data are, at birth, considered to bear its taint, and any data that cannot be proved to be independent of Chance are forthwith and irrevocably assigned to its hell. The theology is a severe one. It is held that the mark of Chance can never be erased completely from any data. The best that we can be presumed to do is to determine that specific data have a low probability of belonging to Chance, and with some trepidation, we accept such data into the fold. If they do not belong to Chance, they belong to Science. Thus data are accepted into science by exclusion. They possess no positive virtues, only the negative one of being due to chance with a low level of confidence.

The concept of chance does not mean to science what it means to the man in the street. To him, chance is synonymous with unpredictability. But there exists a science of chance. And who ever heard of a science whose subject matter is unpredictable? In fact, there exist *laws* of chance, and whenever there is law there is predictability. It is the existence of such laws that permits scientists to evaluate the reliability of their data against baselines provided by statistical theory.

Suppose, for example, one has performed two sets of quantitative observations, one under control conditions and the other following some experimental manipulation. Two sets of numbers will then be available for comparison. Now, is the difference between, say, the means of the two sets of numbers reliable? That is to say, if the experiment had been performed with both sets of observations obtained under the control conditions alone, might a comparable difference have occurred simply because of chance variations? The conscientious experimenter will argue that the difference is not a reliable one, and that it did arise by chance. Then he will set about to prove himself wrong. If chance alone were operating, and if the experimental variable really had no effect, then the two sets of obtained numbers would have to come from a single parent population that possesses certain quantitative characteristics. He will then make some assumptions about the distribution of numbers within the parent population, after which he will determine whether the obtained numbers might reasonably be expected to have been drawn at random from such a distribution. If his calculations tell him there was only a low probability that the two sets of observed values were drawn from the same parent distribution, he will conclude that the difference was real and that the data were reliable.

Statistical analysis has its merits for certain kinds of experiments, but a number of serious difficulties are associated with it. For example, the parent population with which the empirical data are to be compared presents one problem. Ideally, the form and parameters of the parent distribution will have been empirically determined, but this is rarely the case. Postulating the properties of such a distribution involves great risks, for there are an infinite number of distributions from which to choose. Particularly risky, because of its circularity, is the once general practice of deducing the properties of the parent distribution from the data one is testing. This practice is now declining in popularity. Even the so-called distribution-free statistics do not wholly escape from this dilemma, however, for some distribution is always required as a baseline with which to compare the empirical observations.

The question of whether the experiment, if repeated, would yield a comparable difference between the experimental and control observations raises a second type of reliability problem—not the same problem as that involved in asking whether chance can account for the difference obtained in one experiment, but rather a problem in replication. A given experimental operation may, in reality, have no significant effect. But a series of replications is likely to yield a few estimates of statistically significant differences between experimental and control observations. In a series of replications of the same experiment, a statistically significant difference may be expected to occur a certain number of times on the basis of chance alone. Similarly, even if the experimental variable does have a real effect, a series of replications is still likely to yield a few instances of statistical nonsignificance. A single experiment without replication is, then, subject to either of these two types of error. A statistical judgment of significance or nonsignificance may itself be the product of chance.

We are left, finally, with the basic problem of what is meant by "chance." Are experimental observations ever the result of chance? To some experimenters, chance is simply a name for the combined effects of uncontrolled variables. If such variables are, in fact, controllable, then chance in this sense is simply an excuse for sloppy experimentation, and no further comment is required. If the uncontrolled variables are actually unknown, then chance is, as Boring has pointed out (14), a synonym for ignorance. Science is presumably dedicated to stamping out ignorance, but statistical evaluation of data against a baseline whose characteristics are determined by unknown variables constitutes a passive acceptance of ignorance. This is a curious negation of the professed aims of science. More consistent with those aims is the evaluation of data by means of experimental control, an alternative set of techniques which will be the major concern of the succeeding chapters.

One can accept that chance is synonymous with ignorance but argue that statistics are necessary in order to evaluate the degree of one's ignorance. On the basis of the information so obtained, one then utilizes experimental control to identify and decrease the role of uncontrolled factors. The procedure, if it is successful, cannot be condemned. But, as I shall point out later, the evaluation of uncontrolled variability must take into account a number of factors which are not amenable to any known statistical treatment; which are often, in fact, quite subjective and idiosyncratic to a particular experimenter or a particular laboratory. Even among those who profess to find statistical evaluative techniques useful, these other considerations can be found to take precedence.

To some experimenters, chance means the same thing that it does to the man in the street: unpredictability. Yet true unpredictability would put a natural scientist out of business. If he refers to the kind of statistical unpredictability that has become popular in physics, then he should feel obliged to seek the statistical laws governing such "unpredictability," and to base his tests of the reliability of data upon these rather than upon the assumptions that have developed out of the statistics of inference.

GENERALITY

PROBLEMS such as those raised above are not new ones. They and others have been recognized for a long time by statisticians and by psychologists who use statistics, and solutions are continually being sought.

A similar situation exists with respect to evaluating the generality of data. Statistical methods have actually become almost a *sine qua non* for determining generality. But generality has several meanings, and statistical methods, even if they were free of their own intrinsic difficulties, would not be applicable in evaluating all the types of generality.

SUBJECT GENERALITY, OR REPRESENTATIVENESS. If a given experimental result has been obtained with a single subject, how representative is the finding for other organisms of the same species? This is a deceptively simple question. Which aspect of the data does one wish to test for generality? Is it simply the fact that a variable is effective? Is one interested in the general shape of a functional relation? Or are the quantitative values, the actual numbers, of critical importance? It is in answering this question that the intent of the experimenter must be taken into consideration. Often, in psychology, some aspects of the data in an experiment display considerable orderliness, while other features appear chaotic. The experimenter will then be concerned with the representativeness of those portions of the data which display order. Science rarely tries to make a case for disorder, for progress occurs when we gain control over seemingly chaotic data. For this reason, one does not criticize experimental data when they fail to display regularity in all their aspects. The one exception occurs when we can reasonably suspect that the variability may have obscured, or interfered in some way with, the critical data.

Once the experimenter has pointed out those features of the data with which he is particularly concerned, how does he go about determining their generality? This problem will be discussed in detail in the chapters on replication, but a negative comment belongs here. We cannot dispose of the problem of subject generality by employing large groups of subjects and using statistical measures, such as the mean and variance of the groups. It is not true that the larger the group, the greater is the generality of the data. Representativeness is an *actuarial* problem to which the currently prevalent statistical design is not applicable. Suppose, for example, one exposes a group of subjects to a given experimental condition and comes up with a behavioral measure stated in terms of the mean and standard deviation. Then one asks, "How representative are these data? To how many subjects in the population do they apply?"

The first problem is to select that aspect of the data whose generality one wishes to test. One may inquire concerning the generality of the particular shape of distribution that was obtained. The addition of subjects to the group will, indeed, help to answer this question, and we may eventually even be able to state, with a high degree of confidence, that all subjects in the population will fall somewhere within the obtained distribution. For a simple reason, no experimental investigation in psychology has ever been carried sufficiently far to provide such information: The labor would be tremendous and *not worth while.* Such a latitude of specification would produce a degree of generality to which there could, by definition, be no exception. Any data would automatically be representative.

Typically therefore, a more restricted aspect of the distribution is selected for emphasis. For example, we may ask how representative the *mean* value is of all the subjects in the population. In actual practice, this question is seldom answered. If it were, we should read, in published papers, not only the mean value for the group but also the number of subjects who actually fell at the mean value. If the group were sufficiently large, we would then be able to state that, for example, 30 per cent of the subjects will yield a mean value, y, of the behavioral measure. This would be a true statement of the degree of representativeness of the group mean. It is the kind of information that would be useful to the insurance statistician, or to the psychologist who is interested in the population distribution of behavioral characteristics. Actually, few experimental psychologists are concerned with such population distributions. If there were a great interest, we would see more experimental data expressed not simply in terms of behavioral measures but rather in terms of the *number of subjects* that yield each value of the behavioral measure. Unless experimental data are expressed in this way, the use of large groups of subjects does not add to the representativeness of the findings. Also, unless the form of the population distribution is known, it will be impossible to determine representativeness within the species simply from the mean and standard deviation of an experimentally obtained sample distribution.

Statistical methods for ensuring subject generality undoubtedly seem necessary because of the great amount of variability commonly observed among subjects in behavioral experiments. Unfortunately, because of a narrowly conceived design of experimentation, the fact of variability seems to have had relatively little experimental exploration. With the growth of interest in the behavior of the individual, however, some elementary facts about variability seem to be emerging, facts which make possible a different approach to the problem of subject generality. In the traditional, and still popular, psychological experiment, two groups of subjects are each exposed to a different value of some independent variable. While each group may display a different mean value of the resulting behavior, there will be a spread around these means, with possibly some overlap between the two groups. The traditional question of generality in such a situation has been, "How representative of the total population, if all its members could have been exposed to one or the other of these values of the independent variable, are the subjects of the two groups?"

The question serves only to deceive the asker. A sufficient number of experiments have demonstrated that the behavior of the individual subject is an orderly function of a large number of so-called independent variables. Indeed, we may now presume such orderliness to be the rule rather than the exception. Variation among subjects often derives from differences in the parameters of the functional relations between behavior and its controlling conditions. For example, the functional relation between two variables may be a linear one, with individuals differing in the slope and intercepts of the function (see Figure 1). Or the curves relating the two vari-

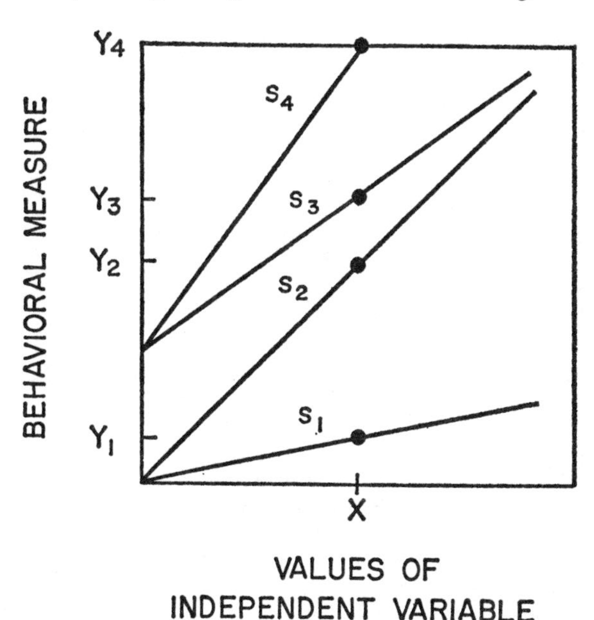

FIGURE 1. A set of curves from a hypothetical population of experimental subjects. The behavior of each subject is related linearly to the independent variable, but the slopes and intercepts of the curves differ.

ables may pass through a maximum, with subjects differing in the position of the maximum (as in Figure 2). Any sufficiently large group of subjects will display behavioral variability consistent with the population distribution of the parameters of the functional relation. In Figure 1, for example, most of the population may resemble Subject S_2. If the sample, presumably an adequate one, is exposed to the value, X, of an experimental variable, the behavioral measures will concentrate about the value, Y_2. But some of the subjects will also react to the experimental variable with the behavior represented by Y_1, Y_3, and Y_4. The number of subjects in each of the classes will depend upon the population distribution of those factors which produce the differences in slope and intercept of the individual curves.

Figure 2 can be analyzed in the same manner. The curvilinear type of relation shown here will also serve to bring out more clearly another aspect of variability. Subjects S_3 and S_4 will show very *similar* quantitative responses to the value, X, of the experimental

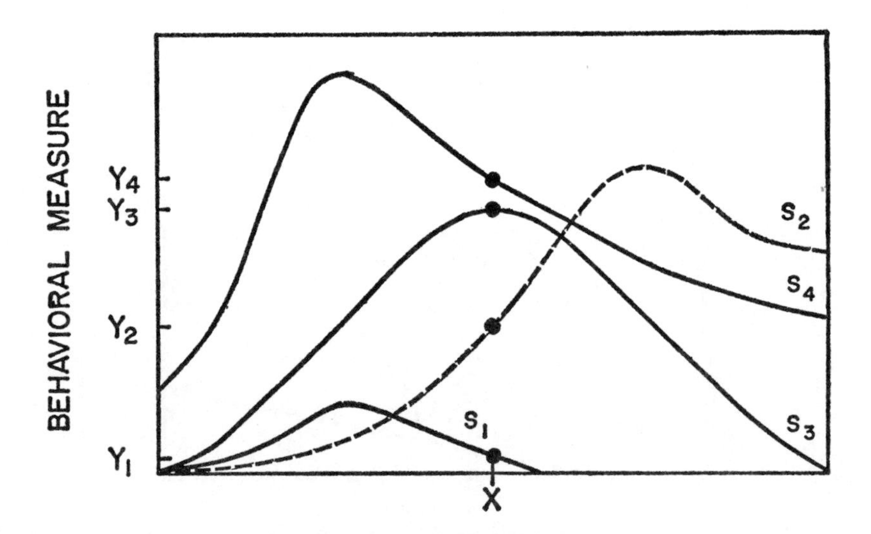

FIGURE 2. A set of curves from a hypothetical population of experimental subjects. The behavior of each subject passes through a maximal value as the independent variable increases in magnitude, but each subject reacts maximally at a different value of the independent variable.

variable. In fact, however, this value of the independent variable catches Subjects S_3 and S_4 at markedly different phases of the process that is represented by the curvilinear function. Traditional group design will not reveal this fact, because the individual functions are not examined nor even obtained. We have here a case in which generality will falsely be attributed to the data. The quantitative similarity of the subjects' behavior is an artifact of an experimental design which does not permit analysis of the causes of variability.

Quantitative differences or similarities among subjects at single isolated points of a functional relation do not provide appropriate criteria for evaluating the representativeness of experimental data. Furthermore, nobody really cares, except possibly for certain practical applications, how many rats, for example, emit 100 extinction responses after 20 reinforcements, and how many emit 200, etc. Such variability concerns the systematic experimenter only insofar as it tells him that he does not possess the information and technical skill to obtain the data in which he is really interested. It tells him he has a considerable amount of work to do before he can even begin to assess the representativeness of his data. The spread around a mean value gives little information about the orderly relations, such as those of Figures 1 and 2, whose variability such a spread reflects. If it can be shown that a given factor produces the same *kind* of lawfulness in the individuals of the population, then the finding has great generality, in spite of the fact that quantitative differences are still observed. It is the generality of such lawful relations that should be of primary concern, and not the representativeness of specific numbers taken out of context.

All this is not to suggest that quantitative variability can be ignored, as later chapters will indicate. The topic was brought in here only to illustrate the inadequacy of traditional conceptions of variability in determining the representativeness of experimental findings. It is probably worth while, at this point, to pay some attention also to the complaint, "But what about those experimental problems that are, by their very nature, not amenable to investigation with individual subjects? Is not the traditional statistical evaluation of generality the only course open to us in such cases?"

The first answer to this plaintive question is that such situations are becoming increasingly rare. New and ingenious techniques have greatly reduced the number of behavioral phenomena that seem amenable only to group-statistical treatment, and more may be expected to fall by the wayside as experimental control becomes more refined. But the key to most of these techniques lies in the reversibility of behavioral phenomena. If an experimental manipulation produces an irreversible change in the aspect of an individual's behavior that we are observing, it may prove extremely difficult, if not impossible, to obtain functional relations of the sort depicted in Figures 1 and 2. And, although the evidence is hardly conclusive at present, some behavioral processes may indeed prove to be irreversible.

If true irreversibility should be encountered, there is a straightforward solution available: to study such processes *as they occur in nature*. An irreversible process must be accepted as such, and the techniques for studying it must take the property of irreversibility into account. Irreversibility, if it can be demonstrated unequivocally, will be a fundamental property of any behavior that displays it, and it cannot be side-stepped. Group statistics is certainly not the answer. An irreversible behavioral process exists in the individual, and has no continuity from one group of subjects to another.

Let us take, as an example, the classical problem of the relation between number of reinforcements and resistance to extinction; and let us accept, for now at least, the assumption that an original exposure to experimental extinction exercises an irreversible influence upon later exposures. This assumption would seem to preclude any attempt to use an individual subject to determine the functional relation between number of reinforcements and resistance to extinction, for this would require repeated exposures of the subject to the extinction procedure following interpolated periods of reconditioning with varied numbers of reinforcements. But the successive extinction operations would supposedly be contaminated by the previous ones, and the resulting data would not be a pure function of the number of reinforcements; they would be a function also of the preceding extinction operations.

The usual solution to this problem has been to expose separate groups of subjects to each value of the independent variable, number of reinforcements, and then to expose each group just once to experimental extinction. The results of this procedure will provide us with some useful practical information. If the data are properly treated, we will be able to make an estimate of the number of reinforcements to give a subject if we wish, for some experimental purpose, to generate a given resistance to extinction. The degree of precision with which we will be satisfied will depend upon the task at hand. But the function so obtained does not represent a behavioral process. The use of separate groups destroys the continuity of cause and effect that characterizes an irreversible behavioral process. "Uncontaminated" extinction data obtained from separate groups will yield a functional relation that has no counterpart in the behavior of the individual. The function obtained from the individual is the result of an interactive process that extends from one segment of the subject's behavior to another. The empirical points on the function obtained from separate groups bear no such relation to each other.

If it proves impossible to obtain an uncontaminated relation between number of reinforcements and resistance to extinction in a single subject, because of the fact that successive extinctions interact with each other, then the "pure" relation simply does not exist. The solution to our problem is to cease trying to discover such a pure relation, and to direct our research toward the study of behavior as it actually exists. If reversibility does not exist in nature, it does not exist in the laboratory.

The fact that a group function may have no counterpart in the behavior of the individual is independent of the problem of whether a group curve can have the same form as the individual curve. The latter problem has had ample discussion in the literature (5, 27, 41, 55, 68). The case I have been discussing is one in which the individual and group curves simply cannot provide the same information, even if their forms should be identical. The distinction between the two types of function can be made not on the basis of mathematical or logical reasoning but rather on the grounds of the behavioral phenomena they represent. Where irreversibility is met, there is no individual curve that can answer the questions one may put to the group curve, or vice versa. The student should not be deceived into concluding that the group type of experiment in any way provides a more adequately controlled or more generalizable substitute for individual data.

If my point strikes home, it should lead the student to re-evaluate much of the supposedly systematic data of experimental psychology. He will find that this distinction has not often been made, and that the two types of data, group and individual, are frequently intermingled within a single systematic framework. In consequence, there is a large job of disentangling to be accomplished. When this is done, the student may find that he must abandon many of psychology's cherished generalizations. He is also likely to find himself faced with a choice. For the two types of data represent, in a very real sense, two different subject matters. He will find, in fact, that some experimenters and systematists have already made their choice as to which of these types of data, individual or group, will form the bases of the science they are trying to build. This choice does not necessarily represent narrowness of interest. It is often the result of a well-considered and conscious decision about the type of data most appropriate for a science of behavior. In every area of science, there are critical times when such decisions must be made, and the consequences are far-reaching. If the correct decision is generally accepted, the science will advance. If the incorrect choice is adopted, the science will experience a period of stagnation until the situation is righted. If the decision is not made at all, the result can lead to a hopeless confusion of basically incompatible data and principles. In the argument that eclecticism is the road to generality may lie the trap of indecision.

INTERSPECIES GENERALITY. Are experimental findings obtained with one species generalizable to other species of organism? This is the problem of interspecies generality, and it has an unfortunate historical background. The solution propounded by many psychologists represents one of the last vestiges of the fallacy of man as the center of the universe. The fact of evolutionary change is accepted in other areas of biology; nevertheless, Behaving Human is often held to represent a discontinuous leap from Behaving Subhuman. Even many of those who do consider human behavior to have developed through a normal evolutionary process still think of man as something special. Furthermore, not only is man's behavior held to be different in principle from that of other organisms, but the behavior of *any* species is sometimes alleged to be different from the next lower one. With each evolutionary step, some advance must presumably have been made toward that ultimate achievement of which the psychologist is supposedly an example.

This prejudice has produced a curious solution to the problem of species generality of behavioral data. Comparative psychology has become a discipline devoted largely to discovering *differences* in the behavior of various species of organism. When similarities, the stuff of which most sciences are made, are found, they are dismissed as unimportant phenomena. Differences that point toward the development of higher-order processes as man is approached along the phylogenetic scale are selected as the only worthwhile comparative data.

A comparative psychology that seeks to determine differences rather than similarities among species really has an easy time of it. Differences are not difficult to find. Any experiment in which species is the variable of major concern will also involve differences in other important variables linked with the species continuum. For example, cats and monkeys differ not only in phylogenetic classification but also in the kinds and quantities of reinforcers that will maintain their behavior, in the kinds and degrees of deprivation that are feasible, in manipulative skill, in sensory acuity, in life span, etc. Because of the difficulty in equating such factors, differences among species might easily result from them rather than from species classification *per se.*

Let us examine a hypothetical experiment in comparative psychology. A grape is held before a monkey and then, while the beast appears to be watching, the grape is placed under one of two different boxes. A screen is then lowered between the monkey and the boxes so that the animal can neither see nor reach them. After a period of time has elapsed, the screen is raised and the monkey can overturn the boxes. The experimenter observes whether the monkey selects the "correct" box, *i.e.*, the one with the grape underneath. The experiment is repeated with longer and longer time intervals between the lowering and raising of the screen, and the maximum period over which the animal can "remember" which box contains the grape is determined.

A comparative study is then undertaken, with dog as the subject. But dogs do not normally eat grapes, so steak is substituted. It is found (let us suppose) that monkey is able to delay its response without error for a longer time than is dog. Since the delayed response is obviously a "higher function," it is not surprising to the comparative psychologist that monkey, a much closer relative than dog to comparative psychologist, is the superior performer.

But what would have happened if the dog had been deprived of food for three days? Or if twice as much meat had been placed in the box? Or if either or both of the animals had been older or younger? Or if the experiment had been conducted in semidarkness? Or if horsemeat and oranges had been substituted for steak and grapes? It is entirely possible that factors such as these would have altered the results of the experiment, either increasing the apparent superiority of the monkey or giving the dog the advantage.

There is no sure way out of this difficulty. If it were possible to arrange optimal conditions for both species, we could make a comparison of the optimal performances. But we do not have the knowledge at present to set up such an experiment. As matters now stand, variations in any of several known or suspected parameters might reverse our evaluation of the species generality of delayed response experiments. What, then, do we look for in order to gauge the species generality of experimental data? This brings us back to the same question we encountered in the case of subject generality—namely, generality of what? The following is only a partial listing of the types of generality one may seek to determine. (It may be noted also that these aspects of generality are important in their own right, independent of the problems of subject and species generality.)

Generality of variables. In the present relatively primitive state of behavioral science, it is important to determine whether a given variable or class of variables is relevant outside the confines of a particular experiment. Generality so defined may be determined by altering some aspects of the original experiment or by performing new and seemingly unrelated experiments. One may employ the same subjects throughout, or other subjects of the same species or an entirely different species. If it can be shown that a given variable influences behavior in all, or even several, such experiments, one form of generality will have been achieved.

Intermittency of reinforcement, for example, is a variable of wide generality with respect to its effect upon resistance to extinction. If a rat receives a food reinforcement for every lever-pressing response (continuous reinforcement), a certain number of responses will be emitted even after we make the food-delivery mechanism inoperative, so that no further food reinforcements appear (extinction). But if we originally reinforce only those responses that follow the preceding reinforcement after, for example, two minutes, then a much larger number of responses will subsequently be emitted in extinction, after we have disconnected the feeder (81, pp. 133 ff.). The fact that we reinforce only a relatively small proportion of the animal's responses seems to make the behavior more persistent after reinforcement is withdrawn completely. The generality of this variable has been established in a number of ways. Intermittent reinforcement still increases resistance to extinction, for example, when we employ different schedules of intermittency. We can deliver reinforcements after variable, rather than fixed, periods of time, or we can make reinforcements contingent upon fixed or varied numbers of responses. Furthermore, intermittency has a similar effect upon the extinction of behavior that is under other kinds of control than positive reinforcement. If a response is depressed by occasionally punishing it with shocks, it will take a longer time for the behavior to recover after the punishment is discontinued than if the shock had been given consistently for every response (26). Also, if an animal is unavoidably shocked at the termination of, say, a five-minute warning stimulus, its ongoing behavior will ordinarily cease during the period of stimulus presentation (29). The animal will soon recover the behavior, however, if the stimulus is permitted to terminate without any accompanying shock. But if the shocks are originally given not along with every stimulus but only with a small proportion of them, it will take the behavior a much longer time to return to normal after the shocks have been discontinued (76).

In addition to these and other types of experimental situation, intermittency of reinforcement has been shown to exercise a similar effect when other forms of response are studied, and in other species, including human. Even though intermittency does not have the same quantitative effect in all cases—there are even some conditions under which it actually decreases resistance to extinction—

the fact that the variable is so widely effective is an important generalization.

When quantitative dissimilarities are observed, the experimenter is faced with a further investigative problem. In the case of reinforcement intermittency, for example, subsequent study has revealed a number of contributory factors which can serve to attenuate, or otherwise modify, the basic finding. If intermittent reinforcements are made dependent upon the emission of a fixed number of responses, the characteristics of subsequent extinction behavior will be quite different from the case in which reinforcements are delivered after fixed periods of time (81, pp. 293 ff.). The stage of conditioning at which extinction is begun will also be a relevant factor, as will more remote historical conditions. But the qualitative fact that a given variable is effective in several different experimental contexts and/or with different species of organism is a basic form of generality that must be achieved before a more sophisticated analysis can be accomplished.

There is an important distinction between the methods for evaluating subject generality and those for evaluating the generality of a variable. Subject generality can be assessed, at least partially, in terms of the number of successful replications that have been achieved among the members of a given species. There is no straightforward way of assessing the generality of a variable, for each successive experiment that serves to extend such generality is necessarily different in some way from the preceding ones. In the case of intermittent reinforcement, for instance, is greater generality achieved by means of those experiments in which the reinforcement schedule was varied, or in the ones that used techniques of aversive control? No one has yet devised a successful statistical technique for answering such a question. Nor is there any technique to be derived rigorously from the rules of logic.

There is, in fact, no objective criterion, derivable from any source, which permits an unequivocal answer to this question. And, I may add, the same holds true for process generality, to be discussed below. When replication is systematic rather than direct (see Chapters 3 and 4), evaluative criteria necessarily involve areas of judgment which are beyond any presently known methods of quantification. We have here, in miniature form, the unsolved problem of inductive reasoning.

INDUCTION AND THE EVALUATION OF GENERALITY. I have no intention of launching a treatise on induction for it would be well beyond the scope of this book. But I have referred to induction previously, in contrasting it to the deductive method of theorizing (page 14), and I shall have occasion to mention it again, either explicitly or indirectly in connection with the role of experience in the evaluation of data. A few words, therefore, about induction, which I have adapted from Polya's fascinating little book, *Induction and Analogy in Mathematics* (63).

Polya comes, I believe, as close to the heart of the matter as anyone has ever come, in a sentence which describes the *inductive attitude*. "This attitude aims at adapting our beliefs to our experience as efficiently as possible" (63, p. 7). If he were familiar with the language of behavioral analysis, Polya might well have recast his statement to read, "Our inductive behavior is a function of our reinforcement history." Induction is a behavioral process, not a logical one, which is the reason logical analysis has failed to account for it. Whether or not we make an inductive inference, and the degree of tenacity with which we cling to that inference, will depend upon our behavioral history (experience). I refer to this history when I say that the evaluation of generality is a matter of judgment. From an act of induction based upon our own accumulated experience, we judge the amount of generality to be added to a variable when it proves effective in experiments that have little or no operational connection with each other.

Lest the student feel that I have gone too far in interpreting Polya's statement about induction, let me also quote the following; the last sentence speaks for itself:

> Experience modifies human behavior. . . .
>
> Yes, and it modifies animal behavior too.
>
> In my neighborhood there is a mean dog that barks and jumps at people without provocation. But I have found that I can protect myself rather easily. If I stoop and pretend to pick up a stone, the dog runs away howling. All dogs do not behave so, and it is easy to guess what kind of experience gave this dog this behavior.

The bear in the zoo "begs for food." That is, when there is an onlooker around, it strikes a ridiculous posture which quite frequently prompts the onlooker to throw a lump of sugar into the cage. Bears not in captivity probably never assume such a preposterous posture and it is easy to imagine what kind of experience led to the zoo bear's begging.

A thorough investigation of induction should include, perhaps, the study of animal behavior (63, p. 10).

In establishing the generality of a variable, of a process, of a method, etc., we are trying to verify our initial observations within an ever-widening set of conditions. Polya has suggested one basis upon which scientists evaluate the degree of verification contributed by any given extension of the conditions. His discussion is couched in terms of the verification of a "conjecture," but the appropriate substitutions are easy to make:

The mental procedures of the trained naturalist are not essentially different from those of the common man, but they are more thorough. Both the common man and the scientist are led to conjectures by a few observations and they are both paying attention to later cases which could be in agreement or not with the conjecture. A case in agreement makes the conjecture more likely, a conflicting case disproves it, and here the difference begins: Ordinary people are usually more apt to look for the first kind of cases, but the scientist looks for the second kind. The reason is that everybody has a little vanity, the common man as the scientist, but different people take pride in different things. Mr. Anybody does not like to confess, even to himself, that he was mistaken and so he does not like conflicting cases, he avoids them, he is even inclined to explain them away when they present themselves. The scientist, on the contrary, is ready enough to recognize a mistaken conjecture, but he does not like to leave questions undecided. Now, a case in agreement does not settle the question definitively, but a conflicting case does. The scientist, seeking a definitive decision, looks for cases which have a chance to upset the conjecture, and the more chance they have, the more they are welcome. There is an important point to observe. If a case which threatens to upset the conjecture turns out, after all, to be in agreement with it, the conjecture emerges greatly strengthened from the test. The more danger, the more honor; passing the most threatening examination grants the highest recognition, the strongest experimental evidence to the conjecture. There are instances and instances, verifications and verifications. An instance which is *more likely to be conflicting* brings the conjecture in any case nearer to decision than an instance which is less so, and this explains the preference of the scientist. . . .

A case little different from previously examined cases, if it agrees with the conjecture, adds to our confidence, of course, but it adds little. In fact we easily believe, before the test, that the case at hand will behave as the previous cases from which it differs but little. We desire not only another verification, but a *verification of another kind* . . . (63, p. 41).

If we apply this criterion to our own problem (page 58), we might then decide that the experiment involving the warning stimulus and unavoidable shock adds the greatest amount of generality to the intermittency variable. For in that experiment we altered not only the temporal schedule of reinforcement but also the type of reinforcement (from food to shock), and, by making the shock unavoidable, we eliminated any necessary relation between it and the measured behavior. There is a hint here, perhaps, of an objective criterion for assessing the amount of difference between two cases and, thereby, for evaluating the degree of confirmation provided by each. But a simple count of the number of procedural differences does not do the job. All procedural changes cannot be given equal weight, for they are not all equally likely to alter the results of an experiment. The weight to be assigned to any given change in the experimental conditions will depend upon both the general state of existing knowledge in the scientific area in question and the acquaintance that any particular scientist has developed with respect to that area. The degree of confidence that prevails in a scientific community with respect to any particular induction will, therefore, be a function of the extent to which the members of that community share a common history of experience.

GENERALITY OF PROCESS. The term "behavioral process" is generally used in either of two senses. One of these refers to the interaction of variables. When several different variables or experimental operations interact, we often characterize the resulting behavior as a process. For example, reinforcement and extinction operations may be combined in such a way as to yield a behavioral process that we are accustomed to call "discrimination." Or reinforcement contingencies may be set up in such a way that different forms of behavior combine in a process called "timing." The identification of such processes, insofar as they are complex interactions of several "elementary" variables, represents an integrative advance. But the demonstration of process generality among species is sometimes difficult to accomplish. The very complexity of a behavioral process hinders evaluation of all the relevant factors, both quantitative and qualitative.

The problems are multiplied when replication is attempted with a new species. For this reason, the careful worker will not even attempt to demonstrate the existence of a behavioral process in a new species until he has fairly thoroughly explored its varied aspects with his original subjects. An unsuccessful attempt is wasteful not only in terms of time and expense but also in terms of useful data that might have been obtained in its place if the unsuccessful generalization had been postponed. The point at which it is feasible to seek process generality among species is a problem whose solution will depend upon the experience of the particular scientist and of others working in the same general area.

Accumulated experience may indicate that process generality in a given area of research is relatively easy to achieve, so that many experimenters may prefer not even to attempt the demonstration for a given process. In such a case the problem may be passed on to a student working for his master's degree, or even to the members of an undergraduate laboratory course. It is important that the experiments be performed, if only to keep those working in a given area from taking too much for granted. They may serve the important function of pointing up the need for further exploration of phenomena that were thought to be well understood.

On the other hand in some areas process generality may be notoriously difficult to achieve. The experimenter will then be cautious in his program of research. It must be pointed out, however, that a failure to demonstrate generality in other species does not negate the possible importance of a behavioral process. Variability, whether within or between species, results not from the precocity of experimental subjects but from ignorance on the part of the investigator.

The behavior of the subject is lawful with respect to controlling variables. Failure to replicate a finding, within or among species, is a result of incomplete understanding of the controlling variables. This positive approach, as contrasted to the negative attitude that failure to replicate must brand a process as nongeneral, is actually the only road to an adequate evaluation of generality. Most experimenters are careful about claiming that an effect is "real." But scientific caution does not so generally prevail when experiments fail to demonstrate a phenomenon. Yet the false negative is just as costly an error as the false positive. Acceptance of the latter may undermine the usefulness of later work, but the former will prevent much useful work from being attempted and may impede progress for a considerable time.

There are occasions when demonstrations of process generality may appear trivial. What is gained, for example, when it is shown that the phenomenon called "transposition" (88) is common to both humans and monkeys? Actually, each time we successfully extrapolate a process to another organism we are likely to accomplish more than the extension of a restricted phenomenon. This is particularly true if the process in question is only a segment of a wider systematization. In such a case extension of one aspect of the system increases the likelihood that other aspects possess a similar degree of generality. Suppose, for example, that a process we might call "discriminated extinction" is observed in both Species *A* and Species *B*. Discriminated extinction is a name for the observed gradual decline in extinction responding over a series of alternating reconditioning and extinction experiments (62). Confirmation of this particular process in Species *B* will also extend our confidence in the applicability to Species *B* of many related principles of conditioning and extinction.

Satisfactory process generalization never requires exact replication of every part of a system. How many individual demonstrations of generality do we require before accepting the generality of a whole framework? There is no simple quantitative answer to this question. The stopping point will vary with such considerations as the complexity of the successful generalizations, their obviousness, the reputation of the experimenters who are involved, the magnitude of the demonstrated effects, the cohesiveness of the system as a whole, the particular species to which generalization is achieved, and other qualitative judgments in which the maturity of a science and of its member scientists plays a dominant role.

The second sense in which we use the term, behavioral process, actually represents the quantitative aspect of variable generality. By determining the effects of a wide range of quantitative values of a given variable, one can obtain a more complete picture of its mode of action. The picture can be presented in the form of a curve which quantitatively relates some measure of behavior to different values of the experimental variable. We might find that the behavioral measure increases linearly as the experimental variable increases in magnitude; or that the behavior increases, passes through a maximal value, and then decreases; or any of an infinite number of other possible functional relations. We often then characterize the observed functional relation as a behavioral process. It tells us how the state of behavior changes in response to systematic variations in at least one of its controlling conditions.

Generality may then be investigated by attempting to replicate the function under new experimental conditions and/or with other organisms. When the function is determined for different species, we have the foundations of a true science of comparative psychology. The question we are asking is whether a given variable influences behavior similarly in various species. Does the variable act similarly over its whole range of possible values? Does it generate the same behavioral process in several species? We might find, for example, in rats, that the rate of avoidance responding under certain conditions bears a logarithmic relation to the length of time each avoidance response postpones shock (see Figure 27, Chapter 8). We might then seek species generality by determining whether the logarithmic relation also holds for cats, pigeons, monkeys, and humans. If it does hold up, we will have achieved more than simple variable generality. We will know not only that the variable is effective in all the species we have checked but in addition that it exercises its effects in a quantitatively similar fashion over its whole range of values.

Even here, however, a negative answer cannot be accepted as final. Suppose we find, for example, that, with cat as subject, the functional relation is linear rather than logarithmic. We still do not know whether changes in other parameters of the function might be responsible for the difference. Perhaps shock intensity is critical. We might find that in both species the functional relation gradually shades over from a logarithmic to a linear one as we systematically vary shock intensity. Changes in other variables may thus produce similarities where only differences had previously been found. It is for this reason that the investigator should refrain from checking species generality until he has first checked the generality of the process under varied conditions with the original species. Premature attempts to demonstrate species generality may be wasteful of time and effort; they may also produce misleading conclusions.

How close a replication should satisfy us in evaluating the generality of a functional relation? Shall we seek exact quantitative replication from one species to another, or from one set of auxiliary conditions to another? The precision one will demand in evaluating the generality of a functional relation will depend upon the current state of development of the science. In some cases one might be content if the various species all yielded, say, an increasing function, regardless of whether that function were linear, logarithmic, exponential, etc. In other cases, one might be satisfied with similarity in the *form* of the functional relation, as it is described by the appropriate mathematical expression, without insisting upon an exact correspondence among the constants of the expression. Rarely, in psychology, are we in a position to require exact numerical replication of a functional relation. Our techniques of experimental control are, in general, not adequate for such a task. What degree of generality we can achieve will be determined in large part by the precision of our experimental techniques.

METHODOLOGICAL GENERALITY. Demonstrations of the generality of experimental techniques from one species to another are an important type of scientific advance. This is particularly true of behavioral control techniques. Take as an example the control of behavior through manipulation of reinforcement schedules. While there is still much to be learned about the properties of reinforcement schedules, a wide degree of generality has been achieved with respect to their effects upon the behavior of different species, from octopus to man. One reason for the importance of demonstrating the generality of such techniques stems from the fact that not all species are equally convenient as experimental subjects. Laboratory control techniques may and should possess a degree of rigor and precision that would be unthinkable under the prevailing ethical code if human beings were the experimental subjects. Thus those investigators whose ultimate interest is human behavior have two courses open to them. They may use humans in their laboratory experiments, deliberately renouncing a high degree of rigor and precision in the hope that the variables they manipulate will prove sufficiently powerful to yield meaningful data; or they may get a satisfactory degree of experimental control by using lower animals as subjects in their experiments in the hope that their data will later prove generalizable, directly or indirectly, to humans.

With the latter course, demonstration of the species generality of the control techniques is of paramount importance. When one technique is shown to be applicable to several species, we gain additional confidence for related techniques. Some techniques—for example, aversive control methods—are not likely to be testable with humans as subjects. This situation is not peculiar to psychology, and the solution of the problem for psychologists must be the same one as that employed in such other sciences as pharmacology. The techniques must be applied to a variety of lower organisms approaching man as closely as possible. The greater the number of species to which a technique can be extended, the greater can be our confidence that it is also applicable to humans. The final extension to human behavior may then be made not on the basis of the method itself but rather on the basis of information gained from the use of the method with lower organisms, applying the principles derived from the method to human behavior and performing, with humans, permissible experiments based on a rationale derived from the earlier work.

Sometimes a technique of behavioral control will prove to be effective in manipulating human behavior but will not replicate the data obtained from other species. As a hypothetical example, a fixed-interval reinforcement schedule may produce a characteristic temporal pattern of responding in a human subject, but this pattern may not be quite the same as that displayed by a pigeon. The schedule exercises a controlling effect in both cases, but the types of control are different. The first task of the experimenter would then be to determine whether other parameters than species might be responsible for the differences. By manipulating other variables, can the pigeon behavior be made to look like the human behavior, and vice versa? Even if the attempt proves unsuccessful, extension of the control technique to human behavior would remain a worthwhile contribution. Another avenue of approach to the study of human behavior would have been made available. Nor would the application of the technique to lower species represent wasted effort. For we would then have a true difference among species, perhaps an important difference, which could never have been properly evaluated without the background of information gained through the study of lower organisms.

Part II
Replication

OFTEN, SCIENCE is thought of as a methodology for the objective evaluation of evidence, a methodology rigorous enough to eliminate most human error. By this definition we should be able, by means of experiment, to find unequivocal answers to all natural problems, both animate and inanimate. Both professional writers and scientists, in their attempts to popularize science, tend to encourage the impression that science is infallible, at least within its own domain. Theories can be incorrect or inadequate—Einstein's destruction of Newtonian physics is a modern fable—but experimental facts, it is assumed, are incontrovertible.

The myth that science is a discipline in which a fact may be accepted as a fact on grounds divorced from personal or other arbitrary considerations is still accepted by many scientists themselves. Facts are indeed, by definition, unassailable. But a close look at experimental method as it is actually practiced will lead one to wonder just what a fact is. To the neutral observer it will be obvious that science is far from free of human bias, even in its evaluation of factual evidence. Experimental findings, furthermore, are so fragile when considered within the total matrix of natural phenomena from which they are lifted, and conclusions from such data often so tenuous, that one can only feel surprise at the actual achievements of experimental methodology. What must we work with in any experiment? Uncontrolled, and even unknown, variables; the errors of selective perception arising out of theoretical and observational bias; indirect measurements; the theory involved in the measurement techniques themselves; the assumptions involved in making the leap from data to interpretation. In short, we have a margin of error so great that any true advance might be considered an accident were it not for the fact that too many genuine advances have occurred in too short a time for the hypothesis to be entertained seriously.

Modern logicians are attempting to systematize the rules of scientific evidence, in order to characterize the adequacy of such evidence in terms of numerical probabilities. Their success thus far has not been substantial probably because scientific *practice* in the evaluation of evidence remains essentially pragmatic. Insofar as they exist at all, rules of evidence have developed out of a long history of scientific experience. The criteria scientists utilize range from objective considerations, such as the precision of the measuring instruments, to highly personal judgments concerning the adequacy of the experimenter. Some types of evidence are given more weight than others; a given sample of evidence may be considered more or less adequate depending upon the questions being asked by the experimenter. The remaining discussion is intended to describe some of the major evaluative criteria as they are actually used.

The soundest empirical test of the reliability of data is provided by replication. There are, however, several types of replication;

some command greater respect than others; some provide more than simply an indication of reliability. The value placed on specific replicative techniques results not from *a priori* logical considerations but from a background of scientific accomplishment. The experience and judgment of the individual scientist are always involved in the evaluation of data.

Chapter 3

Direct Replication

THE SIMPLEST REPLICATIVE TECHNIQUE is the repetition of a given experiment by the same investigator. Direct replication may be accomplished either by performing the experiment again with new subjects or by making repeated observations on the same subjects under each of several experimental conditions. Depending upon whether the data are presented as group statistics or in terms of the behavior of individual subjects, we term replication with *new* subjects, "intergroup," or "intersubject," replication, respectively. When the *original* subjects are retained, we use the terms, "intragroup," or "intrasubject" replication.

In psychological experiments that employ large populations and group-data techniques, repetition is rare. I noted earlier that such repetition would indeed help to establish the reliability of the central tendency, but would bear little, if any, relevance to the question of generality or representativeness with respect to individuals. Replication of individual data, however, may permit a direct assessment of both the reliability and generality of a phenomenon.

INTERSUBJECT REPLICATION

When an experiment is performed with a single organism as the subject, intersubject replication is often demanded on the grounds that the original subject may have been a "freak." Another school of thought argues that there are no freaks, that any carefully obtained data are real data, never to be ignored. Whether an experiment is to be replicated with other subjects will depend upon the experimenter's judgment of the adequacy of the techniques and his confidence in the consistency of his data within an established body of knowledge.

If the investigator has some reason to suspect that his technique may have been faulty, or if the technique is a new one with which he has not had much experience, he is likely to employ additional subjects. Similarly, if his findings seem to be at variance with other data, or if that rare case occurs in which the data seem to open up a new area of research for which there is little, if any, background, the experiment is likely to be repeated. As long as the techniques are considered sound, however, the experiment is never repeated solely for the purpose of finding out whether the observed phenomena are "real." The reality of the original finding is taken for granted. The purpose of intersubject replication is to determine whether uncontrolled and/or unknown variables might be powerful enough to prevent successful repetition. If this proves to be the case, failure of intersubject replication will serve as a spur to further research rather than lead to a simple rejection of the original data. I will return to this topic below, and again in the chapters on Variability, for its implications do not seem to be widely understood among psychologists.

Direct Replication

Experimenters who decide whether or not to attempt intersubject replication on the basis of their own experience with their techniques and with a particular area of knowledge must accept an inevitable consequence. An investigator may, on the basis of experience, have great confidence in the adequacy of this methodology, but other experimenters cannot be expected to share his confidence without convincing evidence. This evidence takes time to accumulate. It will consist of demonstrated replicability of his work by other experimenters and internal consistency of the findings as demonstrated by systematic replication (see Chapter 4).

Even the personality and character of the experimenter will be taken into consideration by his colleagues and peers. For example, a man may reveal, in casual conversation, an inordinate ambition for political success within his profession, or serious deficiencies in his personal ethical standards. In which case, his scientific products are likely to be regarded as outgrowths of his extrascientific activities and therefore as requiring an even greater amount of validation than usual.

As a criterion of reliability and generality, intersubject replication is a more powerful tool than intergroup replication. Intergroup replication provides an indicator of reliability insofar as it demonstrates that changes in central tendency for a group can be repeated. With respect to generality, however, intergroup replication does not answer the question of how many individuals the data actually represent. With intersubject replication, on the other hand, each additional experiment increases the representativeness of the findings. Indeed, replication of an experiment with two subjects establishes greater generality for the data among the individuals of a population than does replication with two groups of subjects whose individual data have been combined.

In contrast to group-statistical experiments, in which intergroup replication seldom occurs, individual subject experiments that utilize more than one subject automatically contain intersubject replications. Each subject constitutes at least an attempted replication of the experiment. In biological research, for example, it is common to find every subject listed as a separate experiment even when the same operations have been performed in each case.

Upon how many individuals must an experiment be replicated before the data can be considered representative? Psychologists have not given this question the intensive analysis its importance warrants; for one reason, because only recently has the number of investigations employing individual subjects become large enough to make a perceptible impression upon the mass of psychological data published each year. The problem is only now becoming critical to psychologists. A more important set of contributing factors arises from the subtle considerations of both a qualitative and quantitative nature involved in deciding how many replications of a given experiment are desirable. At this point I will only indicate some of the gross problems that must be faced in any attempt to develop a "statistics of replication." Such a methodology would have to take actual scientific practice as its point of departure, foı there is no question of the efficacy of the practice, however informal its rules may be.

Let us start off with the example presented in Figure 3. It will be necessary to describe the experimental procedure in some detail,

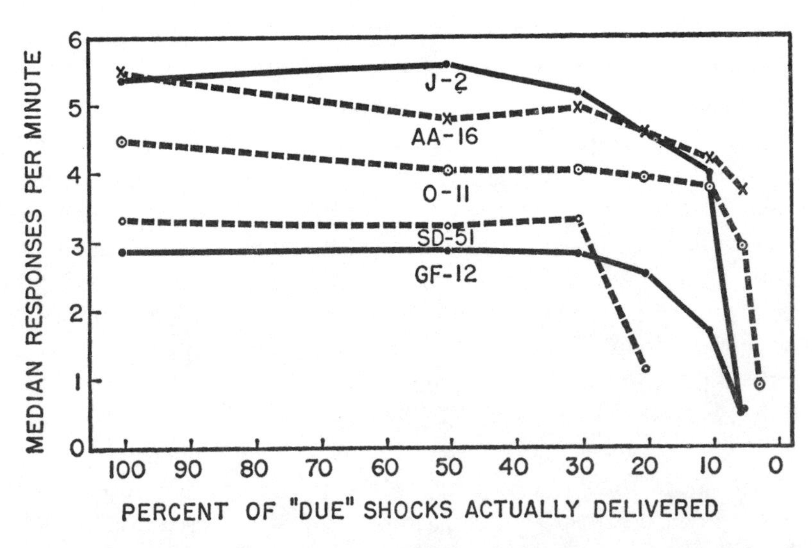

FIGURE 3. A set of five curves, each from a different experimental subject, showing the relation between rate of avoidance responding and the percentage of shocks delivered to the subjects. (*From Boren and Sidman*, 13.)

for, as we shall see later, data cannot be evaluated adequately in terms of numbers alone.

These data are from an experiment on avoidance behavior, with rats as subjects (13). At the start of the experiment, the animal received a brief shock every 20 seconds. Shock could be avoided, however, if the animal pressed a small lever. Each downward excursion of the lever postponed the next shock for 20 seconds. Thus, by pressing the lever often enough, the animal could keep postponing the shock indefinitely. No rats actually attain such a peak performance, but most of them do learn to press the lever and thus avoid the large majority of shocks, with some receiving less than ten shocks during a six-hour experimental session. In the curve of Rat J-2, in Figure 3, the point at the extreme left represents the average rate of lever pressing (about 5.3 responses per minute) on the procedure just described.

The procedure may be thought of as one in which a shock becomes "due" every time the animal waits 20 seconds without pressing the lever. As described thus far, the animal receives a shock every time it waits 20 seconds without depressing the lever. One hundred per cent of the shocks "due" the animal for failure to press the lever are actually delivered. The remainder of the experiment was directed at the problem of what would happen to the rate of lever pressing if some of the "due" shocks were not delivered. Thus, Rat J-2's rate of avoidance behavior was subsequently observed when only 50 per cent of the "due" shocks were actually delivered, and then 30, 20, 10, and 5 per cent, in that order. At the lowest value, for example, the animal received a shock on only 5 per cent of those occasions on which it waited 20 seconds without pressing the lever.

In carrying through the experiment, the problem of how long to expose the animal to each of the shock percentages arose. On the basis of preliminary experimentation, it was decided to run the experiment for seven six-hour sessions at each shock percentage. The first three sessions were then discarded as constituting a period of transition, and the median of the average response rates for the final four sessions at each shock percentage was taken as representing the final stable state at that value.

Let us now examine the curve that represents the behavior of

Rat J-2. Over a wide range of shock percentages, from 100 to 30 per cent, there is little change in the response rate. There is then a marked drop in response rate as the shock percentage drops from 30 to 5 per cent. These two features, the initial flat portion of the curve followed by the final drop in rate, provide a general picture of the data. There are, however, many other details, such as the slight rise at 50 per cent, the extremely sharp drop almost to zero between 10 and 5 per cent, and the actual numerical values of each of the individual points on the curve. All of these features must be taken into consideration in making a decision as to whether to attempt intersubject replication.

Mitigating against replication is the over-all orderliness of the data. With six points on the curve, there was considerable opportunity for irregularities to occur, yet the changes are essentially continuous, certainly within the limits of variability that most experimenters have come to expect in behavioral investigations. The regularity of the curve also compares favorably with other work done in the same laboratory. Such considerations lead to a high degree of confidence in the trustworthiness of the data. In fact, if subsequent replication with other animals did not confirm the findings, our course of action would not be to reject the data of Rat J-2, but rather to inquire experimentally into the reasons for the differences.

In the present case, however, one major consideration called for replication of the data. The flat portion of the curve from 100 to 30 per cent did not seem consistent with the results of other related experiments. It will be worth considering this apparent inconsistency in some detail, for its nature must be taken into account in determining how many replications will be necessary. Disagreement with a well-established finding makes new data more suspect, and requires a greater degree of confirmation, than does a discrepancy with data that are themselves tenuous. The logician or statistician who wishes to quantify the adequacy of replication must find some way to translate this criterion into numerical terms. That is to say, when replication is called for because of disagreement with previous findings, the required amount of replication will be a function of the degree to which the previous findings were solidly established.

What is the problem raised by the curve of Rat J-2? If we consider first the 100 per cent shock schedule, we see that it is possible to specify the extent of the time interval by which *every* lever-pressing response postpones the next shock. This interval, *controlled by the experimenter*, is 20 seconds. The shock delay accomplished by each occurrence of the response has been termed the "response-shock interval." The effects of the magnitude of the response-shock interval upon the rate of behavior that postpones shock have been extensively investigated in a number of species, with several variations in the basic procedure and even with other noxious events than electric shock. The general finding, with some qualifications in detail, has been that the rate of response is an inverse function of the response-shock interval (see Figure 27). As we increase the duration of the time interval that may elapse between a response and the next shock, the rate of occurrence of the response declines.

Let us now examine the 50 per cent shock schedule in terms of the effect this manipulation may have on the interval between response and shock. Let us suppose the experiment is in progress and the animal has just pressed the lever. The next 20 seconds passes without a lever press, and a shock may then be delivered. But according to the 50 per cent shock schedule we have set up, there is an equal probability that there will be *no* shock at the end of the 20 seconds. In that case, an additional 20-second period may elapse without a response, and after the total of 40 seconds without a lever press there is again a 50-50 chance that the shock will be delivered. (Note: At the end of each consecutive 20-second interval of no responding, the probability of shock will be 0.5 only if the sequence set up in the programing apparatus is a random one. Although a random sequence was not employed in this experiment, the main point of the discussion remains valid.) Let us suppose that the shock does occur at this point. Forty seconds will have elapsed between the shock and the preceding lever press. This amounts to doubling the 20-second response-shock interval that inevitably occurred on the 100 per cent shock schedule. On the basis of previous findings, we should expect a corresponding decline in response rate.

We can apply a similar analysis to the 30 per cent shock case. Here the probability that a shock will occur after 20 seconds of no response is only 0.33. There is thus an even greater likelihood that the animal will experience response-shock intervals greater than 20 seconds. But the data do not seem to be consistent with these probabilities. Our previous generalization that response rate is an inverse function of response-shock interval does not seem to hold up in the case of Rat J-2. In spite of the longer response-shock intervals which the 50 and 30 per cent shock schedules seem to make possible, there is no decline in response rate over this portion of the curve. The first step, therefore, was to determine whether the data obtained from Rat J-2 were reproducible, or whether they were the result of some unknown variable over which experimental control had not been well established.

The magnitude and importance of the discrepancy between J-2's data and the previous findings concerning the effects of response-shock intervals warranted initial replication with four new animals. How was the number *four* arrived at? It would be pleasant to be able to present a logical chain of reasoning, leading inevitably to the conclusion that exactly four, no more and no less, was the optimal number of subjects required for replication in this case. But no such logic was employed. One is more likely to find the reasons for the choice in the reinforcement history of the experimenters, and in the economics of their particular laboratory set-up. It had been the usual experience in this laboratory that when as many as four animals (usually less) yielded the same data, subsequent experimentation rarely failed to achieve replication.

Here, then is a second problem for the student of confirmatory logic who would like to quantify the evaluation of data. How to take account of the experimenter's past successes and failures? There does not seem to be any logical justification for such criteria, for what bearing can successful replications of entirely different experiments in the past have upon the likelihood that a present experiment will also be replicable? The answer is that no experimental data are independent of the experimenter. His past and present experiments are not independent of each other. The experimenter constitutes a thread of correlation running through them all, a correlation arising not from the experimenter's physical presence or from his name, but from his techniques of experimental control.

If his techniques have been proved adequate by successful replication in the past, there is a high probability that subsequent experiments will also have relevant variables under rigorous enough control to make the same standards of replication applicable. This statement is not a logical one, but a behavioral one. It is an empirical principle that applies to the behavior of scientists.

The laboratory is not the place for excessive modesty. While the careful scientist will not allow his reputation to soften his judgment of the adequacy of his own work, he must, nevertheless, be prepared to appraise realistically the standards that are actually met by his experimentation. If the standards of behavioral control in his experiments are high, he must recognize this fact and let his work be governed appropriately. Science is an expensive, time-consuming, and serious business. Too low a judgment of one's own experimental adequacy, in the face of contrary evidence, will cost too much time, energy, and money in unnecessary demonstrations of one's competence.

This is not a dangerous philosophy, even though the most conscientious and able scientists are capable of error. As for those who overrate their own competence, they cannot ignore their shortcomings for long. Other replicative techniques, of either a direct or systematic nature, will eventually expose a man's lack of judgment. This is true also of the proven scientist who makes one of his relatively rare technical errors. We cannot really expect more.

Returning to Figure 3, we see the results of the four replicative attempts. Have the data of Rat J-2 been, in fact, replicated? Or are there discrepancies that must be resolved before any conclusions can be stated?

Some discrepancies are evident. The absolute values of corresponding points on the curves show marked variability from one animal to the next. We cannot claim, for example, that all rats will respond at a rate of 5.5 responses per minute when only 50 per cent of the shocks are delivered. We notice also that certain small variations in the individual curves are not consistent from animal to animal. The slight rise from 100 per cent to 50 per cent in Rat J-2's curve, for example, did not prove to be consistent, though there is a suggestion of similar change over a wider range in some of the other curves. Although there is undoubtedly a discoverable reason for these changes, in spite of their inconsistency, they were not pursued further, for variability of this magnitude was well within the limits normally observed and tolerated in this laboratory. Attempts to reduce the variability were not considered economical, since the behavioral changes of major interest were sufficiently large to overcome such a relatively small amount of "noise" in the baselines. It should be kept in mind, however, that later and better-controlled work may prove these small variations to be real and important.

Meanwhile, within our present limits of experimental error, it seems possible to conclude that at least one feature of Rat J-2's data has been replicated. Over a wide range of shock percentages there is little, if any, change in the rate of avoidance responding. A second major feature also seems established. The eventual drop in response rate is a relatively sudden one, when the range of percentages within which the drop takes place is compared to the range over which constancy is observed.

Some of the criteria upon which the experimenters based their judgment of successful replication are roughly statistical. The replication in five animals was compared with other replicative attempts in the past, often involving fewer animals. Five was judged more than sufficient to make the case. The observed variability was compared with that seen in other experiments, in the same and in other laboratories. The magnitude of the change in rate at low shock percentages was evaluated against a baseline that contains a certain amount of variability. Inasmuch as such comparisons must inevitably be made among phenomena that display a greater or lesser degree of variability, statistical judgment will be involved, however implicitly. But the statistical processes employed have not yet been written into any textbooks. The complexity and subtlety of the considerations involved permit a judgment that is far more rigorous and exacting than any statistical procedure yet devised.

For one thing, data from entirely different experiments are taken into account. The degree of solidity of related data is an important consideration. Furthermore, a single exception is never buried in a standard deviation, but is evaluated in terms of the adequacy of the control techniques. The quantity as well as the quality of both the immediate data and more remotely related findings are evaluated, as is the degree to which related findings have been systematized.

Because some aspects of the data are irrelevant to the major findings, they are often disregarded in evaluating replications. In Figure 3, for example, the absolute values of the rates can be ignored in comparing the curves with respect to the features of major concern. The wide range of relatively constant rate and the narrow range of decreasing rate appear in each of the curves, regardless of their overall height on the ordinate, suggesting that these features of the data are independent of the initial rate. Some statistical tests would, by taking into account the absolute rate differences among the animals, yield the conclusion that the data obtained are too variable to be accepted. In actual practice, the consistency of the individual curves in the face of the individual differences in rate serves to extend their reliability and generality. Every demonstration that a behavioral phenomenon is independent of variables that one has reason to suspect would be important factors serves to extend the generality and reliability of that phenomenon. The significance that will be assigned to such a demonstration is not basically a statistical matter.

The success of our replicative attempt brings us back to the problem which was the major consideration in the original decision to repeat the experiment. This was the apparent discrepancy between these and other well-established findings. On the basis of the latter, the wide range over which rate constancy is observed was not to be expected. Where do we go from here? Shall we continue replicating both this and the former experiments until some exceptions turn up? Such a course would be contrary both to statistical and to experimental common sense. Shall we attempt a rigorous quantitative evaluation of the evidence for both sets of experiments, and then throw out those data which seem to have the least support? Not many scientists would subscribe to this course of action either, for science progresses by integrating, and not by throwing out, seemingly discrepant data.

A third course would be to develop a theory that is consistent with one set of data, and then to ignore the other. One usually finds two pious statements accompanying this procedure. One, "We will, of course, modify the theory when new data require it," completely ignores the fact that the new data are already available.

Another contradictory precept, "It takes a theory to overthrow a theory," is the one most often advanced; many theorists thus immunize themselves to the challenge of any contradictory data presented without an alternative theory. Those who do not subscribe to the original theory, however, live an uneasy life until the empirical differences are resolved.

A fourth course, even more basic than direct replication, is to inquire into the factors that might explain the discrepancies and bring them into line with each other. This attempt may involve a theory in a minor way, for one may begin by guessing as to the variables that may be involved, although to call such guesses "theories" is a trivial use of the term.

But guesswork is not always necessary. In fact, the reverse process may prove more profitable. An apparent discrepancy between two sets of data may be the *result* of implicit and unrecognized theoretical assumptions. This was actually the case in the experiment summarized in Figure 3, and the discrepancy was resolved by recognizing the unwarranted theoretical reasoning and by taking a closer look at some more relevant features of the data than those represented in Figure 3. I have noted that omission of a certain percentage of the shocks permitted the occurrence of periods greater than 20 seconds between lever-pressing responses and shocks. Increasing response-shock intervals had previously been shown to decrease the rate of responding. The problem arose because there was no decline in response rate over the 50 and 30 per cent shock levels in spite of the longer response-shock intervals that these schedules made possible.

The flaw in the original reasoning arose out of the unstated assumption that the *possibility* of longer response-shock intervals was actually realized in fact. If the per cent shock findings of Figure 3 and the earlier rate vs. response-shock interval data are both reliable, then a reasonable unifying assumption would be the opposite; namely, that even though longer response-shock intervals were possible, they actually did not occur. If they did not occur, then the rate constancy with decreasing shock percentages would be consistent with the previous body of data. The plausibility of such a notion is enhanced when one recognizes that in the later experiment, response-shock intervals were to a great extent a function of the animal's own behavior. In the earlier investigations, however, the experimenter had exclusive control over the time intervals between responses and shocks.

There is no need to go into greater detail. Examination of the time intervals between successive responses indicated that the animals permitted few such intervals to last much longer than 20 seconds, in spite of the omitted shocks. The data were, in fact, consistent with previous findings, and the major reason for suspecting their reliability was eliminated. The point I wish to emphasize here is that the reconciliation of the data with an existing body of information provided a far more satisfactory demonstration of reliability and generality than did the straight replication with four additional animals. Such a demonstration constitutes another type of replication to which I shall return in greater detail in Chapter 4.

INTRASUBJECT REPLICATION

INTRASUBJECT and, to a lesser extent, intragroup replication provides a unique demonstration of a technique's reliability. When an organism's behavior can repeatedly be manipulated in a quantitatively consistent fashion, the phenomenon in question is a real one and the experimenter has relevant variables well under control.

Figure 4 summarizes some data from an experiment (17) in which rats, by pressing a lever, caused a brief electric current to pass directly into their brain through permanently implanted electrodes. The experiment investigated the effects of two levels of water deprivation upon the rate of lever pressing for the intracranial electrical stimulus. Instead of running two groups of animals, one at each deprivation level, the experimenters changed the deprivation level in alternate sessions for an individual animal. On odd-numbered experimental days, the animal was deprived of water for 46 hours prior to its lever-pressing and stimulation period. On even days, the animal was permitted unrestricted access to water right up to the beginning of the experimental period. Figure 4 demonstrates marked changes in response rate, corresponding to the varying state of water deprivation during alternate experimental sessions. (An intersubject replication is also shown in Figure 4.)

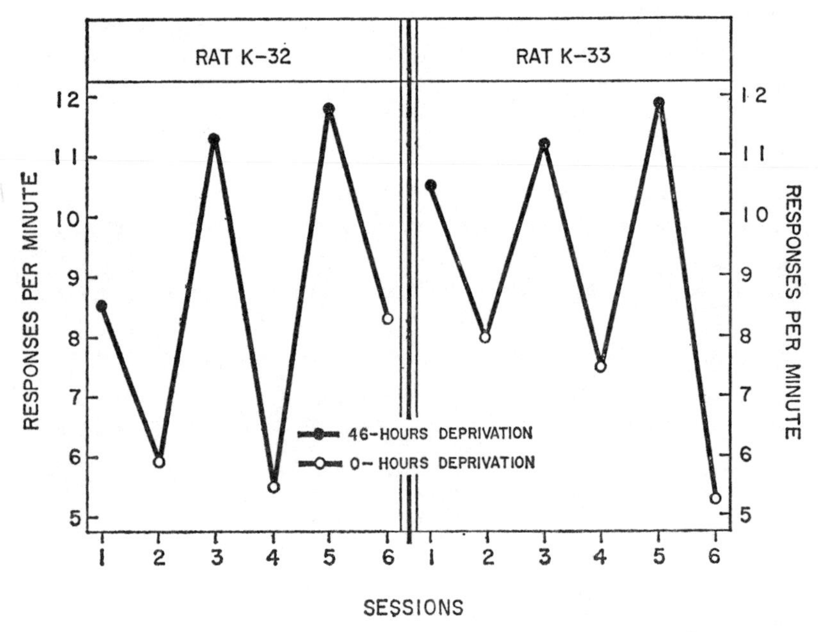

FIGURE 4. Curves from two individual subjects showing the fluctuations in response rate as the degree of water deprivation was alternately increased and decreased in successive experimental sessions. (*From Brady, Boren, Conrad, and Sidman,* 17.)

Such experimental manipulation has considerably greater elegance than a statistical demonstration of the experimental variable. Statistical designs are generally, though not always, one-shot affairs. That is to say, each value of the independent variable is generally administered only once, and the difference between the treatments is evaluated against a theory which assesses the likelihood of such a difference occurring by chance. In a series of manipulations within a single subject the possible role of chance diminishes rapidly with each successful replication.

Statistical criteria are implicitly involved, but statisticians have not yet evolved an explicit set of rules to cover this case. The problem, stated generally, is: How many replications of an experiment are required to express a given degree of confidence in the reliability of the findings? The problem is a difficult one for the statistician. He must first answer the question, "What constitutes a replication?" The answer is likely to vary considerably from one experiment to another. Experimenters take into account such factors as the magnitudes of the observed effects, their confidence in the adequacy of their experimental control, the consistency of their findings with related data, the stability of their baseline conditions, etc. Most scientists make such judgments intuitively, unaware that they are continuously making complex computations involving advanced and as yet unformulated probability theory. Such evaluations are almost second nature to them, carried out informally along with the normal everyday activities of planning experiments, watching their progress, changing their course, and interpreting their results.

Once it has been determined what constitutes a replication in a given case, a decision must then be made as to how many replications are required. This judgment will vary from field to field, from laboratory to laboratory, from experiment to experiment. Sometimes a single repetition will suffice, sometimes two, sometimes more. Eventually the experimenter will reach a point at which he decides that further replication would be less profitable than a new experiment. If a series of experiments in a given area is planned, or has been accomplished, the number of direct replications is likely to be small, for greater reliance will be placed on systematic replication (see Chapter 4). For example, in the experiment from which Figure 4 was taken, further intrasubject replication was considered unnecessary because intersubject replication had also been obtained, interspecies replication was successful, and replication was also carried out with other reinforcement schedules employed to generate the baselines, and with another method of altering deprivation levels.

Intrasubject replication has an elegant and powerful feature impossible to obtain with a one-shot statistical approach: the ease with which experimental control can be exercised, *at will*, over the course of time. Figure 4 provides an excellent example. The figure could have been drawn differently, with one line connecting the high points at 46 hours of deprivation, and another line connecting the low points at zero hours of deprivation. The method of connecting temporally successive points with a single line was selected because it emphasizes the successive reversals of response rate as a function of water deprivation. Alternation of the rate according to

elegant, powerful
eliminating ?!

a temporal pattern *determined by the experimenter* increases our confidence in the reality of the effect. The imposition of a deliberate pattern of change upon the response rate eliminated the passage of time *per se* as a relevant variable. Such a demonstration of control relatively independent of time in the experiment actually makes possible a reduction in the number of replications required to establish the effect on a firm basis.

Intrasubject replication also has the obvious virtue of eliminating intersubject variability as a factor in the evaluation of an experimental finding. Group statistical procedures generally operate against a baseline of intersubject variability. If, for example, the difference between two treatments is less than the intersubject variability between each of the groups, the difference is not considered "significant." Intrasubject replication is free from this source of error. It operates in terms of a baseline of intrasubject variability only. As a practical technique, intrasubject replication is possible only when the behavioral baseline from which changes are measured has attained a steady, recoverable state, or when the baseline is changing in some known, orderly fashion.

Figure 5 offers an example of a relatively stable behavioral baseline, departures from which constitute the measure of a variable's effectiveness. A monkey's lever-pressing behavior was maintained by occasionally permitting a lever press to produce a food reinforcement (variable-interval reinforcement schedule). Responses are cumulated along the ordinate and time is continuously recorded along the abscissa. The slope of the curve, therefore, represents the rate of lever pressing (responses per minute). The relatively constant response rate normally generated by the variable-interval reinforcement schedule provides an admirable baseline for the observation of a behavioral change such as is represented in the prolonged flat portion of the curve of Figure 5. At the first arrow, a stimulus (a series of rapid clicks) was presented to the animal. The stimulus was present for five minutes and then terminated simultaneously with the administration of a brief, unavoidable, electric shock to the animal's feet. The second arrow in Figure 5 marks the point at which the shock was delivered. After several experiences with the clicker-shock combination, the animal displays a profound behavioral change while the stimulus is on. Its ongoing behavior is

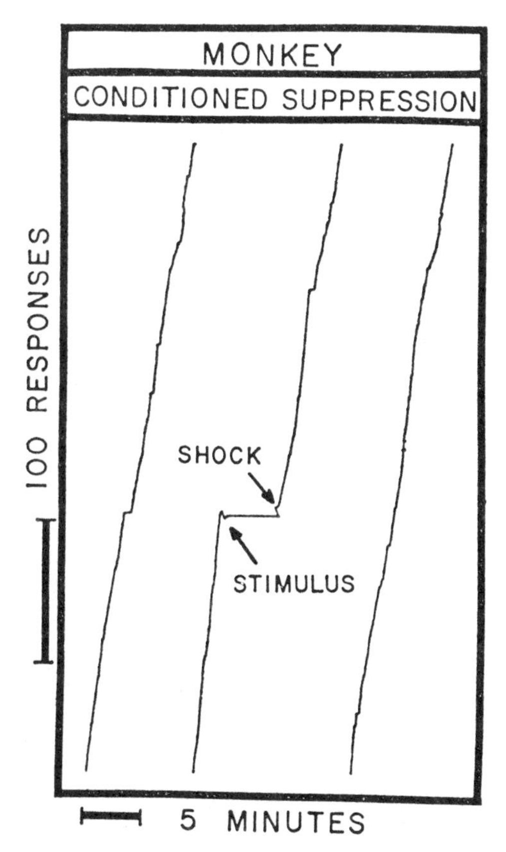

FIGURE 5. A cumulative record of a monkey's lever-pressing behavior, showing a clear disruption of the ongoing baseline behavior by a stimulus which precedes unavoidable shock. After the shock the animal returns to its normal performance.

completely disrupted, with lever pressing being replaced by intense, agitated locomotor behavior alternating with periods of complete immobility.

In Figure 5, the cessation of lever pressing throughout the five-minute stimulus duration is easily apparent. The stability of the baseline prior to the onset and following the cessation of the stimulus provides ample evidence that the five-minute suppression of responding was, indeed, correlated with the presence of the stimulus.

Intrasubject replication, however, makes the case even more convincing. In Figure 6, representing the behavior of a different monkey, the stimulus is presented during alternate five-minute periods. The session begins with the lever-pressing response being reinforced occasionally, according to a variable-interval schedule. After five minutes, the clicker begins, its onset indicated in Figure 6 by the slight downward displacement of the curve and by the label, "cl." The clicking stimulus remains on for five minutes and then terminates contiguously with a brief unavoidable shock to the animal's feet. The first shock is marked by the slight upward movement of the pen and by the label, "sh." The cycle then starts anew, with five-minute periods of stimulus-off alternating with five-minute periods of stimulus-on. Shock comes at the end of every stimulus.

We see in Figure 6 that a suppression of response rate accompanies each clicker stimulus, while the baseline rate recovers during the periods between stimulus presentations. There are, in all, nine replications of the behavioral suppression during a period of one and one half hours. The number of replications and the precisely controlled temporal sequence of behavioral changes leaves no doubt that the effect of the stimulus is genuine. The simple directness of this demonstration, made possible by the stability of the behavioral baseline, is a feature of intrasubject replication that is in the best tradition of scientific methodology. No statistical demonstration of a similar effect averaged over a group of subjects could be as convincing.

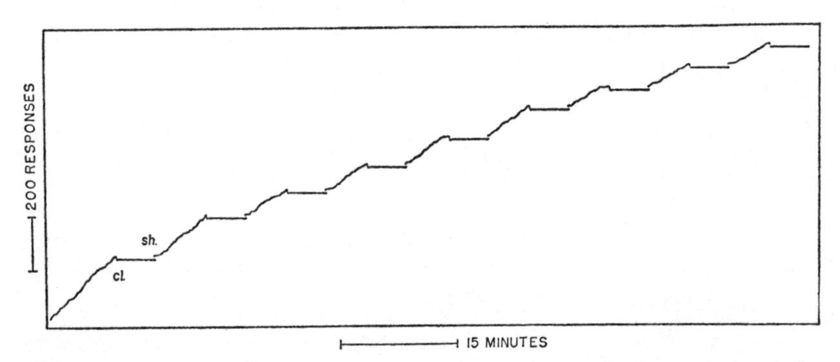

FIGURE 6. Nine intrasubject replications, within a single session, of the behavioral change that was illustrated in Figure 5.

Direct Replication

Another consequence of baseline stability, combined with the repetitive control that is a feature of intrasubject replication, is the reliable demonstration of smaller effects than would be possible otherwise. A small effect obtained in a group-type experiment is likely to be washed out in intersubject variability. The more stable an individual baseline one can achieve, however, the less likely one is to dismiss small, but consistent, effects. Small behavioral effects by themselves are always suspect because of the ever-present possibility that they have been produced by some uncontrolled factor of which the experimenter is not aware. But if they are consistently observed as a result of repeated application of a variable to a single subject, and if the baseline stability generally suggests adequate experimental control, then the experimenter is more than justified if he attempts to discover relevant factors which will serve to increase the magnitude of the effect. In this way he can gain a better experimental "handle" with which to establish the observation more firmly and to ground it securely within a systematic context.

Stable baselines to be used as a foundation for intrasubject replication do not necessarily imply constancy or even simplicity. A baseline may be continuously changing in a most complex fashion. But if the changes are orderly and are, themselves, replicable, their utility as a baseline is in no way diminished. An ingenious employment of a complex baseline is illustrated in Figure 7. The subject of this experiment (24) was a hungry pigeon which had been taught to peck an illuminated disk on the wall of the experimental chamber. The pecking behavior was then placed under multiple stimulus control (see Chapter 11). When the disk became blue, 15 minutes had to elapse before a pecking response could succeed in bringing up a grain feeder from its position below the floor. Behavior in the blue light soon took on the temporal characteristics normally observed on this fixed-interval reinforcement schedule, illustrated in the upper curve of section D, Figure 7. For several minutes after onset of the blue light, there is no pecking behavior. As the end of the 15-minute interval approaches, however, responding gradually accelerates to a high terminal rate, and the cumulative record displays a curvature characteristic of this reinforcement schedule.

An additional complication was introduced into this already

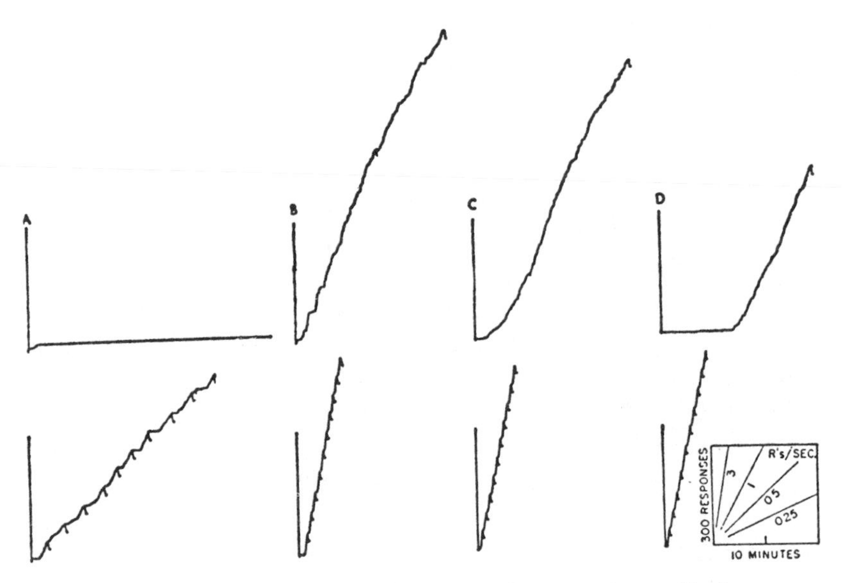

FIGURE 7. Cumulative records illustrating the use of a stable but complex behavioral baseline to follow the temporal course of drug action. The upper curves show the fixed-interval behavior, initially almost completely destroyed by the drug and then gradually recovering its normal characteristics. The lower curves show the initial, short-lived changes that take place simultaneously in the fixed-ratio behavior. (*From Dews,* 24.)

complex baseline. When the disk color changed from blue to red, the grain feeder was made available to the bird whenever it had pecked at the disk 60 times. That is to say, a ratio of 60 responses per reinforcement prevailed when the light was red. Behavior in the red light assumed a high rate, characteristic of this fixed-ratio reinforcement schedule and markedly different from the behavior in the blue light (see the lower curve of section D, Figure 7).

Thus we have a behavioral baseline in which two patterns of behavior are "on call" simply by changing the disk illumination. The behavior is neither simple nor constant. It not only changes with the disk color but also varies systematically as time elapses in the presence of the blue disk. But though it is complex, it is also orderly and reproducible, and its utility is nicely demonstrated when one employs it to evaluate behavioral effects of phenobarbital sodium.

Figure 7 follows the effects of this drug through time on each of the components of the baseline. The first action of the drug is to wipe out the fixed-interval behavior and to disrupt the smooth course of the ratio behavior (section A, Figure 7). In its second stage (section B) the interval behavior returns, but *without* the characteristic acceleration. The ratio behavior is essentially normal at this point. The interval behavior then partially recovers (section C) and, finally, both components of the baseline display their pre-drug levels (section D).

In this experiment, the employment of a complex baseline actually made possible a highly sophisticated differential analysis of drug action. The controlled orderliness, and the recoverability of the baseline after the drug wore off, make possible an intrasubject replication of the drug effects. Complexity, *per se*, is no bar to intrasubject replication.

Often, especially in a young science, an experiment is performed for the sole purpose of determining if it is *possible* to obtain a certain phenomenon. In such an experiment, demonstration of the phenomenon in *one* organism, with reliability established by intrasubject replication, is all that is necessary. The experimenter's judgment of its importance will determine the degree of effort to be expended in establishing the generality of the effect. Having demonstrated that a variable *may* produce a certain effect, his major interest in that variable may be simply in the direction of eliminating it from future experiments. If, however, the variable is considered important for its informational rather than its nuisance value, he will try to determine its generality.

But note that failure to replicate in all subjects does not relegate a finding to the limbo of "chance." Once we find that repeated manipulation of a variable produces consistent behavioral changes *in a single organism*, a failure to get consistent intersubject replication simply points the way to a more intensive functional investigation. Parametric studies of the variable in question, combined with manipulation of other contributory factors, will often reveal quantitative conditions under which all subjects display similar forms of behavior. The systematic manipulation of variables as a technique for establishing both reliability and generality will be discussed more fully below.

This method of dealing with replicative failures compounds the problem faced by the logician who seeks mathematical expression of replicative success. He will be forced to balance successes and failures in some manner in order to arrive at a probability statement that will express the degree of confidence with which we may accept the finding in question.

Successful replications, however, cannot be balanced out by any number of failures to replicate. In the event of mixed replicative failure and success there are only two possible courses open, short of dropping the problem completely. One of these is to demonstrate that the successful replications were the result of some experimental artifact. The second is to demonstrate that failures to replicate can be prevented by experimental identification of and control over the variables relevant to the phenomenon in question. There is no middle ground. A finding is either genuine or it is not, and determination of the conditions under which either of these statements may apply is an experimental, not a logical or statistical, problem. A natural process exists independently of our degree of confidence in its reality. This point is an important one, and the student should not be confused by the modern scientific philosophy that holds that truth is a statistical phenomenon. In the evaluation of theory, of course, we know from experience that new data will eventually come along to demonstrate the inadequacy of any theoretical formulation. Our acceptance of a theory must, therefore, be qualified in some probabilistic fashion. Data, too, can be true only within certain limits of probability, but these limits are imposed by our inevitable errors of measurement. There is always a degree of precision beyond which the accuracy of measurements becomes more and more doubtful. Before this point is reached, however, the truth or falsity of the data can admit of no equivocation. If a datum fails to achieve consistent replication, the scientist cannot afford to ease his conscience with the rationalization that we live, after all, in a probabilistic world, where truth is only a relative matter. The proper inference to draw from variability is that one's control techniques are inadequate.

Some of the most difficult problems of behavioral analysis arise when intersubject replication is successfully achieved while all attempts at intrasubject replication fail. Any of several factors may contribute to such a situation, but they can all be reduced ultimately to failures in recovering the individual's original behavioral baseline. This is not necessarily a serious problem. If the baseline is changing as an orderly function of time, independently of the particular experimental operation that is being superimposed upon the baseline, then the change can be taken into account in evaluating the replication. I know of no case in which this technique has actually been employed. But its potential usefulness seems sufficiently promising for the solution of some of psychology's persistent replication problems to warrant the following detailed, though hypothetical, example.

A long-time problem area of interest to many psychologists has been the influence of a number of variables upon behavioral resistance to extinction. When reinforcement for some behavior is discontinued, the organism will continue to emit that behavior for a limited period of time even though reinforcement is no longer forthcoming. The procedure of withholding the reinforcement for a previously conditioned response has been termed, "experimental extinction." The longer a response continues to be made in the face of nonreinforcement, the greater is its "resistance to extinction."

The effects upon resistance to extinction exercised by such variables as the number of reinforcements previously given the behavior, the schedule of reinforcement, the level of deprivation during both conditioning and extinction, etc., have been particularly interesting problems. Let us examine the last case more closely, and note the problems it presents for intrasubject replication. We can simplify the case by disregarding some of the more subtle complicating factors, and by considering the effects of only two deprivation levels upon resistance to extinction.

The naive expectation might be that the experiment could be carried out in the following way. First, condition the response with a large number of food reinforcements. Then extinguish the behavior after the subject has been deprived of food for, say, 48 hours, and record the total number of extinction responses. Recondition the behavior with an equal number of reinforcements and then extinguish again, this time after the subject has been deprived of food for, say, 12 hours. Then compare the number of responses emitted during the two extinction periods to determine how resistance to extinction is affected by the organism's state of food deprivation at the time. Following this, replicate the experiment with the same subject, perhaps reversing the order of exposure to the two deprivation conditions.

The problem is not, unfortunately, this simple of solution. The above procedure is based on the assumption that the extinction baseline is constant. More specifically, that, if the subject were exposed repeatedly to cycles of alternating reinforcement and extinction under a *constant* level of food deprivation, the resistance to extinction would also be constant from one cycle to the next. This assumption is not valid in fact. The number of responses in extinction declines with successive exposures to the extinction procedure, even though the response is reconditioned between each such exposure (62). Thus, in our original experiment, as outlined above, we could not claim that a lower resistance to extinction under 12 hours of deprivation than under 24 hours is correlated with the state of deprivation. The second extinction period is likely to have yielded a smaller number of responses even if the deprivation level had not been changed. Additional intrasubject replications of the experiment would also be ruled out by virtue of the fact that the extinction baseline is continuously changing.

If the extinction behavior varies in an orderly fashion, however, the orderliness can be put to use both for the original experiment and for succeeding intrasubject replications. Since no investigation has been reported in which this problem has been attacked with a sufficient degree of experimental rigor to reveal the type of order yielded by the individual subject, I have invented the data shown in Figure 8, section A. This is a hypothetical plot of the number of responses emitted by an individual subject in successive extinction sessions, each one separated by a reconditioning session, with food deprivation held constant throughout. For expository simplicity I have made the curve linear. The first step in attacking the problem of extinction as it is related to deprivation level would be to determine the form of this function for a number of individual subjects.

If we are dealing with a consistent natural process, and if we have sufficient control over the relevant variables, we are likely to obtain

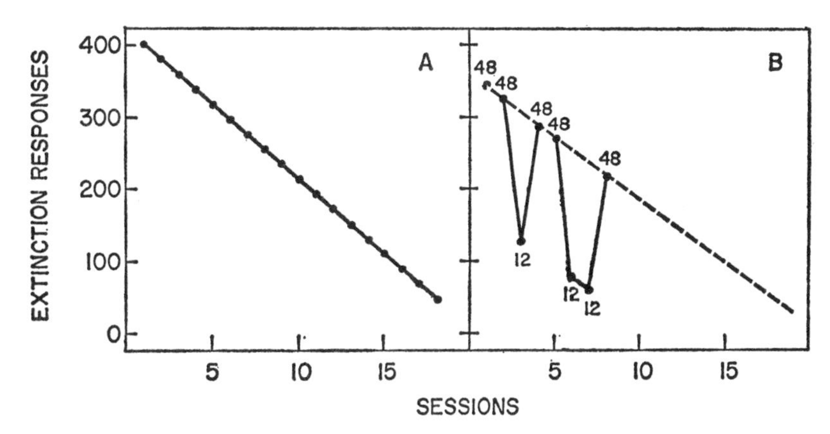

FIGURE 8. Intrasubject replication against a changing baseline. Curve A represents hypothetical data from an experiment in which a response was alternately conditioned and extinguished, with food deprivation held constant at 48 hours. This curve is then utilized in B as a baseline from which to evaluate any changes in the behavior that result from a decrease in deprivation to 12 hours.

a similar curve for each subject, with variations perhaps in the slope and intercept constants. Once we are convinced that we can obtain the function for any subject, within narrow limits of intrasubject variability, we can proceed with our main objective, the manipulation of deprivation levels.

Let us now take a fresh subject and determine only the first two points on his extinction function, carrying out both conditioning and extinction at a deprivation level of 48 hours. Once the first two points have been determined, the remainder of the curve can be drawn, since its linear form is known from the previous experimentation. This has been done, hypothetically, in Figure 8, section B. The dashed portion of the curve is the extrapolation from the first two empirical determinations at 48 hours of deprivation. Let us now carry out the third extinction period after the subject has been reconditioned at the original 48 hours of deprivation and then deprived of food for only 12 hours. The number of responses during this extinction session is plotted as the first 12-hour point in Figure 8. Note that the decline in extinction responding is considerably greater than that which would have occurred normally if the deprivation had been maintained at 48 hours. If the first 12-hour point had fallen on the broken line, then we would have to conclude that the lower deprivation had no effect upon the extinction behavior.

The experiment can be replicated, with the same subject, by first recovering the baseline performance. This is done by running two more cycles of reconditioning and extinction at 48 hours of deprivation. The extinction results appear in Figure 8 as the second pair of 48-hour points. Another extinction session is then carried out with the subject deprived of food for 12 hours. This is plotted as the second 12-hour point. We see again that the decrease in extinction responding is much greater than would have been the case if the deprivation had been maintained at 48 hours. The fact that the second 12-hour point is lower than the first one reflects the normal decline in extinction responding which occurs with successive reconditioning and extinction operations. Additional replications can be accomplished in the same manner, and even with variations in the sequence. The result of a third replication is indicated by the final 12-hour point on the graph.

We have, then, in Figure 8, section B, the representation of an original experiment and two subsequent replications, all carried out with the same subject, and all successful even though the baseline is not constant. The vertical distance between each 12-hour point and the broken line tells us how much of the decline in extinction responding can be attributed to the decrease in food deprivation. The differences between the successive 48-hour points, and between the successive 12-hour points, show the normal decline in extinction responding at each of these levels of food deprivation. The intrasubject replications thus yield data that both confirm and extend the original finding.

Additional information might also have been secured. We could, for example, just as well have chosen a third level of deprivation as our baseline against which to evaluate the effects of both 12 and 48 hours. We could also have employed more than two levels of deprivation during the test-extinction sessions. The technique can be generalized also to other types of experiments in which a changing baseline might appear to preclude intrasubject replication. If the course of the change is known, it can be taken into account when evaluating the replications.

Other problems may enter the picture. In our example, to cite one instance, there may be interactions between the two deprivation levels. The difference between 12- and 48-hour levels might be a compound function both of deprivation and of the number of extinction sessions through which the subject has passed. If this is true, the points at 48 hours will not coincide with the extrapolated curve in section B. Perhaps, for example, following the first extinction period at 12 hours of deprivation, the remainder of the 48-hour function would lie above the broken line. But such possibilities can be checked experimentally and, if they exist, can also be evaluated.

The task will be a difficult one. In order to refine the baseline data to the point where excessive variability does not destroy its usefulness, one must attain a degree of experimental control far more rigorous than that to which most experimental psychologists are accustomed. In order to evaluate possible interaction effects between the changing baseline and the experimental operations, the investigator may have to perform a number of painstaking and time-consuming experiments on what appear at the time to be side issues. But that's the way behavior is. Where such complications exist, there is no profit in trying to escape from them. This would be the same as escaping from the subject matter itself. To the experimenter who has a deep interest in behavior, and who possesses the traditional scientific virtue of investigating a problem thoroughly in all its relevant aspects, such complications offer a fascinating challenge. Tracking them down is likely to add new and significant dimensions to the relatively simple problem with which the investigation started.

There is a second type of situation in which intrasubject replication may seem precluded: for example, in studying behavior while it is in the process of changing from one state to another. A limited case of such a transition stage is the phenomenon often called "learning," in which the initial state of the behavior in question often has a value close to zero. Many investigators have noted that the initial transition state is often not recoverable. For example, we may place a hungry animal in an experimental chamber for the first time. Accessible to the animal is a lever; if he depresses it, a food pellet will automatically drop into a tray from which the animal may pick it up and eat it. We are interested in the rapidity with which the animal learns to press the lever. To measure the course of learning we may record lever-pressing responses cumulatively as a function of time and observe how the response rate changes from near-zero to its final level. A sample record is shown in Figure 9, section A. We see that the animal at first emits a few widely spaced responses, but that its rate gradually increases until a final stable level is reached. We might now, if it seems useful, fit an equation to this "acquisition curve." This would give us a mathematical statement of the state of the behavior, in terms of its rate of occurrence, as it passes through its transition stage.

Our interest now turns to replication. Is there some way of checking our observations by obtaining a second acquisition curve from the same animal? An apparently simple method might be to extinguish the response by disconnecting the pellet delivery mechanism. After the rate of responding has returned to its original low level we could connect the feeder again and observe acquisition a second time. If this is done, however, we are likely to observe a record similar to that of section B in Figure 9. Instead of a gradual increase, the response rate changes relatively abruptly from its ini-

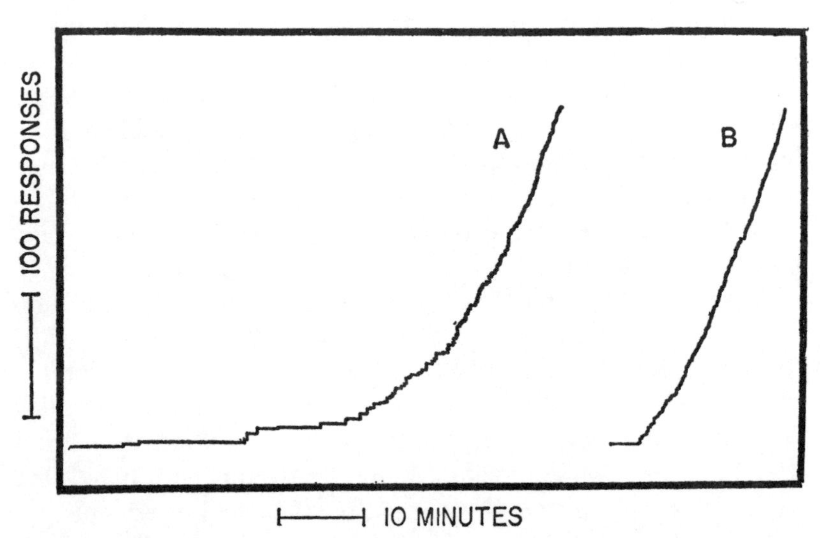

FIGURE 9. Curve A represents relatively slow acquisition of a lever-pressing response by an experimental animal. Curve B illustrates rapid reacquisition of the response following a period of extinction.

tial to its final state, with only a brief intermediate transition phase. If this situation is accepted, as it usually has been, without further critical analysis, intrasubject replication must be abandoned as a technique for establishing the reliability of our original finding. If a transition state is not recoverable, it is not amenable to intrasubject replication.

Such observations have led many psychologists to conclude that initial learning produces an irreversible change in an organism's behavior. Some even postulate an irreversible change inside the organism, preferably somewhere in the nervous system. The search for the "seat of learning" within the brain and elsewhere continues to occupy the experimental and speculative attention of scientists in many fields.

There is, however, an alternative conception. We may have been unable to recover the initial transition state not because of an irreversible change in behavior or in the nervous system, but rather because of incomplete experimental control over the variables involved in the transition. The variable explicitly introduced in the acquisition experiment described above was the contingency between lever pressing and the delivery of the food pellet. We know, however, that other variables, uncontrolled by the experimenter, are also introduced along with this directly manipulated contingency. Such "hidden" variables, although they automatically accompany the introduction of the contingency, may then require independent operations to eliminate their effects. For example, the extinction operation in this case serves largely to destroy the relation between the lever-pressing response and some of the succeeding links in the chain of events leading to ingestion of the pellet. But other links in the chain are not affected because they do not occur during the extinction procedure.

Before going into a specific analysis, let me summarize my point in general terms. The problem is one of apparent nonrecoverability of the original transition state. If nonrecoverability is indeed a fact, intrasubject replication is not possible. I have brought up the consideration, however, that the irreversibility may be elsewhere than in the organism or in his behavior. It may be a consequence of incomplete experimental control over the relations between the organism's behavior and the controlling environment. The extinction operation, as it is normally carried out, only destroys some of the relations that were established during original acquisition. Closer experimental attention to all of the factors involved, including those that entered through the back door, so to speak, might revise some of our notions about irreversibility.

The conditioning experiment I have described above is often termed "simple," but is only deceptively so. The lever-pressing situation has been analyzed, both conceptually and experimentally, into a complex sequence in which the lever-pressing response stands out only by virtue of the fact that we have chosen to record it (81, pp. 52-55). Among the many behaviors involved in the sequence are approaches to the vicinity of the lever, rising up to, or reaching toward, the lever, pressing the lever, releasing the lever, approaching the food tray, reaching for the pellet, picking it up, placing it in the mouth, chewing and swallowing it. Among the many stimuli involved in the sequence are the sight of the lever, the motion of the lever, the food tray, the noise from the pellet delivery mechanism, the sound of the pellet dropping into the tray, the sight of the pellet, its texture, its taste, etc. None of the responses is completely independent of the others. None of the stimuli exercises control that is independent of the other stimuli in the situation. Even more to the point is the fact that *all* of the responses in the sequence had to be learned, as did their relation to the appropriate stimuli. Our recorded data provide only a most indirect picture of the whole process. The animal not only learned those responses that succeeded in depressing the lever but also learned to go to the tray, to pick up the small pellet, to bring it to its mouth, etc. And these responses were learned in their correct sequence, because their reinforcement was correlated with the appropriate stimuli both from the environment and from the preceding behavior. The tray approach, for example, could be reinforced only after the sound from the food magazine; reaching for the pellet could be reinforced only after the pellet had dropped into the tray, etc.

With these complexities in sight we can now analyze the extinction procedure that we employed in our attempt to return the behavior to its preconditioning level. What did we extinguish when we disconnected the feeding mechanism? A glance at that point in the sequence at which we introduced the change will help to answer the question. The critical point lies somewhere between the lever depression and the response of approaching the tray. Following the actual lever depression, most of the remaining stimuli are no longer presented in extinction. There is no magazine sound, no pellet sound, no visual pellet, no tactual pellet, etc. Tray-approach is still possible, but only in the absence of some of its controlling stimuli. The responses involved in picking up and ingesting the pellet can no longer occur in their originally learned context.

While our extinction procedure may have returned the lever-pressing response to its preconditioning level, other components of the total learned sequence could not have undergone complete extinction. Many of these components could not even occur in order to permit the nonreinforcement operation to exercise an effect upon them. And insofar as the later members of the chain formed part of the conditioned reinforcing complex for the lever-pressing response, even the latter was probably not reduced all the way to its preconditioning level. When reinforcement was again introduced, in the attempted replication, the animal did not have to relearn the whole sequence, because the whole sequence had not been extinguished. The new lever-pressing curve was influenced by a number of variables that were not present in the original experiment. The learning process being measured was not the same in the two cases.

If explicit experimental attention were applied to all the components in the sequence, the behavior might be returned to its true initial level, thus making intrasubject replication possible. For example, more complete extinction of the total sequence might be achieved by allowing the empty feeding mechanism to produce its characteristic sounds. This would probably not be sufficient, however. Pellets could also be permitted to drop into the tray but be made inaccessible by interposing a barrier between them and the animal. It would probably be even more effective to substitute a nonnutritive, neutral-tasting pellet which the animal could pick up and ingest until even these responses extinguished. If operations such as these could be carried out, one might approach more complete reversibility.

The example I have cited is specific and difficult, but the principle involved is capable of general application. When apparent irreversibility seems to preclude intrasubject replication of a transition state, take into consideration the possibility that uncontrolled variables have entered the picture during the transition. Although such variables were not introduced deliberately, they may require deliberate manipulation in order to erase their influence. The task may be complex and technically difficult. But, as I have pointed out before, although complexity in nature may be simplified in principle by integrating phenomena within a systematic context, such integration is *not* synonymous with experimental simplicity. The neatest, simplest, and most satisfying systematizations are usually the result of painstaking, arduous, and compulsively thorough experimental labor.

Lest the preceding illustration be considered too hypothetical, since the suggested experiments have not been carried out, let me describe another example essentially as it actually happened. The investigators were interested in bringing under experimental control a type of avoidance behavior that had been relatively little explored. Instead of using electric shock as the stimulus to be avoided by the subject (pigeon), they wished to employ a stimulus which had, in the bird's experience, been associated with nonreinforcement, or extinction. They set up the experiment in the following way (60).

Two illuminated disks, or keys, were available at which the bird could peck. Pecking on the left-hand key when it was illuminated by a red light sometimes produced the grain hopper. Occasionally, however, the left-hand key changed in color from red to green. While it was green the food hopper was disconnected and pecking responses were no longer capable of producing the reinforcement. The subject eventually learned to cease pecking at the green key, while it maintained a steady rate of responding when the key was red. Then the color of the left-hand key was placed under the control of the subject's own behavior. Whenever the green color appeared, it could be terminated and replaced by the red if the bird pecked the right-hand key. Furthermore, if the bird pecked the right-hand key while the left key was red, the onset of the green color was postponed. The pigeon could, therefore, control the left-hand key color in two ways: it could prevent the green color from appearing by pecking sufficiently often at the right-hand key; or, if it permitted the left key to change from red to green, it could reverse the colors by a peck at the right key. Thus, pecking at the right-hand key could, depending upon when it occurred, either postpone or terminate the green color which was correlated with nonreinforcement.

Up to this point the experiment was successful, in that avoidance behavior of the type described seemed to have been brought under experimental control. Several pigeons learned both to avoid the onset of the green stimulus by pecking at the right-hand key and to escape from the green color each time they had failed to avoid it. A substantial rate of response was maintained on the right-hand key. But the experimenters were not satisfied with only intersubject replication of the finding. Since they wished to investigate the phenomenon more intensively in the individual subject, it was necessary to determine whether they had achieved sufficient control to accomplish this. Intrasubject replication was therefore demanded.

The first step was to determine if the effect was reversible. Could the behavior on the right-hand key be extinguished and then brought back again at the experimenter's convenience? In order to answer this question, the experimenters disconnected that part of the apparatus which turned on the green light. The color of the left key now remained red at all times, regardless of the pigeon's behavior with respect to the other key. This is analogous to disconnecting the shock in a shock-avoidance situation, where the usual result is eventual disappearance of the avoidance behavior. But at this stage the experiment struck a snag. The bird continued to peck at the right-hand key, even though such pecks no longer served any apparent function. As a consequence, intrasubject replication seemed to be out of the question.

Fortunately, the experimenters did not abandon this line of inquiry. Although faced with a situation in which intersubject replication was achieved but intrasubject replication did not seem possible, they were convinced that they had a genuine example of avoidance behavior. Previous experiments had shown that birds did not peck at the second key simply because it was available. The avoidance and escape contingencies in which the second key participated must, therefore, have been responsible for the original increase in the birds' rate of pecking it. Some other variable, the experimenters reasoned, must have entered the picture at a later stage. After the avoidance and escape contingencies were eliminated, this other factor must have been responsible for the maintenance of the behavior. Instead of abandoning the technique, therefore, the experimenters addressed themselves to the problem of identifying this uncontrolled factor. If it could be identified it might be eliminated, and intrasubject replication of the basic finding could again be attempted.

The story from here on is a happy one, the details of which I will only sketch in. The investigators recalled previous experiments in which some behavior not explicitly reinforced by the experimenter nevertheless came adventitiously under the control of a food reinforcement (82). That is to say, the behavior happened, by chance, to take place just prior to the delivery of food. Although the food delivery was not dependent upon the emission of that particular behavior, the chance correlation served to increase its rate of emission. In consequence, the likelihood of adventitious correlations with subsequent reinforcement increased, and a spiraling process was begun. The behavior eventually came under the control of the reinforcement almost as precisely and powerfully as if the correlation had been deliberately set up by the experimenter (see Chapter 12, pp. 348-349, for a more complete description of this experiment).

A similar process could have been operating to maintain behavior on the right-hand key in the avoidance experiment described above. Occasionally the bird might peck at the right-hand key and immediately afterward switch to the left key and produce the food. While only the response on the left key was required to produce the food hopper, its appearance might also serve as an adventitious reinforcement for the preceding peck at the right-hand key. Such accidental correlations between the appearance of food and pecking behavior on the right-hand key may have been responsible for the maintenance of the latter behavior, even after avoidance and escape were no longer necessary. Reasoning along these lines, the experimenters changed the procedure slightly. They arranged the programing apparatus so that a response on the left key never produced the food hopper if there had been a response on the right-hand key within the preceding three seconds. Thus there were always at least three seconds between a peck on the right-hand key and the delivery of food. This delay of adventitious reinforcement served its purpose. Behavior on the right-hand key disappeared. Reinstatement of the avoidance and escape contingencies brought the behavior back, and removal of these contingencies reduced it nearly to zero again. Intrasubject replication was achieved, and a degree of experimental control was demonstrated that permitted the initiation of a fruitful research program.

I emphasize again that intrasubject replication is not an easy road to travel. Problems like those described above require both technical labor and creative ingenuity for their solution. There really is no alternative. A psychology that cannot describe, systematize, and control the primary source of all its data—the behaving individual—will forever be a weak sister among the sciences. Intrasubject replication is one of our most powerful tools for demonstrating the adequacy of our control and, thereby, for evaluating the resulting data.

Up to this point, I have discussed intrasubject replication as if it were always possible, emphasizing the need to achieve such replication even in those instances where it does not at first seem to be feasible. The alternative possibility cannot, however, be dismissed. An initial transition may actually effect a permanent change in the state of the organism's behavior, making the process truly irreversible. I know of few experiments to date that have been specifically oriented toward this problem. In lieu of empirical investigation, one of two possible courses of action has generally been followed upon encountering apparent irreversibility.

One alternative has been to ignore transition effects and to confine investigative efforts to reversible steady states. This approach, which will be discussed in greater detail in later chapters, has an obvious weakness in that interesting data are excluded from study.

A second alternative, and the one most frequently employed, is to use a different group of subjects each time the effect of a given variable upon a transition phase is to be observed. Unfortunately, as I have already pointed out, the relevance of the resulting data depends upon the population distribution of various parameters of the individual behavioral processes in question. The very nature of this statistical technique precludes the determination of such parameter values in the individuals of the population, since the same individuals are never exposed to more than one value. Several writers have demonstrated that data obtained by this method may yield a distorted, or even false, description of the behavior of the individual. The compromise effected by using groups in this manner is thus a strange one. The resulting data are not adequate as a description of individual behavior, nor are they the sort of group data that the social psychologist would claim as his domain. Results obtained in this way may possess a very high order of reliability, and as such cannot be excluded by fiat from the realm of science. But they are generalizable neither among individuals nor among groups of individuals joined together by social interaction.

We see, then, that intrasubject replication as a technique for establishing reliability and generality raises some knotty problems which are not satisfactorily resolved by the techniques currently in most general use. Yet it is possible that the challenge offered by such difficulties can be met by the application of traditional principles of experimentation and by creative experimental ingenuity. I will expand on both of these possibilities in the later discussion of systematic replication and experimental design.

With the replicative techniques described above, as well as those to be discussed below, additional weight is added to the evidence when the experiments are performed by different experimenters or in different laboratories; and data become even more credible when replicated by scientists of rival theoretical persuasion. The individual scientist tends to assume that data replicated by certain of his colleagues are more likely to prove reliable and representative than those of other colleagues. Although there is no logical basis for such decisions, they represent accumulated, practical scientific experience.

But the role of individual experience in evaluating data is even more complex. For example, in biological research in general, and particularly in psychology, some of the relevant technical details of an experiment are omitted from published reports simply because their relevance is not recognized at the time, or because fine details of a technique may be too lengthy and confusing to describe in print. It is common practice in biological science for a researcher to pay a personal visit to the originator or other successful user of an experimental technique in order to learn the required skills firsthand. The experienced "maze-runner" may easily fail to replicate some of the findings of "operant conditioners" simply by employing a variable-interval programing tape with too many long intervals punched into it. Similarly, a failure to orient the rat properly in the starting box of a T-maze may convince the operant conditioner that maze data are unreliable. Failures to replicate must be evaluated in terms of the background and training of the experimenter, even though research in other areas has gained him a respected reputation.

Chapter 4

Systematic Replication

THE EXPERIENCED INVESTIGATOR generally has a more sophisticated estimate of the reliability and limitations of his techniques than would the scientist who has never used them. As a rule, he has performed a large number of unpublished experiments, some of them too trivial to report, some of them failures because of faulty technique, others so greatly at odds with established knowledge that he hesitates to make them public until he can develop a systematic framework within which to place them. He has checked his measuring instruments countless times; he has discovered that the data themselves provide certain danger signals; and he has made many, though unsystematic, observations of incidental or even accidental variables. Out of all these experiences he distills a subjective estimate of the reliability of specific data.

Let us now move from the scientist in general to the experimental psychologist in particular. He has just completed a series of observations in which a single organism has been exposed to a set of experimental operations, and the result has been an orderly relation between these operations and the subject's behavior. He is now faced with the task of demonstrating the reliability of his findings. This may be accomplished either by direct or by systematic replication. This is where gambling on the basis of subjective probability enters the laboratory. If the psychologist's experience has given him confidence in his techniques, he will choose systematic rather than direct replication as his tool for establishing reliability. Instead of simply repeating the experiment, he will use the data he has collected as a basis for performing new experiments and obtaining additional related data.

One of the most sacred restrictions imposed upon experimental design in psychology is the requirement that all subjects in an investigation be treated alike except for the independent variable in question. This restriction effectively strangles systematic replication as a primary method for establishing reliability and generality. For every successful systematic replication demonstrates that the finding in question can be observed under conditions *different* from those prevailing in the original experiment. Where direct replication helps to establish generality of a phenomenon among the members of a species, systematic replication can accomplish this and, at the same time, extend its generality over a wide range of different situations. For this reason, an experimenter who has developed a "feel" for a particular area of research will often deliberately fail to control certain variables. If, for example, he is performing an experiment with lower animals, he may permit his subjects to differ with respect to food deprivation, previous history, age, duration of experimental sessions, and additional variables which may have proven relevant in other contexts. If, in spite of these differences, he obtains similar orderliness from each of his subjects, he will have achieved a successful and more generalizable replication than would otherwise have been possible.

But this procedure is a gamble. If systematic replication fails, the original experiment will still have to be redone, else there is no way of determining whether the failure to replicate stemmed from the introduction of new variables in the second experiment, or whether the control of relevant factors was inadequate in the first one.

On the other hand, if systematic replication succeeds, the pay-off is handsome. Not only is the reliability of the original finding increased, but also its generality with respect to other organisms *and* to other experimental procedures is greatly enhanced. Furthermore, additional data are now available which could not have been obtained by a simple repetition of the first experiment.

This last point calls for at least a brief consideration of what might be termed the "economics of experimentation." The chief commodity of experimental science is data. For the investigator, economy of time, space, and available budget are important determinants of his experimental program. The scientist is faced with the perpetual problem of using his resources for maximum productivity while maintaining the quality of his product. Systematic replication is a time-tested method for increasing both the quantity and the quality of one's work. An original experiment may have been long and arduous. Direct replication would not only occupy a large segment of the experimenter's time but also tie up costly apparatus that might be used to obtain other important information. On the other hand, systematic replication will buy reliability, generality, *and* additional information.

I should, at this point, emphasize that I am not attempting to justify systematic replication as a labor-saving device. It is not a magic formula that will permit a scientist to spend more time with his family or his hobbies. Actually, the techniques of systematic replication *do not permit* any relaxation of experimental effort; they do help the experimenter to achieve a more efficient distribution of such effort.

THE "BASELINE" TECHNIQUE OF SYSTEMATIC REPLICATION

VERY CLOSE to direct replication is a form of systematic replication utilizing a given behavioral phenomenon as a baseline for investigating other variables. The original experiment is, in effect, actually repeated, but not as an end in itself.

For example, the behavior generated by a given experimental procedure may have exactly those properties required to investigate a hitherto elusive problem. The long series of experiments by Brady and Hunt and their collaborators, in which the Estes-Skinner conditioned suppression technique (29) provided a baseline for the objective investigation of electro-convulsive shock therapy (ECS), is a case in point (18). This baseline was a conditioned disruption of the normally stable rate of lever pressing that is maintained by a variable-interval reinforcement schedule (see Chapter 3, pp. 88-90). The investigators explored a large number of problems involved in the use of ECS to modify behavior. After establishing the fact that ECS abolished the conditioned behavioral disruption, they went on to investigate the duration of the effect, its behavioral specificity, the relevance of number and temporal spacing of ECS treatments, etc. Their experiments not only constituted a research program important in its own right but also served to solidify and establish the Estes-Skinner technique as a reliable and generalizable research tool. The technique was subsequently extended to provide baselines for the behavioral effects of brain lesions and drugs, and for experimental elaboration of relations between behavioral stress and endocrine function. In the process of opening up and systematizing new areas of investigation, the original finding was replicated many times over.

Another interesting effect of the baseline method of replication is worth noting, for it illustrates one of the ways in which new experiments are generated. During the sequence of experiments in which the conditioned suppression served as the behavioral baseline, practical considerations dictated the introduction of many variations on the original procedure. The original subjects, for example, were white rats. In some of the later work, however, monkeys were substituted for rats because monkeys provided a more convenient vehicle for the physiological techniques involved in many of the experiments. In order to increase the amount of data that could be gathered in a limited time, the investigators utilized Azrin's finding (3) that a large number of stimulus-shock pairings (the operation which produced behavioral suppression) could be accommodated within a single experimental session (see Figure 6). The original experiments had applied only one such pairing per session. In order to minimize the effects of shock *per se* upon some of the physiological measures, an "intermittent reinforcement" procedure was employed, in which shocks were administered after only a small percentage of the suppressing stimuli, and in some experimental sessions the stimuli were presented without any shock at all.

These procedural variations, along with many others, seemed to produce subtle alterations in the baseline performance; this created a renewed interest in the conditioned suppression phenomenon itself. A number of studies were instituted to determine explicitly, in behavioral terms, the consequences of the procedural changes. Thus, the manipulation of variables for the more or less practical considerations of scientific collaboration provided the impetus for an additional series of purely behavioral experiments. In consequence, our control over the conditioned suppression phenomenon was enormously increased, so that it became in turn an even more useful collaborative research tool; increased understanding of the phenomenon permitted a closer integration with data from other areas; and the large number of systematic replications, many of them of a type to be discussed later, established the reliability and increasing generality of the whole structure (76).

The baseline technique of replication becomes feasible and valuable only when an extremely stable form of behavior in a given type of experimental situation has been achieved. For maximum usefulness, it must be possible to maintain the baseline at an intermediate level so that other variables can move the baseline in any direction. For example, for a long time avoidance behavior had been studied by means of a technique that imposed an upper limit upon the measure of the subject's performance (92). The method consisted of the presentation of a warning stimulus, followed within a few seconds by a shock if the subject did not emit a particular response. If the response occurred during the stimulus and prior to the shock, the shock was not delivered. This procedure was repeated at selected intervals until a number of "trials" had been observed.

The measure of the subject's performance was typically the percentage of trials on which the avoidance response occurred. Although the avoidance response could be maintained in stable fashion, the measure did not permit the behavior to be used advantageously as a baseline for individual performance. For when the subject was performing at, or near, the 100 per cent level, no variable that improved performance could be investigated. In order to study variables which might increase the level of performance, the only method was to maintain the behavior at a low level of success, for example, 50 per cent avoidance. But a low performance level in this situation also implies poor experimental control. The behavior is weak because the controlling variables are not applied at values that permit successful avoidance.

Under these circumstances it is not surprising that we find few applications of this procedure as a baseline for individual performance. Only at high performance levels does the behavior become amenable to replication by means of the baseline technique.

This analysis of classical avoidance methodology acquires greater cogency in view of the type of development that followed the introduction of a different technique (69). The feature of the technique that is important for this discussion is the elimination of the "success" measure, for success has a natural upper limit at 100 per cent. Instead of measuring the subject's performance in terms of the number of shocks it succeeds in avoiding, rate of avoidance responding is used to describe the behavior. By utilizing a "free responding" situation, *i.e.*, one in which the subject can perform the avoidance response at *any* time, and by permitting every such response to postpone the shock, we can achieve a stable rate of avoidance behavior that can be measured continuously in time.

Though it has a ceiling determined by the organism's physical capacity, the rate measure nevertheless can vary over a range so wide as to reflect the effects of all but a small sample of the variables relevant to avoidance behavior. And, even more pertinent to our discussion, the rate can be manipulated in an orderly fashion well beyond the point at which the maximal number of shocks is being avoided by the subject. Furthermore, the response rate can be reduced almost to the vanishing point without materially decreasing the degree of success in avoiding the shock. At both high and low rates, the baseline remains one of avoidance behavior.

As a consequence of this modified avoidance technique, a sensitive baseline for individual performance was achieved. Its introduction was followed, almost automatically, by increased employment of the baseline technique of systematic replication in investigations of avoidance behavior. A series of experimental studies was carried out in which the original baseline was employed to correlate the effects of environmental and physiological variables with behavior. As with the conditioned suppression technique, modifications of the baseline were introduced and replicated by similar techniques. And again, not only did the baseline prove to be reliable and generalizable to new situations, but its increased utilization in new contexts shed more light upon the baseline itself. The development of a new type of behavioral baseline often permits, and even forces, new questions to be asked about behavior, questions whose existence could not even be imagined until an appropriate technique had been developed. Finally, to come full circle, the classical avoidance technique, approached experimentally from a different direction, achieved new systematic status as a special case of a more general class of avoidance phenomena.

The full story of this development will have to await a more lengthy exposition (77). It is relevant at this point as an example of a method for achieving systematic replication of individual data via the baseline technique. The example is a drastic and challenging one: If an investigator wishes to explore an area in which available techniques do not generate sensitive and precisely controlled individual behavioral baselines, his first task is either to abandon the old methodology or to modify it until it meets his requirements. If he simply adopts the standards of inadequate control and lack of sensitivity that were perhaps necessary in the pioneer efforts in the particular area, his eventual status in the history of his science will be neither pioneer nor synthesizer, nor even intermediate steppingstone. His work will simply be stopgap, representing a sterile period in the traditionally discontinuous progress of science. This, of course, can happen to any investigator, regardless of the significance his contemporaries attach to his work. But it is rather wasteful to accept this status voluntarily.

THE BASELINE TECHNIQUE AND EXPERIMENTS ON LEARNING. Out of an initial finding, then, there may develop a series of experiments, each one different from the others, yet with a common thread in the form of the behavioral baseline running through them all. The notion of a behavioral baseline has not developed extensively until recently, partly because of the uncritical acceptance of the dictum that behavior is too variable to be studied in the individual organism. The terms "variability" and "baseline" are incompatible, for unless a baseline is stable it has no experimental utility.

My use of the qualifier "uncritical" in characterizing the acceptance of variability by psychologists is deliberate. I do not intend to deny the existence of variability; but there are many kinds of variability, and many ways of dealing with it. (See Chapters 5 and 6.)

A second factor that has retarded the development of behavioral baselines is the growth of a research area in experimental psychology that is called "learning." Workers in this field are interested in the acquisition of new behavior, and presumably not in behavior that has reached an "asymptotic" or other steady level. The term "acquisition" commonly refers to the emergence of new forms of behavior which have not existed in the organism's repertoire prior to the experimental manipulations. Because the newly acquired behavior is presumed, for all practical purposes, to exist originally at a zero level, students of learning are seldom led to consider the baseline state of the subject's behavior as a parameter of acquisition. The usual contention is that a behavioral baseline with a value greater than zero would impose a special condition, so that the characteristics of acquisition could not be generalized to other situations.

But is acquisition of behavior from a zero baseline, if indeed a zero baseline is available, any less a special condition than its acquisition from a more active state? Is not a change for example from one pattern of behavior to another a case of acquisition also? The adjustment of existing behavior to a new variable is an example of learning whose consideration would greatly increase the generality of learning principles. In Figure 10 the baseline behavior (lever pressing) had been maintained by a fixed-interval reinforcement schedule that made reinforcements available to the rat every five minutes. The record at A illustrates the baseline performance. Beginning with the record at B, the reinforcement schedule was changed to fixed ratio, with four responses required per reinforcement. The lower curve illustrates the transition state through which the organism's response rate passed as it adjusted to the new schedule. Is this change any less an example of learning than was the original acquisition of the lever-pressing response itself?

The notion of a behavioral baseline is incomprehensible except in terms of the behaving individual. If the experimenter does not have techniques that permit the manipulation and control of individual behavior, he cannot hope to study behavioral transitions, with any high degree of precision, as a function of greater-than-zero baseline states. Many investigators, therefore, choose what is presumably the easy way out. They try to investigate transitions from a zero baseline, neglecting such examples as Figure 10. This relieves them of the necessity of manipulating behavior before they introduce the variables that are to produce learning. In consequence, most contemporary theories of learning are based upon a circumscribed and specialized set of experiments which unnecessarily restricts their generality. The proper domain of learning includes *any* transition that results from changes in the environmental con-

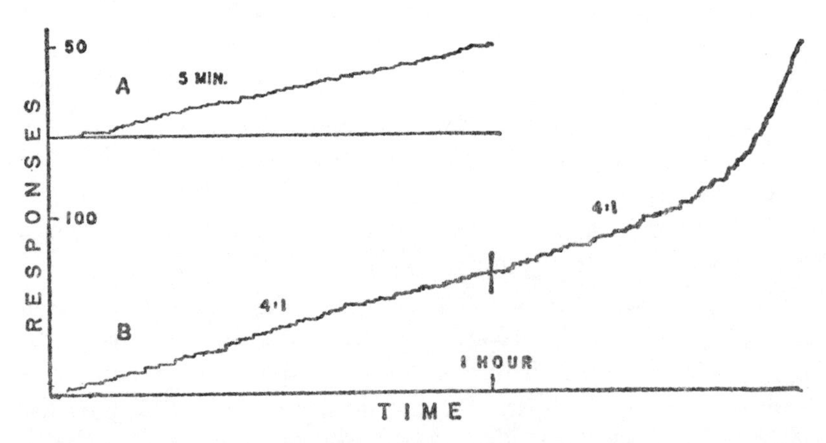

FIGURE 10. Curve A represents a rat's lever-pressing behavior on a five-minute fixed-interval schedule of reinforcement. Curve B shows the transition to a high response rate after the reinforcement schedule was changed to a fixed ratio of four responses per reinforcement. (*From* Skinner, 81, p. 280.)

tingencies maintaining behavior. There are no rational grounds for excluding transitions from a baseline level greater than zero.

An even more pertinent problem, perhaps, is the extent to which traditional acquisition studies actually satisfy the assumption of a zero baseline. Lever-pressing behavior, for example, rarely exists at a zero probability before the experimenter deliberately reinforces the response. Even when this initial level is identified empirically, the custom is simply to subtract the baseline from the final state in calculating, for example, the speed of learning. It is a moot question, however, whether the transition bears such a simple relation to the initial state. There are similar considerations involved in other classical types of experiment, for example, those which measure running speed in a runway, choice behavior in a maze, serial effects in rote learning, etc. In most such experiments the baseline is not zero. It is unknown. But is deliberate ignorance of the baseline state more preferable than a special, but specifiable, state?

It is on this note that our apparent digression returns us to the baseline technique of systematic replication. I suggest that the more general use of systematically replicated behavior baselines in the study of acquisition will produce an increase in generality for this area of research that will be more consonant with its very general title, "learning." The properties of acquisition are a function of the prior state of the behavior. To investigate such relations, however, we must have techniques for generating and maintaining stable levels of behavior from which to measure the transitions. Systematic replication of baselines reveals their properties, thereby permitting increased control. More rigorous control leads to increased utility. The greater the variety of situations in which a given baseline is used, and the more experimental operations that are applied to it, the greater will be the generality not only of the baseline itself but also of the transitions that use it as a point of departure. The baseline technique of systematic replication is a natural tool for the study of learning. Every application of a new operation that turns out to be successful in altering the original baseline automatically yields a curve of acquisition. By replicating the baseline with variations in its own controlling parameters it will be possible to gain a more complete picture of the transitions that follow a particular experimental operation. A science of learning will develop that takes into consideration a qualitative and quantitative variety of operations and baselines.

THE "PROBE" TECHNIQUE OF SYSTEMATIC REPLICATION

THE PROPERTIES of some types of behavior make them useful as probes for illuminating behavioral processes in other situations. When an original finding is of this sort, the experimenter may choose to use the probe technique of systematic replication instead of, or in addition to, the baseline technique.

PROBING THE STATE OF BEHAVIOR. Suppose that behavioral changes must be observed over a long period of time—hours, days, or even weeks. In such a case we must maintain the baseline behavior over the required observation period. But a contradiction may arise. The particular type of baseline we wish to study may be inadequate to keep behavior in progress for as extended a length of time as is necessary. Furthermore, a baseline adequate for this purpose may be insensitive to the variable whose effects we wish to study. The probe technique then becomes applicable. Behavior can be maintained by a baseline which is insensitive to the long-term variable under investigation, and the behavioral changes under study then be probed by applying a more sensitive baseline procedure at specified times. In order to accomplish this, the probing baseline must be one whose properties are already known, and over which we have achieved a high degree of experimental control. The use of such a baseline, then, will not only help to obtain the new information but will also replicate previous findings in which the same baseline was involved.

For example, the probe technique was used to study behavioral changes during sleep deprivation. It was found that a reinforcement schedule requiring pauses of at least three minutes between responses would maintain a hungry pigeon's pecking behavior for several consecutive days, with no pause between responses greater than fifteen minutes and few greater than five minutes (86). The pigeon in this experiment pecked a white disk, and if any peck was preceded by a period of three minutes or more in which no pecks had been made, the response provided the pigeon with brief access to a hopper of grain.

At one-hour intervals, the color of the disk changed from white to either red or green. When it was green, the first response after ten minutes was reinforced (fixed-interval schedule). When the disk was red, the fiftieth response was reinforced (fixed-ratio schedule). The fixed-interval schedule, under the conditions of this experiment, typically generates behavior characterized by a low rate of pecking at the start of the interval, with a gradual positive acceleration as the end of the interval, and reinforcement, approaches. The ratio performance is characterized by a high, sustained rate of response (see Figure 7).

The spaced-responding procedure, then, was employed to maintain pecking behavior over the course of the long-term experiment (our known baseline). Once every hour, however, the color of the disk changed to indicate either the fixed-ratio or the fixed-interval schedule, and any changes in the pecking behavior during the interval and ratio probes indicated the effects of progressive sleep deprivation (87). The fixed-interval and fixed-ratio schedules, by themselves, would not have maintained the pecking behavior in the face of increasing sleep loss. Use of the interval and ratio schedules as probes of the current state of behavior both illuminated the effects of a variable not previously studied in this context and gave additional replication of previous reinforcement-schedule data.

Behavioral probes, utilizing and replicating known relations between behavior and its controlling environment, can also be used to follow short-term changes in the state of behavior. In the spaced-responding technique, for example, interresponse pauses are generated because reinforcement is contingent upon responses that are preceded by pauses. One might be interested in studying the state of behavior as it exists during the pauses, when no instances of the recorded response can be observed. One method of attacking this problem has been to develop a second sample of behavior for use as a probe. A second response is placed under stimulus control in such a way that it will occur, with its known characteristics, only when its stimulus is present. The stimulus is then presented systematically at various points during the pauses that occur in the baseline behavior. The changing characteristics of the second response are observed as a function of its temporal relation to the spaced responses (72). Such a procedure becomes possible only when the properties of the probe are known beforehand, and the technique serves, in turn, to replicate those previously observed properties.

In applying the probe technique of replication, the experimenter makes direct use of known properties of behavior, empirically determined, to accomplish a finer analysis than would have been possible in the absence of such knowledge—a procedure that has, until recently, been relatively rare in experimental psychology. Two developments have made it possible. The first was the growth of the conviction that the behavior of the individual is amenable to a functional analysis in terms of specifiable controlling variables, just as are the phenomena studied in other natural sciences. The second development was the actual achievement of such a functional analysis, an achievement far from complete but increasing in importance as new behavioral phenomena come under experimental control. Not until it became possible to manipulate individual behavior in a relatively precise fashion could the probe technique be used to replicate and refine behavioral data. In order to use behavior as a probe the experimenter must be able to produce the required behavior whenever, and as often as, he wishes to apply it. A phenomenon that appears a certain number of times on the average, among a group of subjects, cannot be utilized in this manner.

PROBING THE CONTROLLING VARIABLES. In the hands of an alert investigator, a closely knit experimental program will yield a set of unifying variables common to many of the related experiments. The discovery and elaboration of these variables constitutes a major type of systematization, and the investigator should track them down whenever the opportunity arises. The nature of the evidence may make this task a difficult one, however. Although the investigator may infer that a single variable is actually responsible for several forms of behavior, all appearing different, these very differences are evidence that his control of the variable in question has been indirect. He must then provide as direct a demonstration as possible of the suspected variable's generality. If he has a well-developed behavioral technology at hand, he is likely to employ the probe technique to determine whether a given variable is the controlling one in different experimental contexts. In the process, he will also replicate and generalize his technology. Such cases are often relatively complex, and involve niceties of the probe technique that will repay detailed examination. Let us take as an example the tandem schedule technique devised by Ferster and Skinner (34).

Among the conclusions that seemed to emerge from a lengthy research program on various types of reinforcement schedules, was the generalization that the properties of behavior over long periods of time are determined by the characteristics which the behavior displays just prior to reinforcement. In a variable-interval schedule, for example, responses are reinforced according to a program set up by a variable clock. The probability of reinforcement delivery increases with the passage of time. Relatively long pauses without responding are, therefore, likely to end with a reinforced response, while short pauses are likely to terminate with a nonreinforced response. The result is an intermediate response rate, determined by the program of reinforcement spacing.

In a ratio schedule, on the other hand, reinforcement delivery is relatively independent of the passage of time, but requires the emission of a particular number of responses. The probability of reinforcement does not increase if the subject pauses between responses. Assuming even slight irregularities in the response rate, reinforcement is most likely to follow a rapid burst of responses. The likelihood that a long pause will terminate with a reinforced response is small. In consequence, a high, near-maximal response rate develops.

This type of analysis seemed to account for much of the behavior generated by a large number of different reinforcement schedules. Both the rate and temporal pattern of behavior appeared to be determined by the spacing of responses just prior to reinforcement. But many of the schedules represented only indirect methods for controlling the prereinforcement characteristics of the behavior. Could this factor be more directly manipulated and its effectiveness analyzed in more precise detail?

In the process of answering these questions the tandem schedule technique was devised. In one experiment, for example, the tandem consisted of two schedules. The first is the variable-interval (VI) schedule that I have described previously. Reinforcement is programed by a variable clock, so that the animal's response is reinforced occasionally, at irregular time intervals. A stable intermediate rate of response was first established on this schedule. The second schedule, the one employed as a probe to determine the influence of the conditions immediately prior to reinforcement, has been called the DRL schedule (*D*ifferential *R*einforcement of *L*ow response rate). The DRL schedule accomplishes the differential reinforcement of low rates by reinforcing a response only if there has been no other response within the preceding ten seconds for example. On a ten-second DRL, reinforcement is available only when the behavior is occurring at a relatively low rate of one response every ten seconds or longer.

Known properties of the DRL schedule were utilized to determine the effects of the conditions immediately prior to reinforcement upon behavior nominally maintained by the variable-interval reinforcement schedule. The two schedules, VI and DRL, were combined into a tandem in such a way that reinforcement was made available to a response at variable intervals, but, in addition, the response could not produce the reinforcement unless at least ten seconds had elapsed since the preceding response. In this way, the variable-interval schedule employed to generate the baseline behavior was maintained. The DRL schedule, added in tandem, ensured precise control over the time interval between the two responses just prior to each reinforcement. If the variable-interval schedule were operating alone, this interresponse interval would be variable, subject to local fluctuations in response rate. With the DRL schedule added, the interval between the two responses immediately prior to reinforcement could never be less than ten seconds.

What was the effect of the added restriction on the reinforcement contingency? Was the intermediate rate which was normally generated by the variable-interval schedule maintained? Or did the ten-second specification of the single time interval between the two responses before reinforcement produce the low rate characteristic of the DRL schedule? The result was the latter. The animals began to space out most of their responses, and the rate fell to the level normally generated by a ten-second DRL schedule. By strategically superimposing the conditions for the low rate upon the variable-interval schedule, a fast-responding organism was converted into a slow one (34).

This experiment, besides demonstrating the validity of a general principle induced from previous studies of reinforcement scheduling, gave an economical systematic replication of the behavioral characteristics of the DRL schedule. If the behavioral properties of the DRL schedule had not been known in advance, the rate decrease that followed introduction of the schedule as a probe would have been an unsystematic finding, unrelated to other data and impossible to integrate under a more general principle.

Systematic replication does not necessarily stamp an experimental finding final—one of its advantages over direct replication. Whereas direct replication reconfirms what is already known, systematic replication may, in addition, yield new information about the phenomenon in question. This is illustrated by another experiment in which a fixed-ratio schedule, in tandem with a DRL schedule, was used as a probe to investigate the control exercised by conditions just prior to reinforcement.

On a ratio schedule, a response is reinforced only after it has been preceded by a certain number of responses. Except insofar as time is consumed by the response itself, reinforcement probability is not a function of the passage of time, as it is in the case of the variable-interval and DRL schedules. Reinforcement is dependent simply on the number of responses that have been emitted by the organism. The fixed-ratio schedule, requiring a constant number of responses per reinforcement, generates an extremely high response rate.

What would be the effect of adding a fixed ratio in tandem to a DRL? Would the resulting behavior be consistent with the generalization under investigation and exhibit the known properties of the fixed-ratio probe? As it turned out, the behavior replicated both the DRL and fixed-ratio properties, and at the same time shed new light on the variables responsible for schedule effects.

The tandem experiment was carried out as follows. The response was first brought to a steady state under a ten-second DRL schedule: no response was ever reinforced if another response had occurred within the preceding ten seconds. All responses that followed the preceding one by ten seconds or more produced the reinforcement. As a result of this contingency, spaced responses occurred at the low rate characteristic of the ten-second DRL schedule. A fixed-ratio of two responses per reinforcement was then added in tandem. Pauses of ten seconds or more still made the reinforcement available, but two responses were now required to produce the reinforcement. Spaced responding "set up" a reinforcement, but a fixed ratio produced it.

The resulting behavior clearly showed the effects of both schedules. The DRL features were maintained, with interresponse pauses of approximately ten seconds continuing to occur. The ratio contingency was evident in the frequent occurrence of closely spaced "bursts" of two responses. The predominant temporal pattern of the behavior was two closely spaced responses, followed by a pause of approximately ten seconds, followed by another two rapid responses, followed by another ten-second pause, etc. (58).

In this case, then, we see a simultaneous replication of two schedule effects, a most economical achievement. In addition, it becomes evident that it is not sufficient to explain schedule effects in terms only of the response rate immediately preceding reinforcement. Our generalization requires modification. Development of the ratio characteristics ensured that reinforcement would always follow two closely spaced responses. But a pause of at least ten seconds was required before the rapid pair of responses could be reinforced. The total reinforced sequence must, therefore, be taken into account, even though the sequence may extend back over a relatively long period of time prior to the reinforcement. This finding not only poses new problems for further investigation but promises also to extend the psychologist's control over his subject matter, the behavior of the individual, to a degree rivaling the "exact" sciences. Such are the fruits of the probe technique of replication.

Successful application of the probe technique, then, achieves a degree of generality far beyond mere subject generality. The demonstration that a principle encompasses more than just a single set of data represents the highest order of scientific achievement. In its most skillful application, the probe technique of replication provides generality of this sort, *along with* reliability and subject generality. Can there be any really serious comparison between the probe technique and conventional statistical design? To use a term appropriate to the agricultural history of statistical design, the "yield" of the probe technique is incomparably superior in both quantity and quality. In addition, it has economy of effort, fineness of experimental control, and simple directness—in other words, the indefinable elegance that is one of the scientist's most subjective, illogical, and useful criteria for evaluating experimentation.

REPLICATION BY AFFIRMING THE CONSEQUENT

THE THIRD TYPE of systematic replication is the most risky and, when successful, often the most satisfying. The risk stems from two sources: (*a*) The method has no logical justification; (*b*) There is no set criterion of success. As every student who has taken an elementary course in logic knows, affirming the consequent is a very dangerous procedure. It is, in fact, usually characterized as a "fallacy." The logical fallacy may be illustrated as follows:

We begin with the statement: "If A is true, *B* is true." We then perform an experiment and find that *B* is indeed true. From this, we conclude that A is also true. Our conclusion may be wrong, however, since we did not state that the truth of A was a *necessary* prerequisite for the truth of *B*. A might be false, even though *B* does turn out to be true. The truth of *B* does not logically permit any inference concerning A.

The logician cannot be gainsaid in this matter, but there is a problem. Few students in the elementary logic course have been told that affirming the consequent, despite its logical fallaciousness, is very nearly the life blood of science. There is, in other words, a discrepancy between logical rules and laboratory practice.

To return to our abstract example, every well-trained scientist knows that it is dangerous to make the inference from *B* to A. But establishment of the truth of *B* does tell him something about A.

For one thing, he has eliminated one of the conditions which could have proved A to be false. If *B* had turned out false, then the truth of A could not be upheld. His confidence in the truth of A is, therefore, increased by a small unquantified bit. He will go to explore other consequences of the truth of A. Propositions C, *D*, *E*, *F*, etc., all of which must be true in order to uphold the truth of A, will come in for experimental check. Furthermore, the consequences of the new findings will be tested in the same way, and each successful demonstration will increase our confidence in A.

Even more important support for A will be the over-all systematization that is achieved. When several seemingly isolated experimental findings are shown to be related, each of the individual components of the system gains in stature. Let us take, as an example of A, the following experiment. The subject, a pigeon, was taught to peck an illuminated disk on the wall of the experimental chamber. Reinforcement was the appearance of a grain hopper from which the bird could eat for three seconds. A special type of fixed-ratio reinforcement schedule was employed (in which the subject must emit a fixed number of responses for each reinforcement). In this experiment, the ratio of responses required per reinforcement could assume either one of two values, changing randomly after each reinforcement. Sometimes 50 responses were required, and sometimes 150, with no exteroceptive stimulus presented to "tell" the subject which of the two ratios was currently programed (34, pp. 580 ff).

The behavior of the bird followed the typical fixed-ratio pattern. Extremely high response rates were maintained, with pauses often following the reinforcement. But an interesting phenomenon appeared. At times when the required ratio was 150, pauses similar to those following reinforcements often occurred after the bird had emitted approximately 50 responses. The bird's current behavior seemed to be controlled by the number of responses that had been emitted since the preceding reinforcement. The "count" appeared to be a critical factor in the ratio performance. When the bird had counted out the number required by the smaller ratio, and no reinforcement was forthcoming, the pause, or "strain," characteristic of the larger ratio appeared.

If this interpretation of the pauses that occurred after approximately 50 responses is correct, it should be possible to demonstrate that the count is a variable in other contexts. For example, an experiment with rats was performed in which two levers were available to the animals. In order to produce the reinforcement, the animals were required to press one lever 12 times and then to press the other (54). That is to say, a fixed ratio of 12 responses per reinforcement was scheduled on one lever, and the animals could utilize the count as their cue to change over to the other lever. Their behavior demonstrated conclusively that the animals did utilize the count in this way, and with considerable efficiency. The count was directly demonstrated to be a controlling variable in behavior generated by one type of fixed-ratio schedule. The suggestion that this variable was responsible for the pauses in the original experiment thereby increases in plausibility. As the explanation becomes more plausible, the observation itself becomes more generalizable. An observation that is not real will not long survive the process of systematic replication.

A second set of data that helped establish the original finding arose from observations of behavior during the transition phase from one fixed-ratio schedule to another. For example, after the subjects' (rats) behavior had stabilized on a fixed-ratio schedule of 25 lever presses per reinforcement, the ratio was reduced to 15. Even though the reinforcement was now delivered after the fifteenth response, the animals at first continued to press the lever beyond the count of 15, without stopping to ingest the reinforcement (10). It appeared as though the previously established count of 25 was powerful enough to override temporarily the control exercised by the reinforcement delivery. This observation not only bolstered the original finding but was, in turn, strengthened by it. The support is reciprocal.

Further systematic replication was achieved in an experiment whose connection with the original finding seemed even more remote. It was demonstrated that behavior generated by certain fixed-interval reinforcement schedules is also under the control of the number of responses emitted during the previous interval, even though reinforcement is programed by a clock (32). Here is one of the most illogical aspects of replication by the method of affirming the consequent. The lower its initial plausibility, the more power attaches to the replication. That is to say, the less plausible some consequence of a finding, A, appears, the greater will be our confidence in A if that consequence is verified. (See the quotation from Polya, pp. 60-61.)

Plausibility? This concept is foreign to classical statistics, and with good reason, for the meaning of plausibility derives at least as much from the observer as it does from the thing observed. There is no scale of plausibility common to all observers. Its subjectivity makes the concept of plausibility a most unscientific notion indeed. Yet scientists employ it, and with profit. They have found, through experience, that attempts to prove the obvious turn out to be most exciting when they fail; that such failures generate scientific revolutions. But the demonstration of an implausible consequence is the most satisfactory form of systematic replication. When many factors mitigating against the reality of a consequence can be found, that consequence is implausible. If the consequence can run the gauntlet of intelligent skepticism and survive the blows by empirical test, then the stature of the original finding is greatly increased. It has spawned a hardier-than-usual offspring, and this attests to its own vigor. Is this poetry? Indeed it is. And it is also good science. The two are mixed because both scientists and poets —at least, the best of each—know more things than the rules of logic would permit them to derive from the available evidence. Discovery has nearly always preceded proof, and the two functions are not always performed by the same person. Yet the discoverer is often given credit even when the formally convincing evidence has to be supplied by someone else. Scientists may talk grandly about the bloodless objectivity of their pursuit, but their other behavior is evidence that they really know better.

Because it is illogical and cannot supply a definitive proof of any proposition, the method of affirming the consequent does not permit us to convince doubters, by logical argument, of the adequacy of our evidence. If a systematic structure, achieved by affirming the consequent, is in fact solid, then the data comprising that structure will eventually be taken into the fold and will, themselves, become the basis for further systematization. The ultimate test is a pragmatic one. The following paragraph, published by Thomas Huxley in 1897, illustrates the application of this principle to some data that were once highly controversial, but which have since become solidly entrenched by a means which could not be other than affirming the consequent:

> At no very distant time, the question whether these so-called "fossils" were really the remains of animals and plants was hotly disputed. Very learned persons maintained that they were nothing of the kind, but a sort of concretion, or crystallization, which had taken place within the stone in which they are found; and which simulated the forms of animal and vegetable life, just as frost on a window-pane imitates vegetation. . . . The position would be impregnable, inasmuch as it is quite impossible to prove the contrary. If a man chooses to maintain that a fossil oyster shell, in spite of its correspondence, down to every minutest particular, with that of an oyster fresh taken out of the sea, was never tenanted by a living oyster, but is a mineral concretion, there is no demonstrating his error. All that can be done is to show him that, by a parity of reasoning, he is bound to admit that a heap of oyster shells outside a fishmonger's door may also be "sports of nature," and that a mutton bone in a dust-bin may have had the like origin. And when you cannot prove that people are wrong, but only that they are absurd, the best course is to let them alone (49, pp. 12-13).

Because there are real dangers involved in replication by the method of affirming the consequent, many scientists conservatively choose not to employ the technique until they have first utilized more direct procedures. Where the logical inference from one experimental finding to another is tenuous, or where even the systematic relation of the two experiments may be a matter of the individual's judgment, there is considerable room for error. The experimenter's history in this respect is an important consideration. There are some scientists who seem to be able to affirm the consequent almost with impunity, and it would be foolish not to listen with respect to such as these. On the other hand, it all too often happens that, following the identification of a new variable, a rash of systematic replications appears in which the new variable is incorrectly held to be the connecting link. The new variable rides the crest of a fad, and it becomes possible to attribute all sorts of behavioral changes to its influence. This is especially likely to be the case if the conditions under which the new variable is effective are as yet poorly understood.

At one time, for example, psychologists were prone to attribute all sorts of otherwise unexplainable experimental data to the operation of secondary reinforcement. Many varied types of experiments were considered systematic replications and, therefore, generalizations, of this variable. The trend has pretty well ceased since we have come to realize how little we know about the circumstances under which secondary reinforcement operates. Such situations seldom last very long. It is probably better to learn to live with them than to eliminate them at the cost of losing the priceless contributions of those with a flair for affirming the consequent. The errors will be corrected as later experimentation reveals that many of the assumed connections among experiments were more apparent than real.

A more serious problem arises from the fact that the process of systematic replication by affirming the consequent has no end. At no time can it be stated conclusively that replication has positively been achieved. The implications of an experimental finding may be infinite in number, and a negative instance may be just around the corner.

What happens when a negative instance occurs? There are many factors which will determine the course of action in such cases. The experimenter must evaluate the number of consequences of A that have been confirmed, their plausibility, and the directness or tenuousness of their connection both to A and to the negative instance. He must apply the usual criteria, to all the data concerned, of the rigor of experimental control. These will take into consideration the other types of replication, both direct and systematic, that have been achieved, as well as the reputations of the experimenters who have been involved. The investigator may then find discrepancies in the evidence that had been overlooked. He may find summary statements unsupported by the data, or he may find some data of which no account has been taken at all. Perhaps his own negative instance will fit together with these other facets, in which case his contribution may be a major positive one.

But what if the survey of the area fails to reveal any important weaknesses in the empirical structure? In such a case, the validity of the negative instance must be put to further test. The scientist will direct his attention to replications, direct and systematic, of the negative case. If the negative instance, too, stands up under replication, the scientist will then be inclined to suspect that the conditions that defined the original finding have been inadequately specified. Perhaps the original statement of the conditions relevant to the initial experiments was too general and did not take into account the specific controlling variables. Or perhaps the original statement was too restricted in that not enough controlling variables were recognized. A better specification of the controlling variables might bring the negative case into line, or perhaps reveal the latter to be unconnected.

Black-and-white instances are difficult to find in experimental psychology, but there have been cases of various shades of gray. One type of finding, for example, that has seemed replicable in a wide variety of situations is concerned with the degree of behavioral control exercised by a stimulus as a function of its temporal relation to reinforcement. It has been reported in an avoidance situation that the longer the time interval between warning stimulus and shock, the weaker is the avoidance conditioning (92). Other experiments have shown that, beyond an optimal value, the greater the duration of a stimulus that precedes an unavoidable shock, the less behavioral suppression will be produced by the stimulus (52). It has also been concluded, from some data, that the conditioned reinforcing effectiveness of a stimulus reaches a maximum and then declines as we increase the duration of that stimulus prior to the delivery of a positive reinforcement (7). The generalization that seemed to emerge from all of these studies was that the longer the duration of a preshock or a prereinforcement stimulus, the less behavioral control will be exercised by that stimulus.

These findings have been replicated both directly and systematically by means of a number of different experimental arrangements. There have, however, been some experiments whose findings are out of line, and there are doubtless others that were never published because their results seemed contrary to the weight of the evidence. Experimental attention has recently been directed at the discrepancies, and the overwhelming conclusion is that the original experiments have simply failed to take into account some powerful variables. The data from the early experiments cannot be considered wrong on this account. It turns out that they simply represent special cases within a more general framework. When the additional variables are taken into consideration, both the original data and the apparent contradictions fit under the same roof. Insofar as the earlier experiments did not adequately control the newly discovered variables, however, they no longer constitute valid systematic replications within the general system.

More concretely, one set of experiments has shown that lengthening the interval between stimulus and shock produces less avoidance conditioning only when the stimulus itself is a brief one (trace conditioning) (50). If the warning stimulus continues right up to the shock (delay conditioning), changes in stimulus duration seem to have little effect (19). Other experiments have shown that any evaluation of stimulus duration must also take into account the length of the period between stimulus presentations (90). Stimulus duration *per se* is not always the critical variable. A stimulus of long duration may exercise weak behavioral control if the interstimulus period is relatively brief. If the interstimulus interval is increased, the same stimulus duration may exercise strong behavioral control. Some experiments have gone even further, to show that the reinforcement contingencies both in the presence and in the absence of the stimulus contribute powerfully to its effectiveness (34, pp. 658-702). It is also becoming evident that, in some cases at least, reinforcement variables are basic to an understanding of the temporal factors (42).

More adequate specification of the variables relevant to a phenomenon or to a behavioral process may thus help to explain discrepancies which turn up when replications are attempted by the method of affirming the consequent. Another instance is exemplified by some early work of Schoenfeld, Antonitis, and Bersh (65) on the problem of conditioned, or secondary, reinforcement. These investigators originally performed two experiments to investigate ". . . the possibility that secondary reinforcing properties imparted to a previously neutral stimulus can act independently of the conditions existing at the time of their acquisition" (65, p. 40). This was a sophisticated problem, but its investigation fell flat when the stimulus exhibited no conditioned reinforcing function at all under any of the experimental conditions. The collaborators were unable to replicate the phenomenon about which they were seeking more general information.

As a next step, the experimenters performed as simple an experiment as possible which would conform to the prevalent statement of the conditions necessary for the establishment of secondary reinforcement. With these procedures, they found it impossible to create a conditioned reinforcer. Evidently the specifications for establishing a stimulus as a conditioned reinforcer were far too indefinite. A re-examination of the procedures and parameters in both the successful and the unsuccessful earlier replications led the investigators to a discovery (implicit also in the earlier writings of B. F. Skinner [81]) of the vital role of operant chaining in the phenomenon of conditioned reinforcement. When the presence or absence of such chaining was taken into account, they were able to produce systematic replications of secondary reinforcement. Both sets of findings became consistent with each other once the controlling factors had been more adequately specified.

I spoke earlier about the problems that arise when irreversible processes prevent direct replication of an experiment with a single organism. The technique of affirming the consequent offers one solution to these problems. Instead of attempting to replicate the data themselves, one may achieve replication by investigating the *implications* of the data. If a series of experiments is performed, each of which yields results consistent with the other, the reliability and generality of the individual experiments are greatly enhanced. The number of such experiments that must be performed cannot be prejudged. It will depend upon the same personal, subjective, pragmatic criteria that science and individual scientists have learned to use in evaluating all types of data.

DATA AND THEORY. The technique of affirming the consequent is frequently employed as a method of theory testing. It is just as applicable, though less often applied, to testing the reliability and generality of experimental data. If a certain experimental result is indeed reliable and general, *and* if we possess an adequate understanding of the variables involved, then the results of other experiments should be specifiable in advance. This process is not necessarily a deductive one; the inference from one experiment to another may be by induction, or even by analogy. The experiments may be so different operationally that their sole connecting link is the inductive leap itself. When this is the case, confirmation of the finding may add greater weight to the original data than if the successive replications were more obviously similar—an extension of the principle that an unlikely confirmation gives us more confidence than a highly probable one.

Although the technique of affirming the consequent may be used for evaluating either theory or data, it is usually reserved for theories. Criteria for evaluating data are largely statistical, and are relatively rigorous. A variable is often rejected (considered to be ineffective) if it can be shown that the observed changes in behavior might have resulted from "chance" as few as two times in a hundred. It is nearly always rejected if the level of chance is found to be as high as five out of a hundred. On the other hand, a fifty-fifty numerical split in the evidence for and against a theory will rarely cause the psychological theorist to abandon his position.

The reason becomes evident upon examining the theoretical controversies of the past decade. Even the most rigorously stated theories are so loosely specified that crucial experiments are impossible. That is to say, the conditions under which A is true are never fully stated in advance. If an implication of the theory fails to be confirmed, the theorist can always point out some aspect of the experiment that might have accounted for the failure.

I bring up this point only to make it clear to the student that the practice I have just described is not a weakness of the method of affirming the consequent. It is, rather, a weakness on the part of those who employ the method. The usefulness of the method as a test of theory is limited by the specificity of the theoretical statements in question. It is folly to evaluate a theory by affirming the consequent when the basic statements of the theory are subject to equivocation. Similarly, it cannot be used for evaluating data which have been obtained under poorly understood conditions. The loose theorizing to which so many of us have been addicted has thus served to conceal a major strength of the technique of affirming the consequent. When this technique of systematic replication is applied successfully, one gains confidence not only in the reliability and generality of the data but also in one's understanding of the data. When its application is unsuccessful—that is to say, replication is not achieved—then the data or the interpretation or both must be rejected. There can be no equivocation. Negative instances are fatal. A quotation from Polya describes the situation beautifully:

> The mathematician as the naturalist, in testing some consequence of a conjectural general law by a new observation, addresses a question to Nature: "I suspect that this law is true. Is it true?" If the consequence is clearly refuted, the law cannot be true. If the consequence is clearly verified, there is some indication that the law may be true. Nature may answer Yes or No, but it whispers one answer and thunders the other, its Yes is provisional, its No is definitive (63, p. 10).

The scientist who attempts to use the technique of affirming the consequent for evaluating either data or theory must display an accompanying willingness to abide by the stringent rules the method imposes. If he does not, he demonstrates his own inadequacy, not that of the technique.

THE DESIGN OF SYSTEMATIC REPLICATION

THE TECHNIQUES of systematic replication that I have cited by no means comprise an exhaustive classification. Nor are the various methods always distinctly separable from each other. There are many possible variations and combinations. How does the scientist decide what method, or combination of methods, to employ? Is there a set of rules he can follow in any specific case and be certain that he has chosen the correct path? The answer is no; systematic replication is not a logical, nor even a well-defined process. There are few scientists who perform an experiment for the deliberate purpose of systematic replication. I have given the process a name, but this is, to a large extent, artificial. Systematic replication, invaluable and necessary though it is for scientific progress, comes about largely as a by-product of the investigator's interest in his subject matter.

The first-rank investigator performs experiments in order to analyze natural phenomena and to determine their interrelations. He explores the phenomena of major interest to him in all their possible ramifications. In his individual experiments he attends to the most minor details, attempting the finest possible experimental analysis. In his over-all plan of research, he bears in mind a larger conception of nature within which his experimental findings must eventually take their proper place. Such an investigator pursues a consistent and well-integrated experimental program in which systematic replication occurs naturally, and usually without conscious deliberation. Systematic replication is an inevitable accompaniment of systematic experimentation, in which proper control has been achieved over both the independent and the dependent variables. When a phenomenon is found to have characteristics that permit its use as a baseline, the investigator does not sit down and deliberately plan a series of experiments designed to demonstrate its replicability by means of the baseline technique. He does, however, employ the phenomenon as a baseline because he suspects it will be useful in elucidating the effects of related variables.

The fact that systematic replication occurs as a by-product of a more basic interest in natural phenomena for their own sake does not reduce its importance. I make the point simply to emphasize that there can be no explicit rules for determining the most appropriate replicative technique. The method to be employed will be selected from the choices made available by the experimental data and by the control techniques at hand.

There is, however, one feature common to all techniques of systematic replication. They all require the utilization of an existing body of knowledge. This knowledge may consist simply of a repertoire of skills useful in controlling behavior, or it may take the form of a systematic body of interrelated data and principles. Systematic replication of any type is not possible without such skills and data. In fact, the maturity of a science may be judged, in part, by the extent to which systematic replication establishes the reliability and generality of its data. A psychology, for example, whose investigators do not have adequate control over their primary datum, behavior, will be incapable of employing systematic replication in any extensive fashion. Furthermore, the psychologist who does not permit his experimental findings to determine the course of his research program will never discover the utility and elegance of systematic replication. The method is not appropriate to a hop-skip-and-jump type of experimental program. The fact that a scientist employs systematic replication to substantiate his findings is, in itself, almost a guarantee of his scientific integrity. It indicates that his satisfactions, scientifically speaking, are derived from his data; that he permits his data, rather than extraneous considerations, to determine his experimental program.

Part III

Variability

ALTHOUGH ITS GENERAL LAWS can be verified only approximately in the laboratory, the subject matter of classical physics was considered to be constant. Variability was usually attributed to errors of measurement for which the experimenter and his tools were responsible. Although this viewpoint has been altered as appropriate evidence became available, it has also proved to be a useful position. The refinement of experimental techniques and the consequent reduction of experimental error in many areas of physical science have made it possible to confirm natural laws with a remarkable degree of precision. When the findings of responsible investigators have shown discrepancies, it has proved wiser to formulate new principles than to accept the data as basically variable.

Psychology has, in the main, adopted a different mode of operation. Most psychologists accept the premise that the subject matter itself is intrinsically variable over and above experimental error. As a direct consequence of this presupposition, confidence-level statistics has been substituted for replication as a means of evaluating data. Many of those psychologists who recognize the limitations of statistical evaluation justify it nevertheless as the best available method for organizing a recalcitrant subject matter. This philosophy has had considerable empirical support in psychology, as has the opposite tradition in physics. Because the doctrine of natural behavioral variability has appeared to be sound, until recently the data upon which most current systematic interest is centered have been produced by experimenters operating within this doctrine. Whether such data will continue to be useful to a science of behavior will depend upon the alternatives available.

That the assumption of intrinsic variability in behavior is false has not yet been demonstrated by experimental evidence. Furthermore, it may never be demonstrated, for it is difficult to prove a negative. Psychology can hardly be said, however, to have reached the limits of precision in its control and measurement techniques. Before a convincing case can be made in favor of intrinsic variability, we will need to develop a high order of technical precision. Meanwhile, the premature acceptance of intrinsic variability as a basic property of behavior has led to the adoption of experimental designs whose nature effectively prevents further investigation of the problem. Statistical experimental design takes variability as its starting point for the evaluation of data. Variability may be measured, and even used as a datum, but it cannot be eliminated without destroying the experimental strategy.

As an analysis of some types and sources of variability, and the citation of experimental designs that stem from such an analysis will make clear, there are alternatives to the currently prevalent strategy. The major alternative is that of treating variations as examples of orderliness, rather than of capriciousness, in nature. Such an approach, if successful, will severely circumscribe the doctrine of natural variability. In order to treat any given instance of variability as a manifestation of an orderly process, we must not only identify the source of the variability but also control it. Each time such control is achieved, intrinsic variability loses another prop. A more immediate consequence for the practitioner of this strategy will be a growing dissatisfaction with much of the data of experimental psychology. As the notion of intrinsic variability becomes a more and more limited basis for laboratory action, the whole existing body of experimental data based upon that notion becomes less and less relevant to an understanding of one's subject matter. This should not pose a serious problem for students, who are nearly always eager to slough off tradition and start afresh. It is more difficult for those of us who presume to be teachers. We often resist discarding hard-won data which have been gathered by ourselves or by our own respected teachers, colleagues, and contemporaries.

My brief comparison of the treatment of variability in psychology and physics was not a prelude to a more extended plea that psychology ape physics. The contrast has been presented only as a method of clarifying the current situation in psychology. The concept of constancy of classical physics may even be regarded as an error that psychology should not repeat. For modern physics is deeply involved in a realm of phenomena in which variability is the rule. But this shift was not a matter of philosophy; it was forced by the data. And the data which necessitated the change could never have been obtained if natural variability had been accepted from the start. The hard core of intrinsic variability was accepted only after errors of measurement had been reduced to quantitative insignificance and after exploration of possible contributory factors failed to eliminate the variability. Few psychologists would argue that their science has achieved this state of sophistication. We have a long way to travel before we can argue convincingly that the variability observed in any given experiment is irreducible.

Chapter 5

Intrinsic Versus Imposed Variability

SUPPOSE WE TAKE THE POSITION that variability is not intrinsic to behavior. What alternative conception is available to explain the fact that variability is observed? If variability is not a natural property of behavior itself, the only remaining possibility is that we *impose* variability upon behavior by means of our experimental operations.

If variability is imposed upon the data rather than intrinsic to it, then variability can be explained through demonstrations in which variability is eliminated by experimental manipulation. Once the factors responsible for any given instance of variability have been identified, that particular instance no longer exists. It is removed from the realm of indeterminism and takes its place within the growing body of known functional relations between behavioral phenomena and relevant controlling conditions. Experimental identification of a source of variability automatically implies experimental control, and once control has been achieved any subsequent instances of the variability in question must be considered to be a function of the experimenter, not of his subject matter.

VARIATIONS TREATED AS EXAMPLES OF ORDERLINESS

ONE DEMONSTRATES that variability has been imposed upon the data by the experimental manipulation of factors suspected of having produced the variations.

For example, after having established a behavioral baseline of some sort in two subjects, suppose we then perform the same experimental operation on each. We may find that the baseline behavior of both subjects changes, but in opposite directions. Statistical analysis might lead us to conclude that the experimental operation had no effect greater than that which might have occurred by chance. But remembering Boring's admonition that chance, used in this manner, is simply a synonym for ignorance (14), we prefer to take another view of the data. Our own interpretation is that the experimental operation sometimes has one effect and sometimes the opposite effect, *depending upon other conditions of the experiment*. The problem now is how to substantiate this interpretation.

The simplest method would be to search for previously overlooked or ignored differences in the baseline behavior of the two subjects. Suppose, for example, our datum is rate of response, with the baseline consisting of a stable rate maintained by a particular reinforcement schedule. Perhaps, on re-examining the baseline behavior, we find that the response rates of the two subjects were not the same. This might lead us to suspect the baseline response rate as the critical factor contributing to intersubject variability. Perhaps our experimental operation decreases high response rates and increases low response rates. One form such a relation might take is illustrated in Figure 11. We see here that there is a baseline response rate, X, which is unaffected by the experimental operation. Baseline rates below this balance point are increased by the independent variable, while rates above the equality point are decreased.

We may employ either or both of two procedures to check our suspicion that some process like the one illustrated in Figure 11 is responsible for the difference between our two subjects. The first method would be to test additional subjects, and to observe whether there is a correlation between baseline response rate and the direction of change induced by the independent, or manipulated, variable. A low correlation might be misleading, however, because of a type of variability that enters at another level. What turns out to be a high response rate for one subject, as measured by the effects of our experimental operation, may well be a low rate for some other

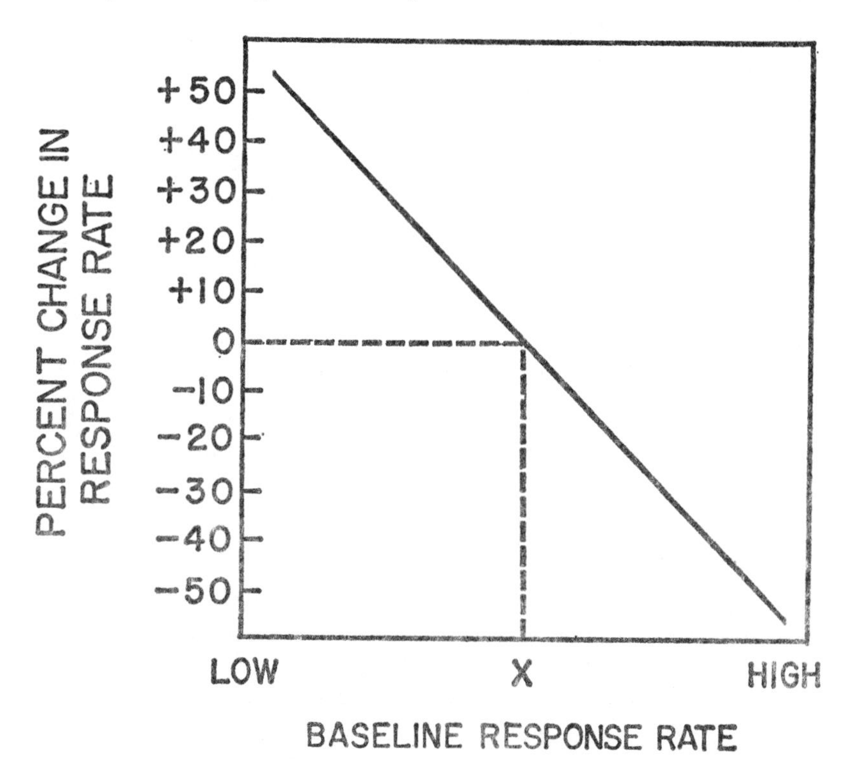

FIGURE 11. Hypothetical data indicating how the effect of some experimental operation upon response rate may depend upon the rate of the baseline behavior from which the change is measured.

subject. Another way of saying this is that the location of the equality point shown in Figure 11 may vary among different subjects. Thus, the same baseline rate might increase for one subject and decrease for another subject. Depending upon the amount and distribution of this second type of variability within our subject population, we may or may not be able to observe the correlation we are seeking.

The second method of checking the source of variability involves the direct manipulation of our original subjects' baseline behavior. If we can establish new baselines, in which the two subjects exchange positions with respect to response rate, they may also reverse with respect to the effect of the experimental operation. There is no statistical problem involved here. What is required is simply a behavioral technology sufficiently developed to provide us with the experimental know-how for manipulating our subjects' behavior to the desired levels. We should, in fact, have several methods for altering the response rates. Only in this way can we evaluate the extent to which the effect of our original experimental operation is a function of response rate *per se*, independently of our method for generating the response rate. If we are able, with our two subjects, to reverse the effect of the independent variable at will simply by manipulating the baseline response rates, then our experiment will constitute a successful demonstration of imposed variability.

What would have happened if the original experiment had been performed according to a traditional group-statistical design? Let us set up such an experiment and examine the possibilities. We first select a large group of subjects according to some random procedure, and proceed to establish the behavioral baseline from which we are to measure the effects of our experimental operation. After the baseline response rate stabilizes with respect to the group mean and variance, we will administer the independent variable. The reader will recall that the effect of the independent variable is going to be a function of the subject's baseline performance, but the experimenter does not know this. His experimental manipulation is going to decrease the response rate of those subjects whose baseline is high, and increase the response rate of the subjects whose baseline is low. The resulting data, therefore, are going to depend

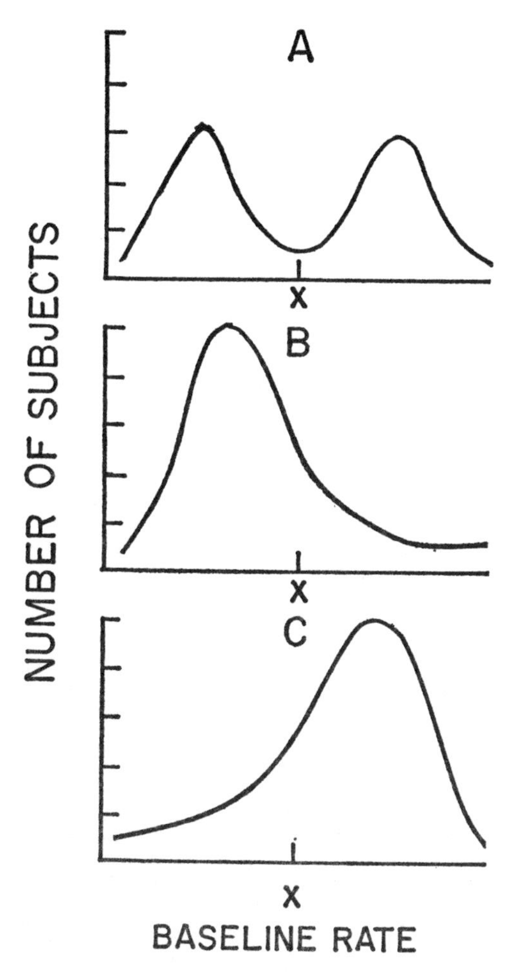

FIGURE 12. Three possible ways for baseline rates of different values to be distributed among a population of subjects.

upon the population distribution of subjects with high, low, and intermediate baseline rates.

Figure 12 illustrates three of the many possible population distributions. In section A we have a bimodal distribution of baseline rates. What would our group data look like if this were a true representation of the population from which we drew our subjects? The experimental manipulation would increase responding in the low-rate subjects and would decrease it in the high-rate subjects. Since the distribution is symmetrical around the intermediate value, there would be no change in the average response rate for the group, though the intersubject variability might decrease. It might easily be concluded that the experimental operation had no statistically significant effect. If, however, there were a marked preponderance of low-baseline subjects in the population, as is represented in section B, the statistics might support a conclusion that the operation increases response rate. With a distribution whose mode is in the high-rate region (section C), the conclusion might be reversed, for most of the subjects would display a lowered response rate as a function of the independent variable. In none of these instances would the generalization be correct.

The original experiment, however, performed with only two subjects, is open to a similar error of population bias. If, for example, the population distribution were peaked in the region of low baselines, there is a good chance that both subjects would have been drawn from this region. Both would then have shown an increased rate, and thereby seemed to justify an incorrect generalization.

Unfortunately, this possibility is often used to justify group data as against small N experiments. A small sample may not pick up all the variations which exist in the population. The strongest likelihood is, of course, that a small sample will represent the modal characteristics of the population. But there is always the possibility that extremes will have been selected out, and that data obtained from these relatively special cases will be generalized to the rest of the population. Such fears are well founded. But is the problem to be solved by group data? The student should recognize that group data not only cannot solve this problem but actually make its solution impossible. As I have pointed out before, group data neither reveal nor eliminate population variability. In a case like the one we have been discussing, where the factor which underlines the variability is itself distributed unevenly throughout the population, group data will even prevent recognition that the problem exists at all.

The problem is one of differences in the functional relations between a set of controlling variables and the behavior of a number of individuals. Unless the group statistics are abandoned and the data of individual subjects examined, there is no virtue in a large N. And if the individual data are so utilized, the "group" experiment is transformed into a design based upon direct intersubject replication, as described in Chapter 3. This provides us with the key to the solution of our problem.

The only way a population bias of the sort that has been troubling us can be detected is through replication, direct or systematic, with individual subjects. Group means may be replicated an infinite number of times, but the population bias will never reveal itself, for it, too, will be replicated, and natural variability will only become more firmly "established." Here we have a case in which the replication of group means can only serve to perpetuate an error, while replication with individual subjects is inevitably self-corrective. If the possibility of error cannot be eliminated, the wisest course to follow is to use procedures that are capable of eventually detecting the error.

To return to our demonstration of imposed variability, we may note that we have actually accomplished a great deal more in this hypothetical experiment. When we reversed the baseline performance of our two subjects we also reversed the direction of their reaction to the experimental operation. By this technique we not only exposed and controlled a source of variability in the data, but we also accomplished a systematic replication that greatly increased our confidence in the reliability and generality of the findings. We were able to take the seemingly discordant data of two subjects and, by manipulating a source of variability, show that the discrepant data really constituted two points along the same continuum. By controlling a source of variability we have increased our confidence in the reliability of both sets of seemingly contradictory data. The replicative technique that we have employed is a variant of the method of affirming the consequent.

In the process of unifying seemingly discrepant sets of data we also greatly extend the generality of the findings. The ultimate test of generality is replication, and unknown or uncontrollable sources of variability are the only potential bars to replication. In the present hypothetical case we now have available a principle by means of which we could explain and even eliminate a portion of the variability that additional subjects might have displayed in any replicative attempt. We have, in a sense, increased the generality of our data even before attempting any additional replication.

Tracking down sources of variability is thus a primary technique for establishing generality. Generality and variability are basically antithetical concepts. If there are major undiscovered sources of variability in a given set of data, any attempt to achieve subject or principle generality is likely to fail. Every time we discover and achieve control over a factor that contributes to variability, we increase the likelihood that our data will be reproducible with new subjects and in different situations. Experience has taught us that precision of control leads to more extensive generalization of data.

Sometimes the opposite case is argued. It is held that the more strictly we control our experimental situation, the less our data will be applicable under different conditions. An extreme form of this position is the often-heard statement that behavioral data from the laboratory are too restricted to be generalizable to the real world, where a multitude of variables must be dealt with. This involves a basic misconception of the technique of eliminating variability through experimental control. Control of a variable does not imply that it has been ignored. The highest type of experimental control over a variable is not achieved by eliminating it. This is, indeed, rarely possible. Experimental control is achieved by deliberately manipulating variables in a systematic fashion, so that their effects may be understood. There is no virtue in using the "real" world as our laboratory if the variables involved have ill-defined consequences, or, as is often the case, if they are not even known. The resulting variability in our data is likely to be greater than the effects produced by the factors upon which our immediate interest is centered. Experimental investigation of the sources of variability in our data leads to increased understanding of the phenomenon under investigation. Acceptance of variability as unavoidable or, in some sense, as representative of the "real world" is a philosophy that leads to the ignoring of relevant factors. When large variability is encountered in an investigation, it is sound practice to assume that a "large" variable (or set of variables) is involved. If the differences among the data from several subjects are so great as to obscure the effects of a deliberately manipulated factor, it is likely that the experimenter has made an error of judgment in orienting his research.

He will find it profitable to change his course and to examine the factors whose uncontrolled effects loom so large in his data. This is a time-tested method for discovering major variables.

Let us return once more to our hypothetical experiment in which we resolved intersubject differences by manipulating a major source of variability. It might be objected that our analysis of the variability between the two subjects of this experiment was only spuriously successful. Our explanation of the variability produced by the experimental operation was accomplished only by appeal to variability at another level—in the baseline behavior. Why, if the organisms were treated alike, was there a difference in their behavior prior to introduction of the experimental variable? Is this, then, the door through which intrinsic variability enters?

Before going on to discuss this question, I must emphasize that the problem is irrelevant to our evaluation of the original experiment. We have demonstrated, in our example, that the original difference between the subjects was a lawful one, capable of manipulation by specifiable and repeatable operations. This difference can no longer be attributed to any intrinsic variability in the effects of our experimental manipulation. The data must be judged to be orderly, and not attributable to chance. Evaluation of the data has been accomplished by experimental rather than statistical manipulation. The baseline variability becomes a problem only if our experimental interest is directed at the baseline behavior as a problem in its own right, or if we are concerned with the general problem of variability *per se*. The question of whether the baseline is intrinsically variable then becomes a relevant issue *in its own right*, independently of the post-baseline data. What is required now is an experimental check upon the nature of the baseline variability in order to determine whether it has been imposed or is intrinsic.

How to go about evaluating the baseline variability? One method is to examine the behavioral history of the organisms in question. One of them, for example, may have been exposed to an experimental arrangement (or even an uncontrolled one) in which efficiently spaced behavior was generated. Perhaps this efficient form of behavior carried over into the conditions we arranged to produce the baseline behavior, and resulted in a low response rate. As before, we may test the possibilities by the systematic manipulation of variables suspected to be relevant. We might, for example, deliberately expose our subjects to conditions which are known to generate efficiently spaced behavior, thus deliberately building a specifiable behavioral history. We can then establish our experimental baseline and observe whether the response rate is indeed a function of this particular historical factor. If an orderly relation is observed we may then proceed to systematic replication, producing similar histories of efficient responding by means of different experimental operations. Success in these efforts would be a complete victory for imposed over intrinsic variability. Even if we were unable to identify the particular history that was responsible for the baseline variability in our original experiment, the explanatory burden will have been shifted from unknown or chance factors to potentially identifiable and reproducible ones. There is, in this case, no appeal to a different level of variability.

There is always the possibility that manipulation of the subject's behavioral history may fail to reveal the sources of the baseline variability. In that case, we might resort to a more subtle type of analysis. No behavioral baseline is as simple as our descriptions tend to make it seem. In describing any natural phenomenon, and behavior is only one example, we always simplify, abstracting those features which are orderly and amenable to systematic integration. When we find that the specifications which we have chosen to abstract from a behavior sample display a variable relation to our experimental manipulations, we may be justified in suspecting the adequacy of our selection.

Perhaps, for example, our original specification of the baseline behavior has customarily not been made in terms of response rate at all, but rather in terms of reinforcement frequency. In the case of behavior maintained by a variable-interval reinforcement schedule we often specify only the average time between reinforcements in describing the baseline. But the demands of a variable-interval programing tape can be met by any of a wide range of response rates. We may find that an experimental manipulation whose effects bear only a disorderly relation to reinforcement frequency will fall nicely into line when related to response rate.

An excellent example of such a case is to be found in an experiment performed by R. J. Herrnstein (42). He used three pigeons as subjects, maintaining their key-pecking behavior by means of a variable-interval food-reinforcement schedule. The experimental operation consisted, in part, of occasional interruptions of the experiment. These were accomplished by turning off the illumination in the experimental space and simultaneously disconnecting the response key from the feeder, so that no reinforcement could be obtained during the "time-out" periods. The second part of the experimental operation was to change the color of the response-key illumination 30 seconds prior to each time-out period. His interest was centered in the birds' performance during this warning signal, prior to the time out. He measured the response rate during this period against a background of several different variable-interval schedules.

Figure 13 shows the ratio of response rate during the warning signal (W) to the rate in the absence of the warning signal (VI). This ratio is plotted as a function of the mean time between reinforcements, as determined by the variable-interval schedule. Two of the animals, S-1 and S-3, displayed a similar and relatively orderly relation. As the reinforcement frequency increased, the ratio of the two response rates decreased. Additional analysis of the data demonstrated that the decline in the ratio was the resultant of both an increase in the VI rate and a decrease in the warning-signal rate as greater reinforcement frequencies were programed.

The third subject, however, was markedly deviant from the other two. For S-2, the ratio of response rates increased with reinforcement frequency. Was this intrinsic variability? Herrnstein thought not, because he had noted an interesting feature of S-2's response rates. Instead of increasing as a function of reinforcement frequency, as was the case with the other two subjects, S-2's VI rate remained constant over a wide range of reinforcement intervals. S-2 had apparently developed what is known as a "locked rate," which makes the response rate insensitive to reinforcement frequency as well as to a number of other variables (see pp. 176-177).

In the light of these data, Herrnstein performed two additional types of operation. First, he took steps to eliminate the locked rate and, once this was accomplished, he redetermined some of the original points of Figure 13. Then, rather than discard his original

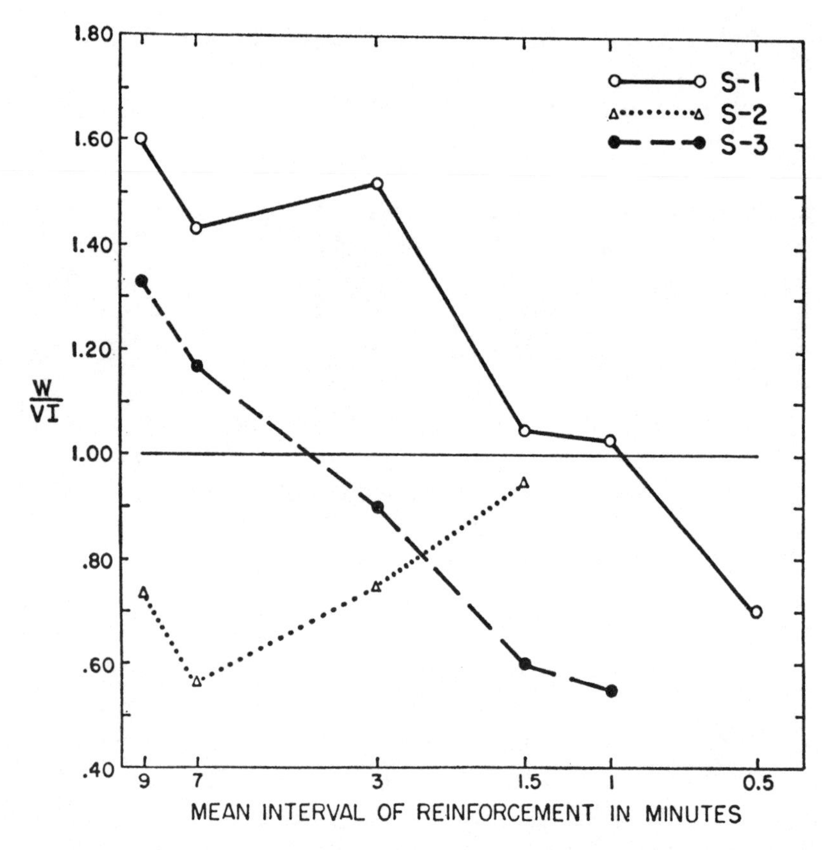

FIGURE 13. An apparent failure to replicate a functional relation in all three subjects. (*From Herrnstein,* 42.)

data, he sought consistency by means of an alternative specification of the baseline. Instead of describing it in terms of reinforcement frequency, he changed to response rate. When the data were replotted as a function of the baseline response rate, instead of reinforcement frequency, the relations of Figure 14 were obtained, consistent in general form for all three subjects and establishing that the original intersubject variability had resulted from an inadequate specification of the controlling variables.

We may expect to run into frequent problems of this sort. As I have pointed out elsewhere, psychologists have not yet reached

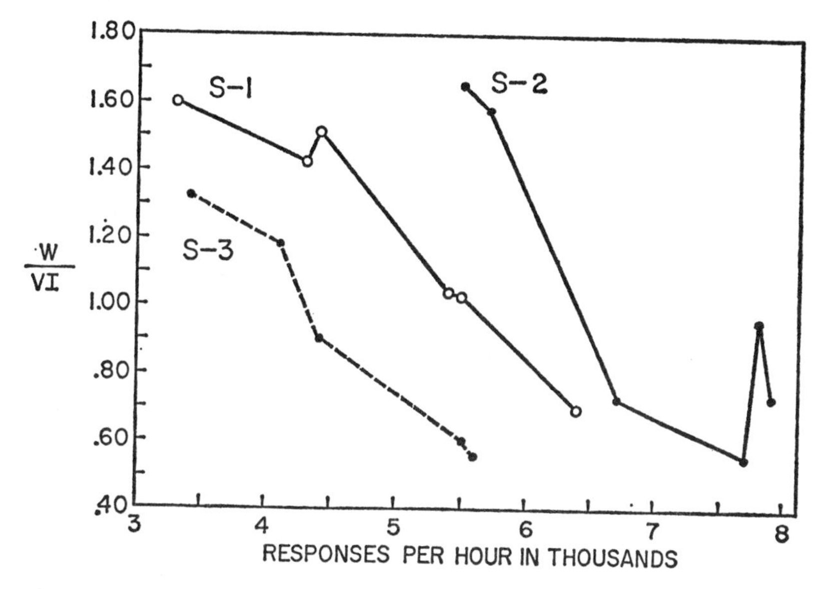

FIGURE 14. Successful replication of the functional relations for all three animals following adequate specification of the controlling variables. (*Data replotted from Herrnstein, 42.*)

agreement on the variables whose specification will form the foundations of their science. Until that time arrives, we cannot treat variability lightly by assigning it to uncontrollable sources.

THE ROLE OF FUNCTIONAL RELATIONS IN EVALUATING VARIABLE DATA

IF AN INSTANCE of variability cannot be explained by manipulation of the behavioral history, or by more adequate specification of relevant current variables, we must turn to a more complex type of experimental analysis. This is the parametric study of variables suspected to be relevant to the phenomenon in question. Behavior is complex enough to make it impossible to study all relevant variables simultaneously. We try, therefore, in classical experimental fashion, to maintain the constancy of all variables except those in which we are interested at the moment. When, by means of systematic replication, we can demonstrate the nonrelevance of certain variables, we are delighted, for we thereby increase the generality of our findings and at the same time make our experimental task lighter. But in our preoccupation with scientific rigor we often forget that the variables we are holding quantitatively constant do not necessarily exert a constant effect throughout all phases of the experiment.

To return to our previous hypothetical example (p. 146); suppose our attempt to explain the variability in terms of differences in baseline behavior was unsuccessful. Appropriate manipulation of historical or current baseline variables did not erase the differences between the two subjects. Can we locate the source of variability in some factor that entered the picture only after the experimental operation was introduced? We may, for example, have data indicating that the state of food deprivation has no effect upon the baseline behavior. In spite of this, related data or even pure "hunch" may lead us to suspect that the variability is explainable as a function of the degree of food deprivation. If our guess is correct, food deprivation must be considered as a hidden variable, exercising no control over the behavior until a new set of maintaining conditions is introduced.

We proceed, then, to vary systematically the level of hunger in the two subjects. If we were fortunate in our guess, we might obtain data similar to that represented in Figure 15. As a background for these data, let us assume that in the original experiment the baseline behavior was generated when the subjects had been deprived of food for 24 hours, and that this level of hunger was maintained during the initial exposure to the experimental conditions. For the sake of illustration let us also select as our behavioral measure the number of responses per unit time, or response rate.

The hypothetical data of Figure 15 were obtained in the following manner. The animals were first returned to the baseline conditions and their response rates measured after several different periods of food deprivation. Let us assume, for simplicity, that the baseline of both subjects was identical and insensitive to food deprivation. This is represented by the horizontal line, which tells us that both subjects maintained a baseline rate of five responses per minute at all levels of deprivation.

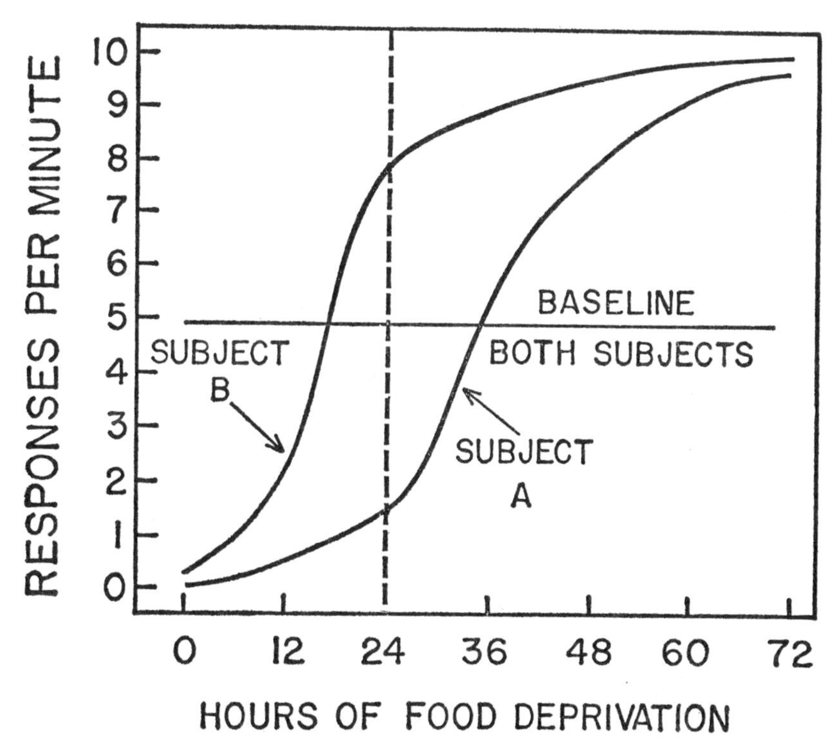

FIGURE 15. An illustration of how food deprivation, which does not influence the baseline behavior, may become a relevant factor following a change in the experimental conditions, and may account for inter-subject variability.

We then introduce our experimental, or independent, variable and again measure the response rates after several different periods of food deprivation. We observe now that the two subjects develop characteristic curves, each sensitive, but differentially so, to food deprivation. Following introduction of the independent variable, the response rate for both subjects increases as a function of prolonged food deprivation. While deprivation was not a controlling factor in the maintenance of the baseline behavior, it enters the picture powerfully after a new independent variable is introduced. When the behavior comes under the control of the new variable it also comes, coincidentally, under the control of deprivation.

The functions which are now found, in our hypothetical example, to relate deprivation and response rate are remarkably similar in shape for both subjects. Most experimental psychologists would be quite content to achieve the degree of consistency from one subject to another which appears in Figure 15. But there are quantitative differences between the two curves, and these differences could well be responsible for the intersubject differences which we observed in our first experiment. The relation between these functions and our original observation of variability will become apparent if we confine our immediate attention to those response rates obtained at the deprivation level of 24 hours. This is the level of deprivation which had been maintained throughout the original experiment.

Under the baseline conditions, established prior to the experimental operation, both subjects respond at a rate of five responses per minute. Following the experimental operation, however, Subject A slows down to about one response per minute, while Subject B increases his rate to approximately eight per minute. One subject's response rate has decreased, while the other's has increased as a function of the same operation. What we did not know in our original experiment was that along with the deliberate experimental manipulation we also introduced deprivation as a relevant variable. In so doing, we located each subject at the 24-hour point on his own rate vs. deprivation curve. For one subject, this point yielded a rate higher than the baseline level, and for the other subject it yielded a lower rate.

If we had employed a 60-hour deprivation period, both subjects would have shown an increased and very similar response rate as a function of the experimental operation. If we had used a 12-hour deprivation level, both subjects would have shown a lower rate. In either of the latter two cases, we would never even have known that there was a problem. Similarly, if we had buried the variability in a statistical evaluation, we would never have become aware of the problem. In either case, we would probably have been caught in a false generalization.

Only by exposing and tracking down major sources of variability can true generality be achieved. As a result of our hypothetical investigation, we would be in a position to make a more complete specification of the effects of our experimental manipulation. In effect, we would have shown that the data of *both* subjects in the original experiment were correct. The large difference between the two subjects following the initial experimental manipulation was the consequence of a relatively small intersubject difference in the slope of the curves relating response rate to food deprivation. Even though food deprivation had been held constant throughout the initial experiment, its effects upon response rate did not remain invariant during both the baseline and the experimental phases. The results of our initial experiment, therefore, actually reflected orderly processes and not some form of near-chaos. Increasing the number of subjects and treating the combined results statistically would not have succeeded in revealing the basic orderliness of the data.

Here again we may have explained the variability of the data in which we are primarily interested, but only at the cost of exposing variability at another level. If we are to push the matter to completion, we are faced with the problem of explaining the difference between the two subjects with respect to the parameters of the rate vs. deprivation function. Our solution has by no means settled the general question of whether there does exist intrinsic variability in behavior. We have simply removed a source of variability from one functional relation and located it a step away in another relation.

The process could continue in infinite regress as long as there remained variables and combinations of variables to be investigated. There is nothing inherently undesirable in this situation. As we continue to identify sources of variability in successive experiments we remove an increasingly large portion of our subject matter from the realm of intrinsic variability. The regress will be halted at any point at which (*a*) variability is no longer encountered; (*b*) variability becomes so small and so unsystematic that we can attribute it to uncontrolled but unimportant variations in our techniques; (*c*) variability can definitely be shown to have been imposed by the experimenter; (*d*) a class of behavioral phenomena is ultimately discovered which does possess inherent variability. As was the case in physics, the last eventuality will open up new and exciting areas of research. But we have a long road to travel before that feat becomes possible. Meanwhile there are a number of other sources of variability to be considered, along with methods for dealing with them.

VARIABILITY PRODUCED BY WEAK BEHAVIORAL CONTROL

One of the most discouraging and at the same time challenging aspects of behavioral science is the sensitivity of behavior to a tremendous array of variables. There are very few conditions to which we can expose a behaving organism without observing some change. Even in the most rigorous experimental setup, the organism is continually exposed to changes in his environment. At the very minimum, these will be confined to changes that occur as a result of his own behavior, and to variables correlated with the duration of exposure to the experimental situation. In the more usual case, there will also be variations in such factors as temperature, humidity, noises, sleep, hunger, thirst, sexual cycles, and many others. There are, in addition, physiological changes whose known function is to regulate the internal economy of the organism, but whose effects may also extend out to behavior. Variables such as these, unless they are, themselves, the subject of investigation, are generally considered "nuisance" factors. The experimenter would prefer not to have to consider them in a specific experiment, though he may be well aware of their importance in a general systematic picture. When he can, he eliminates or stabilizes them by means of experimental control, but this is not always possible. The combination of the required skills, available time, and financial resources is often not available.

The recognition of such factors has contributed to psychologists' unprotesting acceptance of a statistical philosophy of experimentation. Even if such factors were controllable, the argument sometimes goes, why go through additional experimental labor and expense when the effects of "irrelevant" variables can be canceled out statistically?

But variables are not canceled statistically. They are simply buried so that their effects cannot be seen.

The rationale for statistical immobilization of unwanted variables is based on the assumed random nature of such variables. In a large group of subjects, the reasoning goes, the uncontrolled factors will change the behavior of some subjects in one direction and will affect the remaining subjects in the opposite way. When the data are averaged over all the subjects, the effects of the uncontrolled variables are presumed to add algebraically to zero. The composite data are then regarded as though they were representative of one ideal subject who had never been exposed to the uncontrolled variables at all.

Not only is the assumption of randomness with respect to the uncontrolled variables an untested one but it is also highly improbable. There are few, if any, random phenomena in the behavioral world. Perhaps the major reason for this is the interaction that continuously takes place between behavior and its controlling variables. Often behavior, once it changes as a function of some variable, turns about and alters the variable itself. Even when this does not happen, the effect of a given variable is seldom independent of the current state of the behavior. As the behavior changes, the degree of influence of the controlling variable also changes. This is just another way of stating that behavior seldom bears a simple linear relation to its controlling variables. Under such conditions, the assumption of randomness is thoroughly untenable.

Even if the assumption of randomness were tenable, statistical control would not be a satisfactory solution to the problem. The controlling variables interact reciprocally not only with behavior but also among themselves. The effect of a given variable upon behavior depends upon the qualitative and quantitative properties of other variables that are simultaneously present. These include not only the factors that the experimenter manipulates directly but also those "irrelevant" conditions which the experimenter prefers not to consider. Even if specific variables acted randomly in a group of subjects, it is highly unlikely that groups of such variables would combine in such a way as to produce random effects.

There is, finally, the basic observation that behavioral states persist for some time after their controlling variables have been withdrawn. I will have more to say about this characteristic of behavior in the chapters on experimental design. It is relevant here, however, because of the roadblock it places in the way of statistical control of variability. Even if an uncontrolled variable were to exert random effects upon behavior, these effects might persist after the random variable disappeared. When it reappears, or when other variables replace it, the state of the behavior is not the same. It thus becomes possible for a given uncontrolled variable, if it occurs with slightly greater frequency than do other such variables, to assume relatively complete and powerful control over the behavior in question. All that is required is for the uncontrolled variable to reappear each time before the effects of its previous occurrence have faded away. There will thus be a cumulative process by means of which it can gradually build up its control even to the point where it becomes dominant over other factors. This is essentially the process that is involved in the acquisition of "superstitious" behavior (82). Occasional adventitious reinforcements whose effects are relatively long-lasting, have been observed to establish control over behavior powerful enough to override deliberately manipulated experimental variables.

In view of these considerations, it is unlikely that any behavioral measure can be freed of the effects of uncontrolled variables simply by taking an average over a group of subjects. The average will be composed of individual measures which reflect nonrandom differential effects of all the uncontrolled factors in the situation. The uncontrolled variability, though submerged from view, remains present in the data. Any evaluation of group data must take this situation into account. Unfortunately, since the grouping of data hides such variability, it cannot adequately be evaluated.

Again, as we criticize traditional techniques, we must inquire into the alternatives. The fundamental corrective technique is, of course, to secure direct experimental control over as many as possible of the factors that are considered relevant to a given experimental problem. On the other hand, this is not always feasible, or even desirable. It is likely to be technically difficult and expensive to achieve control over all such variables. Furthermore, even if complete control were technically and economically feasible, we will not usually know the relevance of all conceivable factors.

Is, for example, the range of humidity normally maintained in one's laboratory going to produce significant variations in the data? To control humidity in the absence of such knowledge may be a wasteful enterprise; and, unless humidity is a variable in which the experimenter is interested for its own sake or for its systematic relevance, he will be reluctant to organize an experimental program to determine its possible importance What he will do is observe the natural humidity variations that occur and note whether these are correlated in any consistent and major way with his experimental findings. Even if he observes an important correlation, however, he is likely to adopt a different course than to install expensive humidity-control apparatus.

Before describing his procedure, it is important to note a basic feature of his first step. This is the employment of individual data to determine whether humidity is a variable requiring deliberate control. Because of possible interactions both with the behavior and with other variables, individual effects may be large, but discrepant. Averaged data might hide the discrepancies, but individual data will reveal their magnitude and importance. Or there may be large effects in only a few subjects, so that statistical significance would be low in spite of the high experimental significance. Individual data are capable of revealing the effects of variables that group data might hide.

Thus, what happens if it is found that humidity does contribute importantly to the variability of behavioral experiments? Unwanted variables of the type I have been considering exert their maximal effect upon behavior that is being maintained weakly. I believe that this is a general enough principle to justify a rule of thumb: When intolerable variability is encountered, strengthen the variables that are directly responsible for maintaining the behavior in question. For example, in the domain with which I am most familiar, one might increase the subjects' level of food deprivation, increase the size of the reinforcement, increase the shock intensity, provide the behavior with an exteroceptive feedback, employ easily discriminable stimuli, and, in general, make use of as many as possible of those variables and combinations of variables which are known to exercise a high degree of behavioral control. In other words, instead of trying to manipulate extraneous variables directly, one can often override their effects by establishing baselines that are relatively insensitive to their influence.

Successful employment of this technique for dealing with variability depends upon the availability of an established body of information. Unless something is known of the variables that are most effective in maintaining behavior at a high level it will be impossible to eliminate unwanted variability by the technique of strengthening the behavioral control. The degree to which this technique is employed, then, is another criterion for evaluating progress in an area of scientific investigation. Orderly data, unmarred by variability from extraneous factors and secured by means of experimental arrangements in which such factors are not explicitly eliminated, indicate that the investigators have the most powerful variables well in hand.

The extent to which this technique depends upon established knowledge may be illustrated by an example. A project was instituted to investigate the effects of localized brain damage, in rats, upon timing behavior. To generate a behavioral baseline we selected, to start with, a procedure which required the animal to space its lever-pressing responses at least 20 seconds apart in order to secure a food reward (94). A stable rate of spaced responding over a two-hour period was to serve as the baseline from which to measure the effects of experimentally produced cortical lesions.

Well before any lesions were attempted, however, we struck a snag on the behavioral side of this enterprise. After maintaining a stable level during the first hour of the session, some of the animals' response rates became extremely variable during the second hour. Lever-pressing rates declined, and the animals spent a considerable amount of time in an attitude that resembled sleep. This behavior, along with the negatively accelerated lever-pressing curves, suggested that the animals had received enough rewards during the first hour to produce satiation, a condition in which other variables than the reinforcement schedule come to dominate the behavior. Previous data, however, had shown that satiation is a relative matter, controlled by other variables in addition to the amount of food consumed. These data may be summarized, in a not very precise manner, by the statement that the more favorable we make a food-reinforcement schedule, the more the animal will eat. Because of these findings, the course we chose in order to eliminate the variability and prolong the stable baseline performance was different from the one suggested by our initial observations. Our first tendency had been to decrease the size of the reinforcements and thus to delay satiation. Actually, however, we did the opposite. We increased the size of the rewards. By this operation we successfully overrode the effect of the unwanted variables that were interfering with our control over the baseline behavior. The larger reinforcement, instead of producing earlier satiation, increased the control exercised by the reinforcement schedule to the point where uncontrolled variables were effectively immobilized.

It will undoubtedly have occurred to the student that this technique has its limitations. Increasing the effectiveness of the maintaining variables is likely to reduce the sensitivity of the behavior not only to extraneous variables but to the major variables under investigation as well. For example, behavior maintained by certain fixed-ratio schedules of reinforcement, in which a fixed number of responses is required for each reinforcement, is known to be extremely stable and resistant to extraneous influence. It also turns out to be highly resistant to a number of drugs that depress behavior maintained by other reinforcement schedules. If one is interested in assessing the effects of such drugs upon behavior, one does not want to employ the fixed-ratio schedule to generate the baseline, in spite of its relative insensitivity to irrelevant variables. Blough has suggested a pointed analogy, "If, in the study of water waves, a smooth, unruffled surface of water is desired as a baseline, it does not do to freeze the water to achieve this baseline" (8, p. 343). Thus, a certain amount of judgment and trial-and-error must be employed by the investigator in selecting the most appropriate method for achieving relative freedom from unwanted variability. He must not make the error of selecting a method that will make the behavior insensitive to the variables of major interest.

Weak behavioral control may also result from an injudicious selection of the quantitative values of the variables which are to maintain a baseline. Figure 16 presents a potential example. In this experiment, either one of two stimuli was always present, depending upon the behavior of the subject (white rat). When the first stimulus (S_1) was present, each lever-pressing response by the animal served to postpone the appearance of the second stimulus (S_2) for 20 seconds. Whenever the animal paused in its responding for 20 seconds, S_2 appeared. If the animal failed to respond in the presence of S_2, it received a shock and S_1 reappeared. Each response in S_2, however, postponed the shock and prolonged the duration of S_2.

It was found in this study that the behavior in the presence of S_1 was determined, in part, by the amount of time each S_2 response postponed the shock. We see in Figure 16 that the amount of

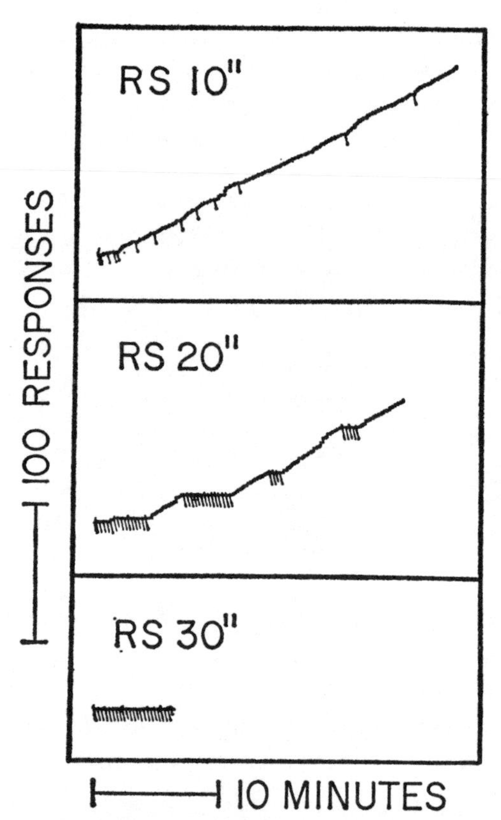

FIGURE 16. The center record depicts a state of behavior which oscillates between the extremes of stability shown in the upper and lower curves. (*Unpublished data from Sidman,* 73.)

responding in S_1 declines as we increase the shock-postponement interval (RS interval) in the presence of S_2. With an RS interval of 10 seconds, the subject emits most of its responses in the presence of S_1. With an RS interval of 30 seconds, there are practically no responses in the presence of S_1. When the RS interval is 20 seconds, the performance in S_1 is intermediate between the two extremes. It is this intermediate curve which is relevant to our present discussion. Note that the response rate is two-valued. Periods of relatively stable rate are interspersed with plateaus of no responding. The stable rate is similar to that of the upper curve, while the plateaus resemble the lower curve. The behavior, then, may be considered to be in a transition stage between the high response rate displayed in conjunction with an RS interval of 10 seconds, and the low rate associated with the 30-second RS interval. The behavior is "teetering" between the two extreme positions.

This oscillating transition state is an example of the weak behavioral control that may result when the control fluctuates between two quantitative values of a variable. The oscillations do not represent chance variability. Because the behavior is being maintained at an intermediate state between two extremes, other uncontrolled factors in the situation will operate to push the performance sometimes to one side of the dividing line and sometimes to the other. In such a situation the baseline variability can be reduced by altering the quantitative values of the controlling variables, thereby strengthening the experimental control.

VARIABILITY PRODUCED BY LOCAL FLUCTUATIONS IN THE MAINTAINING CONTINGENCIES

WE HAVE ALREADY NOTED that behavioral changes often persist for a considerable time after the variables that initiated the changes are no longer physically present. Extinction is a well-known example. Behavior may occur in essentially unchanged form long after reinforcement has been discontinued. There are, however, more subtle cases than this. Small changes in reinforcement contingencies may take place briefly during the course of an ongoing experiment, with effects that long outlive the local fluctuations. Such fluctuations are usually unplanned by the experimenter. They may occur as a consequence of the method of programing the reinforcement contingencies, or they may be a by-product of the reciprocal interaction that takes place between behavior and its controlling environment. In either case, their persisting effects are likely to account for a major portion of the variability, both within and between subjects.

There is one method of programing an experiment that will almost inevitably produce local fluctuations of the type with which we are concerned here. This method is characterized by the use of *random sequences*. For example, the series of time intervals that constitutes a variable-interval reinforcement schedule may be punched into a programing tape according to some random order. Or a series of stimuli to which the subject must respond differentially is presented in a randomized sequence. The random series is generally employed because the experimenter wishes to eliminate any consistent effect that might arise from the sequence itself. For example, the experiment may involve two stimuli of different wave lengths, with a different response being required to produce reinforcement in the presence of each stimulus. The experimenter's interest is in the discriminability of the two wave lengths. He therefore does not present the two stimuli alternately, for if he did, the subject could obtain reinforcement by alternating his response on each exposure, independently of the particular wave length. Since the experimenter's concern is that the subject's behavior be a function of the wave length of the stimulus, and not of the sequence, he presents the stimuli in a random order.

The random order does not, however, eliminate sequence effects. Any series of events approaches true randomness only over an extremely large number of occurrences of its components. Local segments of the series will be found to be nonrandom. They will contain some long successions of single components, some alternating patterns of two components, and many other types of orderly sequence. Such local deviations from randomness cannot be ignored. Behavior is governed by local contingencies, regardless of whether they have been explicitly arranged by the experimenter or whether they occur as uncontrolled fluctuations in an over-all random sequence. If the same response has been reinforced five times in a row, it is highly likely that the next response will be influenced by this sequence, particularly if the stimuli involved are close to the difference threshold. We may expect part of the variability in response to the same stimulus to be a function of such orderly sequences. In a given experimental session there may be no occurrences of five successive similar events, while in the next session there may be several such instances. A considerable portion of the intersession variability is likely to arise from such local fluctuations within a random sequence.

Similar factors may contribute to variability in a behavioral baseline, thereby obscuring the effects of variables that are superimposed upon the baseline. A variable-interval reinforcement schedule, for example, is commonly used to generate a stable rate of responding, deviations from which will provide a measure of the effects of other variables. According to this schedule, reinforcement is made available to the subject after varying periods of time have elapsed since the last reinforcement. The sequence of time intervals could be programed randomly, but it is unlikely that a stable response rate would be achieved in this manner. A sequence of short time intervals between reinforcements will produce an increase in the rate of responding, an increase that may persist long after the sequence of short intervals has ended. A series of long intervals between reinforcements not only will lower the rate but is likely to produce a temporal pattern of response similar to that generated by a fixed-interval schedule. The subject may cease responding immediately after receiving a reinforcement, and then gradually accelerate until the next reinforcement is delivered. Even as low an animal as the rat may reflect, in its rate of response, a sequence of alternating short and long intervals. Such fluctuations in a random series of intervals will, therefore, be reflected in corresponding behavioral fluctuations.

A partial answer to this problem is to use, instead of random sequences, a mixed series of intervals. A random series will be cluttered with local regularities over which the experimenter has no control. A mixed, but *controlled*, sequence of intervals can minimize sequence effects much more effectively. The experimenter can, for example, arrange a sequence in which each interval is followed equally often by every other interval in the series. If necessary, he can accomplish the same arrangement for pairs of intervals, triplets, and so on. It is more likely to be the case, however, that stabler response rates will be secured when some intervals occur with greater frequency than others, for rate is not a simple linear function of the interval between reinforcements.

Few empirical data of the sort required to solve such technical problems are available at present. Many experimental psychologists have not yet felt the necessity of dealing with them. They are content to achieve behavioral stability of an over-all statistical nature in which local fluctuations are disregarded. Thus data are averaged over individual subjects or, within individuals, over blocks of "trials" or over relatively long periods of time. But as the problems with which we are dealing become more subtle, and as our understanding of behavior increases, we will be forced to come to grips with finer details of behavior, details which are now obscured by variability that arises from fluctuations in the maintaining contingencies.

It must be pointed out, if it is not already apparent, that such variability cannot be eliminated completely. Behavior, of necessity, takes place in time, and sequential effects are, therefore, inevitable. If there is any truly intrinsic variability it probably arises at this point. But—and this cannot be emphasized too strongly—variability that arises from sequential effects is intrinsic not to *behavior* but rather to its controlling conditions. Behavior is a lawful function of local fluctuations in the maintaining contingencies. It is the contingencies themselves that change, either because of the vagaries of the natural environment or because of the practical necessities of experimental technique. The only real solution is to evaluate such effects and to take account of them in both our experimental and theoretical descriptions of behavior.

Local fluctuations in the contingencies that maintain behavior may occur as a function of reciprocal interaction between behavior and its controlling environment. The very factors that govern behavior are often, themselves, altered by the behavior they generate. Variability in behavior may thus arise because the behavior changes its own controlling conditions. Such reciprocal interaction may lead to any of several different effects. The interlocking system of behavior and controlling contingencies can be self-regulating. In this case a cyclic process will result. The behavior will fluctuate, in more or less regular fashion, through two or more states, with an average value that may be relatively constant over a sufficiently long period of time. Over shorter periods, however, variability will be evident, and comparisons between segments of a performance will suffer insofar as the segments are abstracted from different stages of the cycle.

Avoidance behavior provides an example in which the experimenter deliberately arranges conditions in such a way that the behavior changes some of the controlling variables. In avoidance experiments the subject is usually shocked according to a temporal schedule programed by the experimenter. The avoidance response, however, alters this schedule. Each time the subject emits the avoidance response, shock is postponed, and the over-all shock frequency thereby decreases. But as the shock frequency declines, the avoidance response becomes weaker and eventually fails to occur in time to prevent a shock. The one or more shocks which are then received serve to "pump up" the behavior, and a new cycle begins. Part of the process is illustrated in the cumulative response curve of Figure 17, which represents an intermediate stage of avoidance conditioning in a monkey. Each lever-pressing response by the monkey served to postpone a shock for 180 seconds. The animal received a shock every 180 seconds as long as it failed to press the lever. The record illustrates cyclicity of the sort I have been describing. After each shock the response rate is high, with a subsequent gradual decline as time passes without a shock. Eventually the rate declines to a point where a 180-second pause again produces a shock, thereby initiating a new cycle.

Early in conditioning, the cycles are generally shorter, with several shocks intervening between each run of responses. At a later stage than that shown in Figure 17, the cycles become extremely long, with some animals maintaining the avoidance behavior for scores of hours without receiving a shock. Thus, not only does the behavior

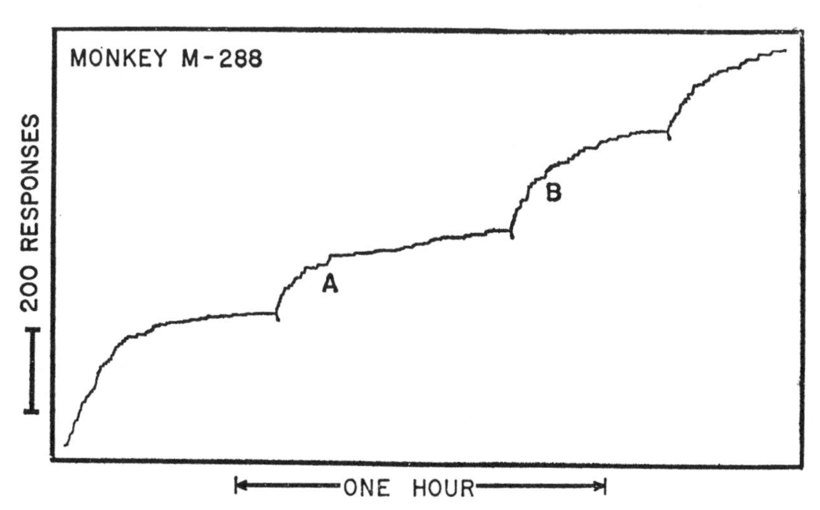

FIGURE 17. Cyclic fluctuations in response rate brought about by interactions between avoidance behavior and shocks. The small, oblique "pips" in the record indicate shocks. (*From Sidman*, 75.)

alter the shock frequency, but it does so differentially in different stages of the conditioning process. The cyclic variability itself therefore undergoes an orderly change. Experiments carried out during the late phase of the conditioning process are less likely to suffer from the cyclic fluctuations.

The interaction between avoidance behavior and shock is of a self-regulating nature. As avoidance responses reduce the shock frequency the response becomes less probable, and eventually a point is reached at which shocks again occur and boost the response probability. Cyclic variability of this self-regulating type is also displayed by behavior which is maintained by temporally specified positive reinforcement schedules. Figure 18 contains a cumulative record of a pigeon's behavior as it is generated by a fixed-interval reinforcement schedule. On this schedule the pigeon's response of pecking an illuminated disk can produce a reinforcement no more frequently than once every four minutes. After each reinforcement is delivered the four-minute interval begins anew, and when it has elapsed, a reinforcement again becomes available.

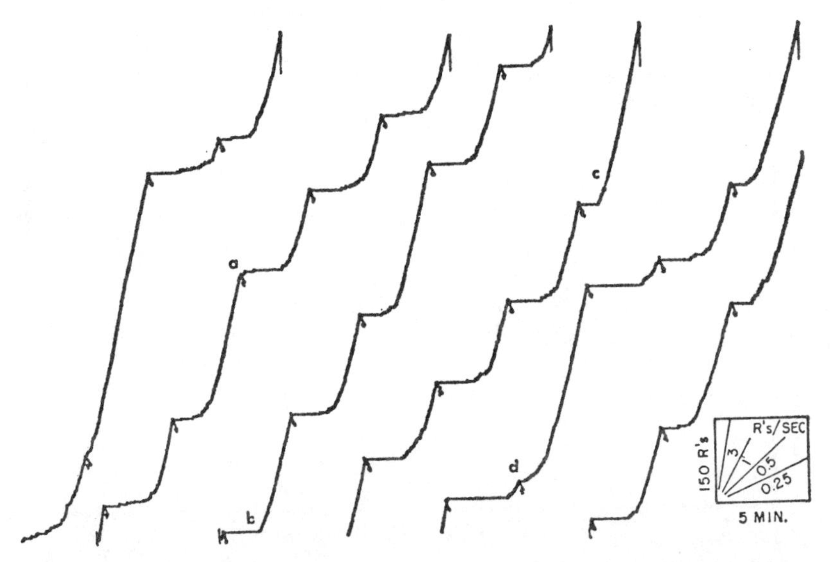

FIGURE 18. Cyclic variability characteristic of behavior maintained by a fixed-interval reinforcement schedule. (*From Ferster and Skinner,* 34, p. 159.)

Intrinsic Versus Imposed Variability

The characteristic behavior generated by this fixed-interval schedule, when other conditions are appropriately controlled, is the positively accelerated responding that may be seen in Figure 18 between most of the reinforcements. The flat portion of the curve immediately following reinforcement, however, may be seen to vary in duration. Occasionally the flat portion occupies nearly the whole segment of the curve between two reinforcements, in which case the typical "scallop" is absent. Such variability provides evidence of a self-regulating process. When the flat portion of the curve is brief, the terminal rate is reached quickly and a relatively large number of responses occurs before reinforcement is forthcoming. The pay-off, in terms of reinforcements per response, is relatively low. One or more such low pay-off cycles weakens the behavior, and the pause after reinforcement becomes longer, perhaps extending throughout the whole four minutes. Such long pauses make reinforcement available after a relatively small number of responses, thus increasing the pay-off in terms of reinforcements per response. The behavior is strengthened and the pause after reinforcement becomes short again.

Again, then, we observe variability resulting from a continuous process of adjustment between behavior and a controlling variable. Such variability cannot be attributed to chance. Each state through which the behavior passes is strictly determined by antecedent and current conditions. Until a more satisfactory degree of control can be established over the cyclic process it may be necessary to employ a statistical *description* of the behavior. But *evaluative* statistics are inappropriate. Once the processes underlying cyclic variation are specified, statistical evaluation can neither make the cycles disappear nor make them more real. Our efforts should be in the direction of securing sufficient experimental control to determine whether the final analysis will require even a statistical description.

Reciprocal interaction between behavior and its maintaining contingencies is not necessarily a self-adjusting process. The interaction may be such as to produce either a complete cessation of behavior or its opposite, "runaway" behavior. Behavior maintained by a fixed-ratio schedule, for example, does not have a built-in adjusting mechanism. If we make the required ratio of responses per reinforcement too large, the behavior in question will simply disappear. Large ratios generate long periods of no response, particularly after a reinforcement has been delivered. Unlike interval schedules, long pauses on a ratio schedule do not increase the probability that the next response will be reinforced. Their effect is simply to decrease the reinforcement frequency. As the frequency of reinforcement declines, the pauses become longer, thus decreasing the reinforcement frequency even further. The spiraling process continues until the behavior ceases completely.

Depending upon the ratio of responses to reinforcements, the behavior may go out suddenly or it may continue in a state of "strain" for a considerable period. In the latter case, not only will the baseline display considerable fluctuation, but it will also yield varying results when it is used to assess the effects of other variables. Some drugs, for example, which have no effect upon a relatively smooth fixed-ratio performance (24), produce marked changes in a "strained ratio" (59). Again, this is not random variability. When a given subject yields discrepant data at different times, or when there are marked intersubject differences, or when different experimenters come up with conflicting data, a strong possibility exists that uncontrolled changes have taken place in the contingencies that maintain the behavior. Such changes will, however, be controllable if the behavior in question has been investigated intensively enough so that its major governing variables have been identified.

Variability arising from a nonself-regulating process of the sort that tends to extinguish behavior is usually easily identified, for the phenomenon is directly observable. When the process goes in the other direction, however, it is sometimes not so easily specified. The maintaining contingencies can change in the direction of producing "runaway" behavior, which may be characterized by high rates of occurrence and relative insensitivity to manipulation by other variables.

For example, when a pigeon has had long experience with a variable-interval reinforcement schedule, responding at a constant high rate day after day, the rate itself becomes an important feature of the reinforcement contingency. That is to say, reinforcement is correlated not simply with the key-pecking response but also with key pecking characterized by a particular rate of occurrence. It is of little consequence that the response *rate* has, in actuality, nothing to do with the appearance of the grain hopper. The important factor is that the presentation of grain is consistently preceded by a given rate of responding. The rate itself becomes conditioned, however, adventitiously. Once this happens, of course, behavior maintained by a variable-interval reinforcement schedule is no longer a satisfactory baseline from which to measure the effects of other variables. The response rate, itself conditioned, loses a great deal of its sensitivity. Furthermore, discrepant data are likely to cause useless controversy if such a "locked rate" is not recognized.

It has been noted, for example, that the response rate generated by a variable-interval schedule of food reinforcement can faithfully reflect the subject's degree of food deprivation. More recently, however, the variable-interval baseline has been reported relatively insensitive to food deprivation (34). In the latter case, however, the subjects had been exposed to the schedule for a much longer period of time than is usual in most laboratories. Furthermore, other conditions of the experiment were such as to produce a relatively high, consistent response rate. It is likely that a locked rate had developed, and that both findings concerning deprivation are correct, given the particular conditions of the experiments.

This example exposes a unique feature of variability among experimental findings that arises from a runaway cycle of interaction between behavior and its controlling variables. Insensitivity of the variable-interval baseline was observed in a laboratory that is noted for its stress upon rigorous control of basic variables. Extraneous factors are characteristically minimized by the use of high deprivation levels, relatively large amounts of reinforcement, sensitive response keys, etc. In consequence, a high degree of reproducibility in the behavior of individual animals is a feature of this laboratory's work. Experimentation characterized by such a high degree of rigor is, by virtue of the stability of its baselines, most likely to reveal effects in which properties of the behavior become, themselves, important determiners of the maintaining contingencies. It is only when behavior displays consistent characteristics over long periods of time that a phenomenon such as a conditioned, or locked, rate can be observed. We have an unusual case, therefore, in which insensitivity may result from extremely rigorous, rather than from inadequate, experimental control. In evaluating findings concerning which different laboratories are at variance, therefore, it is necessary to consider the characteristic modes of operation of the investigators concerned. While orderly functional relations are, in general, a good indication of adequate technique, there is always the possibility that even greater control will produce invariance.

The problems of variability raised when behavior enters into its own control are not necessarily of the type that must be circumvented. Any given response takes place in time, within a matrix of other similar and dissimilar types of behavior. The interactions that take place are part of the real behavioral world. They are also fascinating laboratory problems. The variability arising from such interactions is *determined* variability, not random. It is a type of variability that must be understood before we can provide an account of behavior that will be useful either descriptively or as a basis for theoretical integration and practical application. Experimental techniques designed to *eliminate* reciprocal interaction between behavior and its controlling environment may well be inadequate tools for the task at hand. One common technique, for example, is to employ discrete, widely spaced, "trials." The subject is exposed to the experimental conditions only once, say, each day, and only one response is permitted to occur in each exposure. In this way, interaction effects of the type I have been discussing are presumed to be eliminated.

Certainly the temporal separation between responses ensures that the response *rate* will not enter as an important controlling factor. But it is not so clear that other characteristics of the behavior will be prevented from interacting with each other and with the maintaining contingencies. When a response with given incidental properties is reinforced under certain conditions, then that particular response, with many of its incidental properties, is likely to occur again the next time similar conditions are encountered. This will be true whether the next response is occasioned within two seconds or two years. The action of reinforcement is automatic and lasting, and the artificial spacing of trials does not eliminate cumulative effects. Thus, in an experiment that requires a human subject to press one of two available telegraph keys to obtain reinforcement, a run of five successive and successful responses on one of the keys will have a cumulative effect that is not dissipated over a period of

24 hours or more. While a response rate is not likely to be conditioned adventitiously, different sequences of response on the two keys may well be accidentally reinforced sufficiently often to produce considerable variability in the data.

Unless a given sequence becomes dominant because it is reinforced sufficiently often to initiate a runaway spiraling process, this source of variability is not likely to be revealed by statistical analysis of the data. For the adventitiously reinforced sequences will themselves vary with respect to their particular patterns and with respect to the duration of time within which they persist. Our knowledge that such effects are taking place comes not from analysis of particular data, but rather from an acquaintance with general principles that have been directly demonstrated in appropriate experiments.

This brings us to the major defect of experimental techniques designed to eliminate the variability that results from circular relations between behavior and its controlling environment. Not only are such techniques generally unsuccessful in eliminating such variability, but they actually hide it from direct view and thus prevent an adequate analysis. There is, in addition to interaction among the responses that yield the primary datum of the experiment, an unknown and generally unrecognized chain of events taking place between trials. The behavior that takes place immediately before, for a considerable period prior to, and immediately after the subject is in the experimental situation is not irrelevant to his recorded behavior. The experiment may be confined to a limited block of time, but the subject continues to behave during the in-between periods. Failure to *recognize* that interactions are taking place between recorded and unrecorded behavior is not equivalent to eliminating such interactions from the data.

VARIABILITY AS A PROBLEM OF "CAPACITY"

Apparently no two individuals have exactly the same genetic endowment. In addition to, or perhaps because of, hereditary differences, individuals also vary with respect to their anatomical "geography" and function, their physiology, their body chemistry, and many other aspects of their internal functioning. Such factors as these are all presumed to affect behavior, and there is considerable evidence at a gross level of analysis that they do. The notion of intrinsic variability derives some of its strongest support from this evidence.

When formulated against such a background, intrinsic variability is a somewhat different concept from that which I have discussed previously. Intrinsic variability as we are now looking at it does not imply indeterminism. It is considered intrinsic by the psychologist only because his competence does not usually extend into those physiological realms from which the variability is presumed to stem. The physiologist, on the other hand, who is convinced that his subject matter is intrinsically orderly, may ascribe the variability he observes to the subject's biochemistry. The variability is intrinsic only insofar as the physiologist does not possess the information and the skills required to investigate the relevant biochemical phenomena. The biochemist, in his turn, may save his science from the stigma of capriciousness by locating the wellspring of variability in the gene. The geneticist then carries the whole burden upon his shoulders, although he has recently begun to pass some of the load back to the biochemist. (There is the fascinating possibility developing that the chain of causality may reverse still further. Ultimate responsibility for explaining some of the variability of genetic action may yet rest with the psychologist.)

Some geneticists, as well as many members of those biological disciplines intermediate in the chain that leads from psychology to genetics, accept their burden cheerfully, as an article of faith. What many of them do not realize is the weakness at the top of the structure of which they are presumed to constitute the base. Stated baldly, they are being imposed upon. For, as I have pointed out in preceding sections, psychologists are not yet capable of stating unequivocally whether or not the variability in their data stems from inadequate experimental control, insufficient understanding of the processes involved, or from factors that lie outside their sphere of competence. Or perhaps I am being unfair to the geneticist. His intuitive recognition of these inadequacies may explain the paucity of collaborative experimental investigations of the presumed genetic determination of behavior. Until the psychologist can supply baselines from which other important sources of variability have been eliminated, there will be little profit in uniting the two disciplines in a common enterprise. (The same difficulty, of course, may exist in the reverse direction, but I cannot consider myself a competent judge on this score.) Similar statements may be made with respect to other biological areas which are presumed to have control over some key behavioral variables.

As a consequence, at least in part, of inadequate specification of processes at the strictly behavioral level, research in physiological psychology (which I shall now use as a general term to cover relations between behavior and all other types of biological variables) has oriented itself largely in terms of a gross, amorphous, catch-all concept which we may call "capacity." Experimental subjects (more usually, groups of subjects) are compared with respect to their *ability* to perform stated tasks. One strain of rats may be found superior to another in learning to run a maze without error. The difference between the two strains is often ascribed to variations in "learning ability." In another typical experiment, animals with a portion of their brains removed are found to lose, temporarily at least, a given sample of learned behavior, for example, an avoidance response. That portion of the brain which has been excised is then held to have something to do with, or even to be the seat of, "memory," or "retention ability." Or an animal given electrical stimulation in the brain simultaneously with a stimulus for a choice reaction no longer makes the correct choice consistently. The brain stimulation is then considered to have destroyed the animal's "ability to discriminate."

On the basis of these and similar experimental findings, it has been assumed that uncontrolled physiological variations within the organism can be held responsible for much observed behavior variability. The type of reasoning involved here is sound enough. When it is found that a variable *can* affect behavior, it is reasonable to assume that it *does* so, under appropriate conditions. But what have we actually discovered about the presumed relationship? Strain *A* of rats may learn a particular maze faster than Strain *B*, but Strain *B* may learn an avoidance response, or even another type of maze, faster. If such is the case, what can we say about the relation between genetic endowment and learning ability? It is evident that we have not analyzed the behavioral processes involved in the various "learning" situations well enough to understand where the true relation between gene and behavior lies. Experiments involving other physiological factors are similarly vulnerable. It is not the organism's "capacity" for anything that is being affected. It is rather some behavioral process that may or may not possess generality of the sweeping nature that is implied by such terms as learning, memory, etc.

The point of the above discussion has not been to deny the relevance of physiological factors as determiners of either consistency or variability in behavior. It has been my purpose rather to emphasize the overgeneralized nature of much of the evidence supporting such a conception. It is also possible to suggest some directions research should take to provide a firmer explanation of behavioral variability that stems from physiological factors. Like other sources of variability, this one too must be uncovered and explored before it can be dealt with.

One step is, of course, the refinement of physiological techniques. This refining process is continually going on in physiology, anatomy, and related areas. There is no necessity, and perhaps it is not even desirable, for technical developments in these areas to be influenced in any way by problems in behavioral research. The majority of physiological techniques that have proved useful to the physiological psychologist—surgical techniques, methods for staining nerve fibers, electrical stimulation of and recording from muscle and nerve, hormone assay, drugs, etc.—have developed out of immediate interests that are independent of behavior. Those psychologists interested in physiological contributions to behavior have rarely been guilty of ignoring physiological techniques. Their error has generally been in the direction of employing the techniques too soon, before the data which they make available has been sufficiently well understood.

On the other side of the coin is the problem of developing techniques for behavioral investigation, and of systematizing the resulting data. It would seem to be an obvious requirement that there be firm technical and systematic anchors on *both* the behavioral and physiological side before there can be any fruitful collaboration between the two. Strangely enough, this has become an emotionally loaded issue in psychology and is, even today, debated with considerable heat.

Intrinsic Versus Imposed Variability

B. F. Skinner serves both as villain and hero in much of the most recent discussion. In 1938 Skinner suggested, with all good intention, that intensive behavioral research, for its own sake, is a necessary prerequisite for an adequate understanding of the neurological correlates of behavior (81, pp. 418-432). Along with this suggestion, he presented a forceful empirical case for an independent science of behavior.

A large segment of psychology immediately subdivided into two camps, each apparently reacting to Skinner's suggestion according to its own hopes and fears. Many of those who had no interest in the search for points of contact between behavior and physiology argued that Skinner had demonstrated the futility of such an enterprise. The other group felt that Skinner was attempting to submarine the then struggling science of physiological psychology. He was typified as a proponent of the "empty organism," a characterization which the student is still likely to encounter on some of his examination papers.

Subsequent developments have served to demonstrate that each side has been overstating the case. I frequently hear expressions of bewilderment from investigators on both sides as they come to realize that some of the most significant current research in physiological psychology is being carried out by means of behavioral techniques that were developed by Skinner and related workers. This development has not been the result of any abandonment, by either group of extremists, of their untenable positions. It has been a natural outcome of a growing appreciation, on the part of both physiologists and psychologists, of each others' techniques. The contribution of operant conditioning techniques to an understanding of physiological variables has been made possible, up to now, by the consistency and reproducibility of the behavioral baselines. Other sources of variability have been sufficiently eliminated from some of these baselines to permit their use in identifying physiological and neurological sources of variability.

We are, however, on the verge of more significant advances made possible by the type of functional analysis of behavior that has been carried out in operant conditioning laboratories. It is now feasible to generate baselines which not only are stable for the individual organism but are, in addition, controlled by variables of wide generality. For example, many distinctive characteristics of behavioral performance under a variety of reinforcement schedules have been found to depend upon particular patterns of reinforcement of interresponse intervals. The widespread action of this variable is rapidly being confirmed and extended in the laboratory. More important for the present discussion, it is also possible to generate behavioral baselines that are controlled almost completely by the deliberate reinforcement of specified interresponse intervals. When precisely controlled behavior of wide generality is employed for the study of physiological factors, the data can be applied in diverse situations. We may expect to see the increasing use of behavioral baselines which, as functional analysis reveals, are under the control of variables relevant in a variety of contexts.

The discovery of such variables cannot be accomplished by classifying behavior in terms of "abilities" or "capacities" of the organism. Nor is it sufficient to conceptualize behavior as a "problem-solving" activity. Such terms merely lump different varieties of behavior into classificatory groups, and these fall apart as soon as different behavioral processes are shown to be involved. A detailed functional analysis of the relations between behavior and its specific controlling variables can, on the other hand, produce a useful classification. A descriptive approach will produce a body of interrelated observations that will greatly increase the behavioral generality of any physiological variables.

A similar analysis may be made of the problems on the physiological side. Intensive investigation of physiological variables, by physiological techniques, must precede any application to behavioral studies. A method that produces unknown or poorly understood physiological consequences is of little value as a tool for investigating physiological contributions to behavioral variability.

The investigation of physiological factors related to behavioral processes demands a high degree of descriptive integration and of individual competence in several areas. The growing recognition of this fact has led, in recent years, to a somewhat new approach to the problem of interdisciplinary research in the behavioral sciences. It had been the custom, in forming an interdisciplinary research group, to look for a physiological psychologist, or a biopsychologist, or a psychopharmacologist—an investigator who claims competence in both psychology and another of the biological disciplines. Too often, however, the physiological psychologist turns out to be a competent physiologist and a dilettante psychologist, or vice versa. Or the psychopharmacologist may have been well trained in the techniques of pharmacology, but qualifies as a psychologist only because of his interest in central nervous system drugs.

The newer conception of interdisciplinary research calls for a group of investigators, each competent in a restricted field, be it psychology, electrophysiology, pharmacology, anatomy, endocrinology, or any of a wide variety of possibilities. As each works out his own problems, for their own sake and without interdisciplinary considerations, he will develop his techniques and his understanding of the area to the point where he can apply them confidently to problems requiring collaborative research. In such a setting it is sufficient that each investigator have an intelligent interest in other areas so that he will appreciate potential points of contact. It is not even necessary that the group be, in any sense, an organized "team." For the competent and interested investigator will take pride in seeing his techniques extended into areas in which their relevance was not foreseen. The competences required for collaboration become available as each area pursues its independent course of development. Development and systematization of the individual scientific disciplines involved is the means for an eventual attack upon sources of behavioral variability attributable to physiological factors.

VARIABILITY AND THE SELECTION OF DATA. Students are generally taught that if any data are presented from a particular experiment, *all* the data must be presented. Selection of data is supposed to be a major crime, unworthy of the objective detachment which science claims for itself. Many students, however, soon come to realize that not all their teachers are consistent in applying this standard, particularly in their own work. They find that the rule is, in actuality, that *students* must never select data.

It may sound unfair, but it is wise, for reasons I will clarify shortly. Some students accept the wisdom of the double standard and, as they mature, gradually adopt a responsible and rational attitude toward the selection of data in their own experiments. A few students, unfortunately, never mature in this respect. Their experiments may be plagued with variability that results from poor control but, pure in their objectivity, they tell all. They continue to pepper the literature with reports encumbered by the "ifs, thens, and buts" characteristic of inconclusive data.

Before going on to describe and justify the necessary practice of data selection, it is only fair to point out that the problem is a ticklish one. The most difficult situations arise when experiments are performed to test theory. It is recognized, at least implicitly, that, despite public protestations to the contrary, scientists are usually intensely and personally involved with their theories. Consequently, the selection of data in theory-testing experiments calls for intelligent skepticism. One must ask whether the selection was made on the basis of legitimate practices or, consciously or otherwise, on the basis of consistency with a hypothesis.

I may point out that in a highly systematized science, even the second course is often justified. In some areas systematization has become the rule, and unifying concepts are, characteristically, tightly specified, without apparent loopholes in the reasoning. In such areas, data which are at variance with a generally successful systematic framework may be rejected as having arisen from uncontrolled sources of variability. On the other hand, in a well-developed science such variability is likely to be relatively rare except, perhaps, at its outermost frontiers. Then we may also hear the contrary view expressed: namely, that unusual variability within a well-integrated and highly controlled scientific discipline is of unusual significance, and may require a major revision in the systematization. Psychology has few, if any, theories so tightly formulated and so well documented that this problem becomes important. But there are, at least in the process of development, a number of local empirical generalizations that will require an answer to the problem of whether variant data are to be rejected or are to be accepted as being systematically important.

How is the problem to be solved? The honest answer seems to be the simplest one: Report all data. But this answer is not as honest as it seems; and it is completely irresponsible. If the experimenter has good reason to believe that an instance of major variability arises from uncontrolled sources, he has no obligation to impose such data upon the literature and upon his colleagues. If uncontrolled variability occurs only rarely, he may justifiably not even mention the data in question. No colleague is as informed about the possible sources of occasional uncontrolled variability in a given laboratory as is the experimenter who works in that laboratory. He is in the best position to evaluate such instances, and he cannot pass his responsibility on to others. If the variability occurs frequently enough to be a serious problem, none of the data should be reported until the sources of the variant data have been eliminated. There is no middle ground.

A decision as to whether some observed variability constitutes a serious problem does not have to be an arbitrary one. Nor is it necessary, or even desirable, to appeal to statistical criteria. One of the most important considerations is the orderliness of the variant data. If the exceptions from the main body of the data show evidence of lawfulness, then they require explanation. They cannot be dismissed as examples of capricious variables. No matter how rare the exception, if it displays regularity of its own it must be dealt with. The deviant subject whose curve displays, say, an inverse instead of the usual positive relation to the independent variable, must be respected. It will not do either to ignore his data or to average it out with the other subjects. On the other hand, if an occasional deviant subject displays no apparent order in his behavior, he may be dismissed from consideration. At most, the experimenter may report that the subject existed, but he need not burden his colleagues with his data.

A similar situation exists in the case of intrasubject variability. If a given subject's behavior displays cyclic or other orderly fluctuations, one cannot ignore the variability; for it is likely to be present and to play a critical role in later replicative attempts by the same and by other investigators. On the other hand, if the fluctuations do not seem to be systematic, and are small relative to the phenomena of major interest, they may be treated as inconsequential background "noise."

It is also legitimate practice to ignore even a large deviation if it appears only rarely. Such deviations are by no means undetermined. But their infrequent nature and their lack of any apparent relation to the critical variables in the experiment indicate that they are controlled by factors extraneous to the investigation. They can be ignored because they are not likely to appear in replications, and because their inclusion in a report will probably inject extraneous considerations that serve to obscure the major issues.

Sometimes occasional major fluctuations may occur sufficiently often to be correlated with some specific factor that is outside the range of interest of the particular investigation. For example, an air-conditioning system may occasionally break down during an experiment. If the experimenter observes significant changes in otherwise stable baselines on the occasion of such breakdowns, he is justified in rejecting the variant data on the grounds that the variability was produced by a condition extraneous to the purpose of the investigation. If the variant data were included in an otherwise stable baseline, it is possible that subsequent changes, induced by a deliberately manipulated variable, would be mistakenly rejected because they did not exceed the baseline variability.

I have several times made a distinction between occasional and frequent variability. But, it may be asked, how is one to determine whether the exceptional instance is occasional? What constitutes an acceptable frequency of deviant data? There is no fixed answer to these questions, for each case demands its own evaluation. It is necessary to depend in large degree on the experience and integrity of the investigator. The longer he has worked in a given area, and the more extensive his acquaintance with the work of others in the same field, the greater is his ability to evaluate a given instance.

Mistakes will, of course, be made, but there are general principles of caution to be observed. Early in an experimental program no instance of variability can be ignored, for it is impossible to make a realistic estimate of the probability that such variance will recur. Such an estimate can be made only on the basis of an existing sample of data, and the larger the sample, the more accurate the judgment can be. This is the reason for the double standard under which fledgling experimenters are not permitted to select data, whereas their more experienced colleagues can. The ideal solution is to encourage the publication of relatively long, integrated series of researches. By the time an experimenter reaches the end of such a program, he will have had sufficient experience with his subject matter to permit judgments concerning the acceptance and rejection of variable data. Unfortunately, the modern stress upon frequency of publication, with its economic rewards, mitigates strongly against such a course of action.

One of the consequences is the unhealthy amount of trivial data and extensive explanatory argument that characterizes many doctoral dissertations in psychology. The young investigator, because of pressure from his peers and because of his own insecurity with respect to the area in which he is working, must present all of his data, including every instance of variability. Having included such instances, he is forced to discuss them, and they become woven into an intricate fabric of theory, speculation, and suggested confirmatory experiments to justify small effects whose genuineness he is in no position to judge.

A critical aspect of the problem is the stage of the investigation in which variability appears. A subject may have produced hundreds of hours of stable baseline data, but in the hours just prior to the planned introduction of a new variable, a sudden change may occur in the behavior. Even if the experimenter is an old hand, has never observed such a change in the past, and cannot correlate it with any variation in his controlled conditions, he must not ignore the variation at that stage. He must change his plans and delay the introduction of the new variable until he has additional data. The sudden, unexplained variability may represent a permanent change in the baseline behavior, produced perhaps by an unsuspected process that had been building up slowly. The baseline must, therefore, be continued in order to determine whether the sudden variability can be ignored or whether it must be taken into account in evaluating subsequent results.

It may happen also that the behavior, changed by an unknown but briefly acting factor, will take a considerable time to return to its baseline state. Discussion of this problem will be more appropriate in the sections on reversibility and steady states (Chapter 8), but it represents one of the possibilities that demands caution in accepting variable data. The fact that variability persists for a fairly long time is not an absolute criterion for accepting it as relevant to the behavior under investigation.

Sometimes it is useful not only to reject variable data from a given subject but also to eliminate subjects from consideration when evaluating data. The second procedure is justified, however, only when the experimenter can identify the conditions responsible for the behavior of the deviant subjects. Otherwise he is open to the charge that he has selected data on the basis of preconceptions about the experimental results.

Suppose, for example, that three subjects yield an inverse linear relation between response probability and an independent variable, while a fourth subject is unaffected by the independent variable. Ordinarily the experimenter would have to consider the data from all four subjects in evaluating the reliability of the experimental manipulations. But he finds additional evidence that the difference between the two types of curve can be accounted for in terms of a particular difference in the subjects' behavioral histories. He can then state that the inverse linear relation is characteristic of subjects with a particular behavioral history, and the exceptional subject then serves to clarify, rather than to obscure, the behavioral process under investigation.

One does not lose generality in the data by thus limiting the population to which a given experimental result applies. In point of fact, generality is increased. It is unrealistic to expect that a given variable will have the same effects upon all subjects under all conditions. As we identify and control a greater number of the conditions that determine the effects of a given experimental operation, in effect we decrease the variability that may be expected as a consequence of the operation. It then becomes possible to produce the same results in a greater number of subjects. Such generality could never be achieved if we simply accepted intersubject variability and gave equal status to all deviant subjects in an investigation.

Chapter 6

Variability as a Scientific and as an Engineering Problem

In the preceding chapter I have touched upon some major sources of and methods for dealing with variability in behavioral experiments. The underlying thesis has been that variability is not intrinsic to the subject matter but stems, rather, from discoverable and controllable causes. The door was left open for the admission of intrinsic variability, but only after, and if, a high degree of technical development and systematization of data has forced it upon us.

Any sample of behavior is under the control of a multiplicity of variables, some of them presumably held constant in a given experiment, and others simply unrecognized. Sometimes the variability in a set of data can be located among such factors. Two subjects may be found to differ in their response to variable A, not because there is intrinsic variability in the relation between variable A and behavior, but because they differ in their response to variable B, which interacts with variable A. A solution of this sort explains the variability in a given experiment in a deterministic manner, without assuming it to be inherent in the behavior.

The process of systematically tracking down sources of variability, and thus explaining variable data, is characteristic of the scientific enterprise. Variability, however, may have different implications for the investigators we may call behavioral engineers (without implying any value assessment or even a strict dichotomy between the terms, "scientist" and "engineer"). Among behavioral engineers I include those whose work is concerned with intelligence and aptitude testing, man-machine interactions, behavioral therapy and diagnosis, opinion sampling and control, and related aspects of applied psychology. Such workers cannot, as a rule, deal with variability in the ways I have outlined, and the two sets of problems should not be confused. The behavioral engineer must ordinarily take variability as he finds it, and deal with it as an unavoidable fact of life. For example, basic research may suggest, as it has, that one way to increase the likelihood that a radar watcher will detect infrequent signals is to flash a number of artificial signals on the screen (46). Many problems will arise in applying this suggestion. For example, how frequently should the artificial signals be presented? The optimal rate of presentation will undoubtedly vary for different watchers. It gives the engineer no comfort to tell him that the sources of this variability can be identified. Unless the variability can be eliminated, for example by special training, he must make some compromise with it. He will end up by presenting the artificial signals at a rate that he suspects, or has experimentally determined, will be optimal for most watchers under the greatest variety of conditions.

Cronbach has made a distinction between basic and applied psychology which though broader than the one I am stressing, nonetheless has much in common with it (22). He discusses "two historic streams of method, thought, and affiliation which run through the last century of our science." Calling one of these streams *experimental psychology* and the other *correlational psychology,* Cronbach characterizes them as follows:

> The well-known virtue of the experimental method is that it brings situational variables under tight control. It thus permits rigorous tests of hypotheses and confident statements about causation. The correlational method, for its part, can study what man has not learned to control or can ever hope to control. Nature has been experimenting since the beginning of time, with a boldness and complexity far beyond the resources of science. The correlator's mission is to observe and organize the data from Nature's experiments. As a minimum outcome, such correlations improve immediate decisions and guide experimentation. At the best, a Newton, a Lyell, or a Darwin can align the correlations into a substantial theory (22, p. 672).

The behavioral engineer seldom has the facilities or the time that would be required to eliminate the variability he encounters in a given problem. We may sympathize with his plight and admire his achievements in the face of such difficulties. Some basic scientists, however, go further than admiration. They actually imitate the engineer and attack basic scientific problems as if they were engineering problems. Hence the insistence upon large samples and statistical criteria of generality, stress upon subject generality rather than upon the generality of principles, and the resigned acceptance of intrinsic variability.

But the basic scientist has available for himself a luxury which the engineer cannot afford; which many engineers, in fact, do not consider desirable. This is the luxury of being able to refine experimental conditions until they bear only the most abstract relation to the world as we normally see it. It is a luxury because it requires an amount of time not usually permitted by the pressing demands of immediate practical problems; because it requires a long-term financial investment that could not ordinarily be tolerated if that expense had to be included in the cost and sometimes in the market price of an engineered product. The basic scientist has an obligation to take advantage of this luxury, because it has been found to pay off both in contributions to our understanding of natural phenomena and in practical applications to engineering problems.

Elimination of variability in laboratory experiments may not seem to constitute a rational procedure for finding out anything about the obviously variable world about us. But, as an empirical fact, this procedure has been enormously successful. Principles of great generality discovered inside the laboratory are often found to be operating elsewhere in the world. Laboratory-acquired knowledge of techniques for manipulating and observing relevant conditions is often powerful enough to override natural sources of variability. The obligation of the basic researcher is all the greater because he is the only one working at this task.

Basic research has acquired great prestige and is now, for the first time in history, receiving tangible public support. The basic scientist, in behavior or in any other area, is failing in his obligation when he treats his subject matter as if it were an engineering problem. When he orients his experimental techniques around a fatalistically accepted conception of intrinsic variability, he forfeits his right to the investigative luxuries of fundamental science. He is, in fact, in a peculiar, in-between position. His avowed goals are those of fundamental research, but his techniques are those appropriate to the solution of immediately practical problems. In consequence, he often accomplishes neither.

VARIABILITY AS A DATUM

THE METHODOLOGICAL DISTINCTION between the basic scientist and the engineer highlights the contrast between variability as a problem in formulating behavioral laws and as a problem of experimental technique. As long as variability is seen as resulting from inadequate understanding of, and/or insufficient control over, relevant variables, it remains a purely experimental problem. The basic scientist will bend his efforts toward elimination of the variability, at least to the point where it does not interfere with his major findings. The engineer will, of necessity, accept the variability, evaluate it, and take account of it in his recommendations. The engineer's recommendations are in the form of suggestions for concrete action, for example, how to arrange the dials on an airplane's instrument panel, what items to include in an intelligence test, what therapeutic measures to take, etc. The fundamental researcher makes his recommendations in the form of behavioral laws. These may range from a description of an empirical relation between two variables to a comprehensive systematization of a large number of such relations.

Often, the laws are not stated in such a way as to take account of the variability that was actually observed in the experiments. It is often assumed that it has been reduced to a negligible level with respect to the phenomena covered by the stated laws, and that, if necessary, it could be reduced still further by means of a more rigorous experimental technique. The law is thus often stated as though it existed in pure form, uncontaminated by the variability that can always be observed if fine enough measurements are made.

When the observed variability is orderly, however, the scientist is obliged to take account of it in formulating his laws. The variability may, in fact, be so conspicuous that it will provide the major experimental datum—for example, that provided by behavior observed to oscillate in a lawful manner. The oscillation, and the effects of relevant variables upon the characteristics of the oscillation, can provide the data upon which a statement of behavioral law is based.

We may, for example, program a ratio schedule of reinforcement on a self-adjusting basis. Subjects working on a fixed-ratio schedule display a two-valued rate of responding. Immediately after each reinforcement there is a pause; during this the rate is zero. Once responding begins, however, it continues at a high, near-maximal rate until the next reinforcement occurs. This is illustrated in Figure 19. The duration of the pause after reinforcements is known to be a function of the ratio of responses to reinforcements. The higher the ratio, *i.e.*, the greater the number of responses required per reinforcement, the longer the pauses. Using this information, we can specifically program a ratio schedule in such a way as to produce an oscillating state. We simply permit the ratio size to adjust on the basis of the length of pause following reinforcement (34, pp. 720 ff.).

The number of responses required to produce a particular reinforcement can be made inversely proportional to the duration of the preceding pause. A long pause will then cause the programing apparatus to decrease the number of responses required for the next

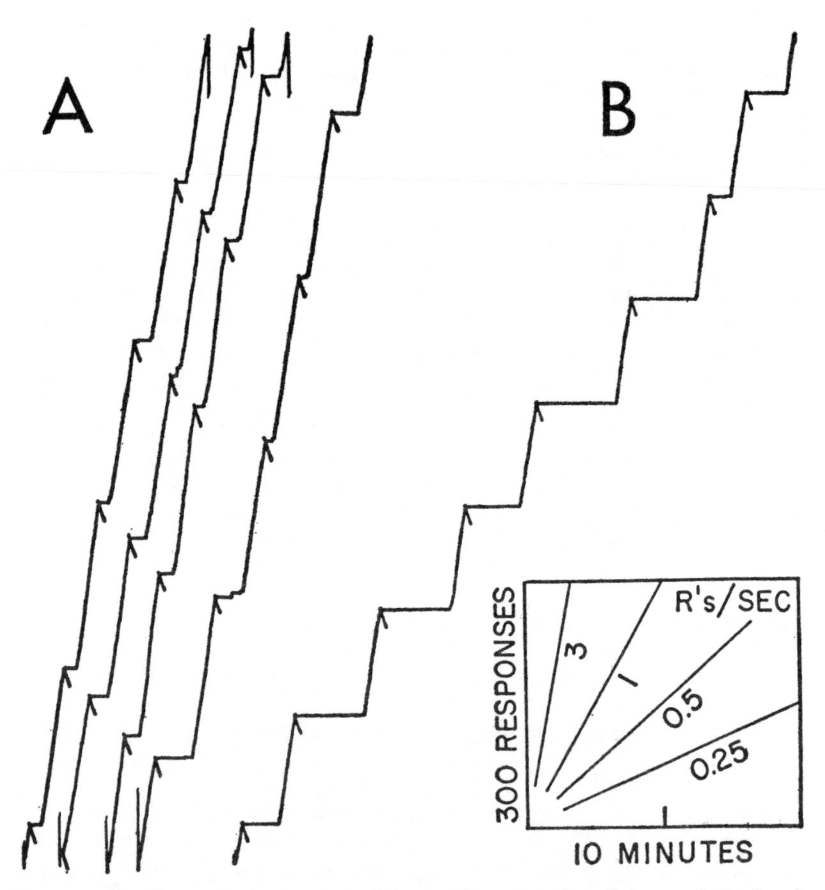

FIGURE 19. Records from two subjects, showing the characteristic fixed-ratio performance of pauses following each reinforcement (marked by the oblique "pips") and rapid transition to a high terminal rate. (*From Ferster and Skinner*, 34, p. 52.)

reinforcement. Such decreases in the required ratio will automatically shorten subsequent pauses. Shorter pauses will, in turn, cause the programing apparatus to increase the number of responses required for reinforcement, and such increases will again produce longer pauses. The behavior, as measured by the duration of the post-reinforcement pause, will oscillate about whatever value is optimal under the particular conditions of the experiment. The period and amplitude of the oscillations will be a function of such variables as the proportionality constant between pause duration and ratio size, maximum and minimum limits upon the ratio size, amount of reinforcement, drugs, and other factors.

The resulting behavior is, in principle, intrinsically variable, and can be described comprehensively in terms of the characteristics of its oscillations. Variability, in this instance, becomes the datum upon which behavioral laws must be based. It is not simply a problem that demands refinement of experimental techniques. The relation of such variability to technique is an indirect one. If, by deliberate experimental manipulation, we can produce and control an oscillating state, we get access to information that permits us to understand similar instances of variability when they occur in uncontrolled situations. The behavioral oscillation in the adjusting ratio schedule helps us understand why it is difficult to maintain a strained ratio performance—*i.e.*, a ratio performance characterized by long pauses following reinforcements—for any extended period of time. The ordinary ratio procedure does not have any self-adjusting mechanism built into it. Since the ratio remains the same, regardless of pause duration, long pauses are likely to generate still longer ones, and the behavior will eventually disappear. Similarly, short pauses initiate a process which spirals in the opposite direction, till the final performance is characterized by extremely brief post-reinforcement pauses.

Systematic information of this sort will have at least two implications for fixed-ratio technology. In generating baseline behavior by means of the fixed-ratio schedule, we have, first, a rational basis for deciding how far to extend the size of the ratio; second, a measuring technique. The length of the post-reinforcement pause has been shown to be a sensitive barometer of the ratio performance.

A discovery that variability stems from the action of a self-adjusting cyclic process, or from the failure of such a process, will have an important implication for the statement of behavioral laws. We cannot assume that the variability can be reduced by more rigorous experimental control. The laws therefore cannot be formulated in such a way as to ignore the variability that was actually observed in the relevant experiments. They must, rather, take account of that variability, and indeed, must take that variability as their point of departure. Such variability is not mere noise in the system. It is the major datum. We have here a case in which laws based upon variability will take precedence over those that assume constancy in the underlying variables.

In the example of the adjusting ratio we observed a technique of investigating and accounting for behavior that varies around an optimal state. The technique can, with a little ingenuity, be applied to a wide variety of other situations. Some of the variability in behavioral experiments, however, stems from oscillations between two or more different forms of behavior, rather than among several states of a single response. Direct experimental investigation will make possible a systematic account of the factors responsible for such "response variability."

In one type of experiment, for example, a pigeon has two keys available at which it can peck. Responding on one key produces food reinforcement on a ratio schedule. But after each reinforcement, the required number of responses, *i.e.*, the size of the ratio, increases. Responding on the second key, however, returns the ratio to its minimal value. The rate of oscillation between the two keys depends upon such factors as the size of the increment added to the ratio after each reinforcement and the number of responses required on the second key to reduce the ratio. These two variables can be balanced so as to produce almost any desired rate of oscillation between the two keys (36). Such experiments indicate that response oscillation is under the control of specifiable and manipulable factors and is not, as many theorists have tended to assume, a source of irreducible, or intrinsic, variability. As multiple-response experiments become more frequent, we can expect additional light on this aspect of variability.

Other experiments have shown that response variability can arise from inadequate restriction of the reinforcement contingency. The extreme case is that in which reinforcement is presented independently of any particular form of behavior. Whatever behavior is going on at the time reinforcement occurs will increase in frequency, but the topography of the adventitiously conditioned behavior will display a gradual drift (82). This is because slight variations in the response can be reinforced, since the reinforcement is, in fact, independent of any specified form of behavior. After a long enough period of time, the response that was originally "caught" by the reinforcement may not even be recognizable in the currently maintained pattern of behavior.

In most experiments the situation is somewhat more restricted than this, but there is, usually, considerable latitude. When a response is specified as "lever pressing," the behavior is restricted only to those actions that succeed in depressing the lever. The lever press may, however, vary through a wide topography, including responses of varying force and duration, and performed with different parts of the body.

It is not clear at present whether variability that results from insufficient restriction of reinforcement contingencies is a problem in experimental technique or is a factor that must be taken into account in the formulation of behavioral laws. We have little experimental data bearing on this question. Its usual formulation is in terms of the definition of response. When a response is defined in terms of its consequences, *i.e.*, reinforcement, the problem arises as to whether a definition in terms of, say, its physical characteristics would give rise to a different and perhaps more successful type of behavioral systematization. It seems likely that the eventual solution to this problem will be a compromise. Responses will be defined in terms of the reinforcement contingencies into which they enter, but the behavioral laws will also include statements describing the effects of permissible variability in response properties. This variability cannot be eliminated completely by any refinement of experimental technique short of transforming the subject into a surgical preparation upon which reinforcement contingencies have no effect at all. The problem at hand is an empirical one, to determine whether, and how, quantitative and/or qualitative restriction of response variability will require changes in our descriptive account of behavior. It may turn out that no such changes will be necessary, but that increasing restriction will simply sharpen the precision of our present descriptive techniques.

VARIABILITY AND ADAPTIVE BEHAVIOR

MANY WRITERS have pointed out that if organisms did not display variability in their behavior, they would not long survive. The environment is never constant, and no organism ever faces exactly the same situation twice. Changing behavior is required in order to deal effectively with a changing environment. Mental hospitals are filled with people who find it impossible to deal with new situations by appropriate alterations of their behavior. In a less protective society, stereotypy would result in death. Such observations have, unfortunately, helped to generate a philosophy of indeterminism with respect to behavior. Since nature requires variability for survival, it is assumed that those organisms which have maintained their existence are endowed intrinsically with behavioral variability.

Variability as a fact cannot, of course, be denied. But variability as a fundamental principle of behavior deserves a closer examination. The simple observation that a behavioral phenomenon serves the useful function of preserving the existence of an organism, or of its species, is not enough reason to take that phenomenon as a starting point in the analysis of behavior. Variability, as I have pointed out in the preceding pages, springs from many sources and is amenable to analysis; its analysis has been a profitable scientific venture.

The basic error in accepting variability as the starting point for behavioral analysis is the failure to distinguish between *useful function* and *lawful process*. The knowledge that behavior performs a function, that different types of behavior serve different functions for an organism, is useful in many ways. The recognition, for example, by some remote and unsung genius that all organisms require food in order to survive marked an advance in biological knowledge whose magnitude has probably never been matched since. But the fact remains that no individual organism engages in food-seeking behavior in order to fulfill a commitment to preserve its species. The function of such behavior can be conceptualized against the grand background of evolution. But the processes that control and are controlled by food-oriented behavior comprise at least part of the subject matter of several biological sciences, from biophysics to psychology.

Behavioral variability falls into a similar category. Species whose behavior was too stereotyped to permit them to cope with altered environmental conditions are no longer present to tell their story. The only exceptions to this picture are those species, such as the lungfish, whose environment has not undergone any significant alterations. But again, no individual example of behavioral variability can be understood solely in terms of its function in preserving the species—if such a function can be seen at all. The experimental investigation of variability reveals behavioral processes whose description provides us with behavioral laws. Variability may be a component of such laws, or a consequence of them. An explanation of variability is to be sought in the conditions under which behavioral processes occur and in the factors that determine their characteristics. The adaptive function of variability is a fortunate by-product of the underlying behavioral processes.

There may actually be a fundamental error even in *seeking* the adaptive function of every sample of behavior. Since the process of evolution has, for the most part, eliminated those organisms and species whose behavior was not adaptive, we base our observations on a biased sample. We see around us organisms whose behavior is under the control of processes that permit survival. Processes that mitigate against survival become visible when we examine behavior in the laboratory. Here, animals in which our experimental operations generate nonadaptive processes are permitted to survive, and the reality of such processes becomes apparent.

We may take, as an example, behavior that is generated and maintained by the fixed-ratio schedule of reinforcement. The fixed-ratio schedule normally generates an extremely high response rate, but if the required ratio of responses to reinforcements is too high, the animal ceases responding. Suppose we require a rat to secure *all* its food by pressing a lever. Every fiftieth lever press brings it a small quantity of a specially prepared diet containing all the ingredients necessary for healthy maintenance. Most rats will, under these conditions, maintain themselves indefinitely. Let us now increase the work load suddenly from 50 to 500 lever presses per reinforcement. Lever pressing will continue for a while at its usual high rate, but longer and longer pauses will develop until the animal responds so infrequently that its food intake is not sufficient to maintain life. Eventually, the animal will die of starvation.

In this example, the environment did change, but not in such a way as to make it impossible for the rat to secure an adequate supply of food. Although the new reinforcement contingency was not capable of maintaining the *high* fixed-ratio rate of lever pressing, the animal might have continued at a lower rate and still secured enough food to more than match its energy output. The animal starves in the midst of plenty because of the specific behavioral processes generated by fixed-ratio reinforcement schedules. When reinforcement is made contingent on the animal's making a fixed number of responses, certain variables combine in such a way as to produce either a high response rate or a zero rate. If the zero rate prevails, no long-term considerations of organism or species survival will alter the process. Process proves stronger than function.

Similar cases, in principle, may well be responsible for the non-adaptive behavior that forces us to commit a large segment of our population to mental institutions. Many psychiatrists proceed on the assumption that the behavior displayed by mental patients, while it is obviously ill-suited for physical survival, does possess some kind of adaptive function. Therapy is often oriented around a search for this hidden, presumably idiosyncratic, function.

The patient, for example, who displays practically no behavior at all is sometimes viewed as the product of a behavioral history in which almost all behavior has produced punishment or trauma of some sort, real or imagined. The subsequent loss of all behavior is viewed as an adaptation to an environment in which "not responding" is the only safe course. It is also possible, however, that this patient is simply displaying the normal, automatic response to an environment which had failed to provide sufficiently frequent reinforcement. The process of behavioral extinction may have been powerful enough to override the survival function of behavior. The distinction is important in practice, as well as principle, for the type of therapy to be employed will differ markedly, depending upon which of the possibilities is suspected by the therapist.

Although it has been customary to regard variability as a fundamental behavioral property that permits adaptation to a changing environment, it is possible to take a different view of the relation between environment and variability. Instead of considering adaptive variability as a primary phenomenon, let us look into the possibility that it is imposed by the environment. There is a subtle reversal in emphasis involved here. Instead of evaluating variability in terms of its adaptive function in controlling the environment, we may regard variability as being generated by a continuously changing milieu, so that its adaptive function is secondary.

The environment may generate behavioral variability in many ways. The most direct method is by brute force. An organism may find one response to be successful the first time it meets a given situation, but the next time the situation arises its original behavior no longer works. Every parent who observes the developing behavior of his children with more than cursory interest has seen instances of this process. A nine-month-old baby, for example, may have discovered that she can elicit smiles and caresses from her parents by performing a little trick, such as clapping her hands. Occasionally, if the parent is preoccupied, this doesn't work. Subsequent crying, however, may succeed where hand-clapping failed. Later on, another trick, "waving bye-bye," may produce the same results. Sometimes it is only necessary for the child to flash a broad smile. Each of these forms of behavior is separately conditioned, and any of them may occur in the parental environment. The child may, in fact, occasionally be observed to run rapidly through the sequence of hand-clapping, crying, smiling, and waving bye-bye until the customary reinforcement is forthcoming.

Similar instances may be multiplied throughout the behaving organism's life history until it becomes impossible to disentangle the interlocking systems of directly conditioned multiple responses. Different responses may be reinforced in similar appearing environments, while seemingly different environments will call forth common forms of behavior. The resulting richly diversified behavior may be highly adaptive, but the diversification does not arise spontaneously for the *purpose* of adaptation. The behavioral variations are directly conditioned. They are adaptive only insofar as the environment continues to provide reinforcement according to the same rules.

What happens when the rules change, and behavior that was formerly appropriate no longer succeeds? Experimental evidence indicates that the extinction process produces increased behavioral variability (2). Here, then, we are faced with a behavioral mechanism that does seem designed to promote survival. Unless organisms can develop new courses of action when the environment fails to reinforce previously appropriate modes of behavior, their chances of survival will be greatly diminished. Extinction-produced variability is as nice an adaptive mechanism as any that have been observed in other biological areas.

But again, the adaptive function may be only secondary to a direct conditioning process. Experimental data on this point are meager. It has been suggested, however, that the variations which occur during extinction consist of behavioral forms that had, in the past, been themselves reinforced (64). The fact that such reinforcement may have been only incidental, or even accidental, does not diminish its effectiveness. Reinforcement is typically forthcoming when behavior produces a certain end effect, but there may be only few restrictions on the path that a sequence of behavior can take in reaching its conclusion.

A chess player receives his prize after he places his opponent's king in a compromising position, but the rich variety of moves by which this objective can be accomplished makes the game an unending source of fascination to its devotees. An experienced player, when he meets an opponent who is not susceptible to his favorite strategy, has a reinforced repertoire of other courses of action from which to draw. The adaptive variability displayed by a master is a hard-won product of a long history of reinforcement and extinction. This principle is taken for granted in the construction of chess-playing machines. The probability that the machine will make a given move depends not only upon the current configuration of the pieces on the board but also on the consequences that similar moves have had in the past under similar circumstances.

Like the chess player, the laboratory animal may vary its responses along many dimensions, as long as they produce their required effect. Lever depressions may vary in force and duration; they may be accomplished with any paw, with the nose, or even with the tail; they may have been preceded by any other response in the animal's repertoire. But as long as the behavior succeeds in closing the switch, reinforcement will be delivered. Eventually, the lever-pressing behavior becomes relatively restricted in its form, but the reinforcement history of the initial variations may show up again during extinction. Quantitative observation should reveal a correlation between the deviant forms of response observed during extinction and the reinforcement history of the variations.

If the latitude permitted by the initial reinforcement contingency was sufficiently wide, the extinction-produced variability is likely to permit the animal to come up with a successfully revised form of response. If, however, the new requirement calls for behavior that is unrelated to previously reinforced forms, the organism may die. When the environment makes reinforcement contingent upon restricted forms of behavior, it also narrows the "reservoir" of behavior that will be available when the requirements change.

Environmental control of behavioral variability may take still another course. If the reinforcement contingencies change frequently, we may expect to observe a correspondingly greater degree of behavioral variability. In an environment that demands constant reorientation and adjustment to changing conditions, variability may become the most prominent feature of behavior. In some circumstances, variability itself may become conditioned. That is to say, reinforcement may be contingent not simply upon the emission of a given response in the presence of appropriate stimuli but also upon the emission of variable behavior. In such cases variability will be the rule, for it will be a primary requirement for reinforcement to occur. Successful creative behavior in science, in the arts, and elsewhere has a strong component of conditioned variability. One consistent lesson of science is that the solutions to experimental or theoretical problems often demand the sloughing off of conventional ways of thinking. Those scientists who persistently question traditional formulations and orthodox approaches are displaying the effects of a history of reinforcement for behavioral variability. They have found that when old responses do not work, new ones must be tried.

Conditioned behavioral variability has an undoubted survival value—look at the behavior of the beast of prey, of the military strategist, of the lover, as well as of the creative scientist. Behavioral variability in such cases is so obviously adaptive that it is easy to assume we have thereby explained it. But the statement that behavioral variability possesses survival value is actually a statement about the availability of reinforcement. Behavior is adaptive insofar as it secures the reinforcements that maintain the organism in life, in health, or in its chosen field of endeavor. If we are to understand the adaptive function of behavioral variability we must first investigate the relations between behavior and reinforcement history. Variability may be conditioned, but the particular behavioral forms that emerge at different stages of a variable sequence are a function of contingencies that must be specified.

Here, then, is the basic problem involved in explaining any given instance of variability, whether it be at the level of physical maintenance or of abstract scientific creativity. What are the specific current and historical variables that brought out the successful behavior? Recognizing the adaptive function of behavioral variability does not help to answer this question.

STIMULUS GENERALIZATION AND RESPONSE INDUCTION. Two phenomena that seem to be examples of fundamental variability and to possess a conspicuous adaptive function are stimulus generalization and response induction. The basic observations defining these phenomena have been known for many years, but until recently they generated only feeble experimental attack. The experiment demonstrating stimulus generalization in its most precise and quantitative form is the following (38).

A hungry pigeon is placed in a darkened experimental chamber; there is an illuminated disk, or key, on one wall of the chamber. By pecking at this key, the pigeon can get access to a small amount of grain. After the pigeon has learned to peck at the key, the grain reinforcement is programed according to a variable-interval schedule, *i.e.*, the pecking response produces food at irregularly spaced time intervals. During the phases of the experiment in which the response is reinforced, the key illumination is maintained at a constant wavelength—550 millimicrons, let us say.

The next, and critical, phase of the experiment is carried out under the condition of experimental extinction. The food-delivery mechanism is disconnected, and the bird receives no further grain in the experimental chamber. The variable-interval reinforcement schedule was employed in the first phase because it is known to generate high resistance to extinction of the previously reinforced response. That is to say, the pecking behavior continues at a relatively constant rate for a long time after reinforcement is discontinued. During the period of extinction in which a stable rate would normally be maintained, the color of the key is systematically varied over a broad spectral range. The colors are changed frequently, but every one is present for an equal total period of time, so that the number of pecking responses in the presence of each color may be compared directly.

Typical results for a single pigeon appear in Figure 20. The greatest number of extinction responses was emitted when the wavelength of the light illuminating the key was 550 millimicrons. This was the wavelength present during the variable-interval reinforcement phase. As the wavelength differs more and more from 550 millimicrons, the number of responses diminishes. This curve has been termed a "generalization gradient." It shows that the subject responds not only to stimuli that were present during reinforcement but also to stimuli to which it had never previously been exposed in this particular situation. As the new stimuli diverge from the original one, however, the probability of response declines.

The generalization gradient provides a mechanism whereby behavior can adapt to an environment that never exactly repeats any combination of stimuli. If a successful form of behavior were to come under the control only of the precise circumstances that were present at the time it was acquired, we should have to relearn the behavior each time the original situation recurred with its inevitable variations. Keller and Schoenfeld have made the point very nicely:

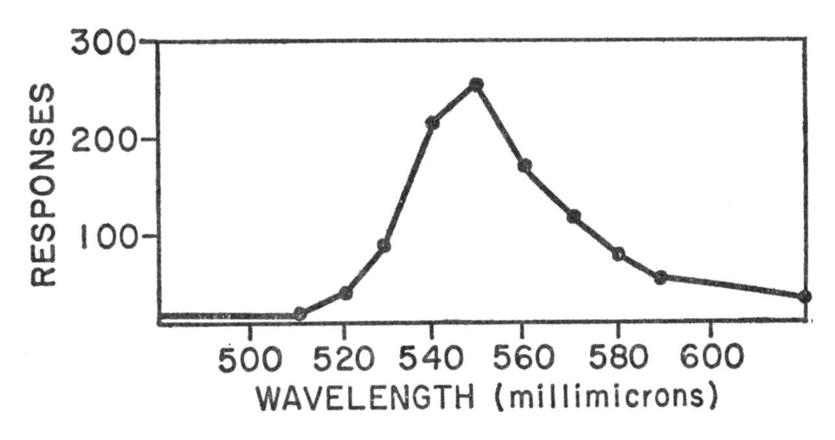

FIGURE 20. A gradient of stimulus generalization. (*Adapted from Guttman and Kalish,* 39.)

Our environment is in perpetual flux, and it is very unlikely that any stimulus ever recurs in identical form. The visual stimuli supplied by a running rabbit to a pursuing fox, or by the face of a friend as you see it from moment to moment, are subject to countless variations in pattern, movement, brightness, and so forth, yet the fox continues its chase, and you do not feel yourself confronted with a procession of strangers. In the ever changing environment, the generalization of stimuli gives stability and consistency to our behavior (51, p. 116).

Although generalization functions to produce consistent behavior, the gradient also has contained in it a source of variability. As shown in Figure 20, the probability of an appropriate response is not constant over the range of stimulus variations. Nature may often present markedly different situations that call, nevertheless, for the same behavior. The likelihood that the appropriate behavior will occur becomes less as the situations differ more sharply. Behavioral variability may thus occur where consistency is called for.

Furthermore, every situation, in the laboratory or outside, contains many stimuli, each of which can vary along a multitude of dimensions. Interacting generalization gradients are a potential source of behavior variability whose influence we have hardly begun to explore. Laboratory observations have been made of the "prepotency" of one stimulus over another with respect to the degree of control exercised over behavior, but nothing is known about the generalization gradients that are interacting in such a way as to produce prepotency. The area is a fascinating one, and its exploration will undoubtedly yield rich dividends in our understanding of and control over behavioral variability.

Striking cases have been observed of the prepotency of stimuli that one would normally expect to have little effect. One example arose in an experiment on avoidance behavior, with a monkey as subject (15). The beginning of every experimental session was signaled by a flashing red light, which remained present throughout the session. When the flashing light terminated, the experiment was over for the day, and the animal could relax. After some experience, the monkey normally initiated a steady rate of avoidance responding as soon as the light came on. One day, however, there was an apparatus failure, in which the flasher did not operate. A steady red light appeared instead of the usual flashing one.

Under these circumstances, one might expect to observe at first a lower than usual rate of responding, or even a zero rate, with an immediate recovery as soon as the animal received a few shocks. It seemed reasonable to suppose that the shock exercised more potent control than the flashing light in this situation. What the monkey did, however, was to sit and take several hundred shocks, one every 20 seconds, without making a single avoidance response. The small change from a flashing to a steady red light actually produced a significant shift along the generalization gradient—presumably that of flash rate. This occurred in spite of the fact that other demonstrably powerful variables, such as the shock, had not changed. Similar unrecorded cases, in greater or lesser degree, are undoubtedly present in many behavioral experiments. As long as the facts of generalization remain shrouded in mystery, the concept of intrinsic variability will continue to be applied. The best of the experiments that have been performed in this area indicate that generalization is an orderly phenomenon. Interpretation of the process in terms of its adaptive or nonadaptive function will eventually yield to a functional analysis based on the type of quantitative data illustrated in Figure 20.

Response induction is sometimes considered to be the response counterpart of stimulus generalization (81). The following experimental observation is typical of the small number of measurements that have been made of induction gradients. In this experiment (47), a hungry rat received a food pellet each time it depressed a lever. The reinforcement contingency, however, had one important restriction. The pressure on the lever had to be 21 grams or more before the food pellet would be delivered. The pressure of each lever response was recorded, and the frequency distribution of pressures in a series of 100 reinforcements is presented in the upper portion of Figure 21. Considerable variability may be observed, the pressures ranging from 13 to 45 grams. Such variability has great adaptive utility, for the environment rarely requires behavior with closely circumscribed properties. Fine tolerances are approached in highly developed skills such as piano playing of concert quality. Normally, however, a considerable range of variation in the dimensions of a particular form of behavior is not only permissible, but is actually required. The dimensions of the environment vary, and behavior must vary correspondingly if it is to be successful.

Response induction gives us one of the most elegant adaptive mechanisms that behavioral research has uncovered. Suppose the environment changes in such a way as to require behavior with properties that have never before appeared in the organism's repertoire. Glancing again at the upper distribution of Figure 21, we might wonder what would happen if the pressure requirement were suddenly increased from the original 21 grams to 57 grams or more. Since pressures of this magnitude are never observed, it is likely that the behavior will extinguish through lack of reinforcement. If all its food had to be obtained in the experimental situation, the animal,

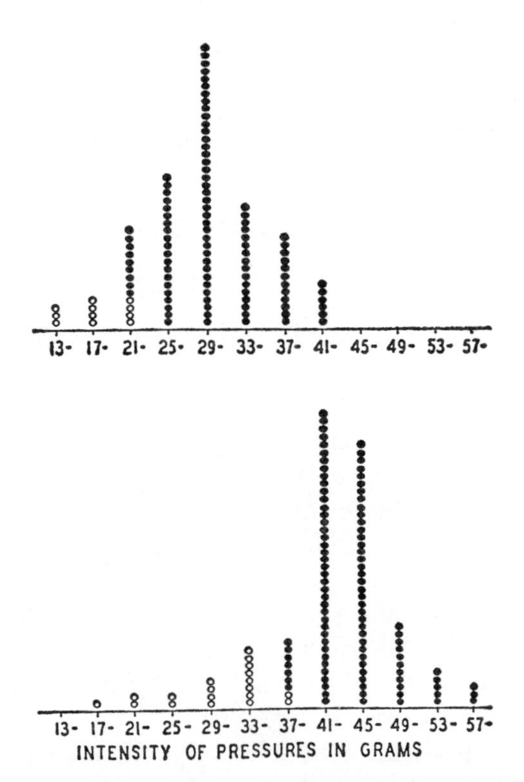

FIGURE 21. The upper frequency distribution illustrates variations in the pressure exerted by a rat in depressing a lever. All lever presses with a pressure of 21 grams or more produced a food pellet. The lower distribution shows the changes that occurred when the pressure requirement was raised to 38 grams or more. (*From Hull*, 47, p. 305.)

too, would be likely to extinguish, along with its lever-pressing behavior.

Suppose, however, that we begin by selecting 38 grams as our new cut-off point. The animal occasionally emits a lever response with 38 grams of pressure or more, so that some reinforcement will be received. The results of this new requirement are presented in the lower distribution of the figure. We note that the distribution has shifted markedly toward the high pressures. The range of variability has also increased. But, most important, we now observe pressures that were not previously recorded. Shifting the pressure requirement to a point within the normal range of variation has brought out new behavior. It is possible now to reinforce lever presses of 57 grams or more. By means of this procedure, force levels equal to the animal's bodily weight have been achieved.

As Keller and Schoenfeld stated, "The reinforcement of a response having a certain intensity apparently suffices to strengthen topographically similar responses having widely different intensities" (51, p. 171). But the "why" of response induction has not yet been satisfactorily resolved. One reason for this is the fact that a pure case of response induction has never been examined in the laboratory. In the experiment, for example, whose results are presented in Figure 21, induction was undoubtedly responsible for the initial appearance of new responses when the pressure requirement was shifted upward. But once the new responses appear, they are subsequently maintained by direct reinforcement and no longer constitute a pure case of induction. The problem, in fact, becomes one of explaining why they occur so seldom.

Until an uncontaminated case of induction is achieved, variability arising from this source will remain poorly understood, and the phenomenon will continue to receive superficial classifications as an "adaptive mechanism." But a demonstration of genuine response induction, through refined experimental technique, will probably be accompanied by a diminishing amount of variability attributable to induction. In an experiment such as that of Figure 21, for example, one could place an upper as well as a lower limit upon the response pressures that produce reinforcement. Instead of reinforcing all pressures above 38 grams, we might reinforce only responses that fall between 38 and 41 grams. Any pressures above 41 grams, then, would represent a more nearly uncontaminated case of induction. But there can be no doubt that the range of variability would be greatly decreased. Another factor that would have to be eliminated is the reinforcement of certain sequences. For example, if "correct" responses characteristically are preceded by one or more "incorrect" responses, we may be reinforcing the latter as members of an adventitious chain. Elimination of this possibility would, perhaps, further decrease the amount of variability that we normally attribute to induction.

It may actually be the case, then, that response induction, in spite of its adaptive utility, is in reality only a minor contributor to behavioral variability. Its major effect is likely to be an indirect one, in that it provides for the initial appearance of new behavior which may subsequently enter into a reinforcement contingency and be maintained directly.

Part IV

Experimental Design

In the preceding chapters I have considered, in a more or less general way, some of the problems that arise in evaluating experimental data. I shall now indicate how these considerations enter into the actual design and conduct of experiments. Wherever possible, I shall draw upon actual experiments for illustration, but occasionally I will need to make a hypothetical demonstration.

The use of published experiments to clarify a principle of experimental design has the virtue of providing the student with sources from which he can obtain relatively detailed descriptions of experimental procedures, and upon which he can draw whenever a need for technical information arises. There is, on the other hand, the danger that a "halo effect" will attach itself to experiments cited as good examples of a given technique. Only the rare experiment is exemplary in all respects. An experiment selected for certain desirable features may well be deficient in other ways. I emphasize this point partly to keep the reader on his toes, and partly to absolve myself beforehand of a charge of immodesty that may arise from the citation of my own and other related experiments as examples of desirable techniques. My examples are drawn, of necessity, from those areas with which I am most familiar. The problems and solutions they illustrate, however, are intended to be general in principle. Those who have an interest and a technical competence in other areas should have little difficulty in making the necessary translations.

A more disturbing possibility is that the examples may be accepted as constituting a set of rules that must be followed in the design of experiments. I cannot emphasize too strongly that this would be disastrous. I could make the trite statement that every rule has its exception, but this is not strong enough. Nor is the more relaxed statement that the rules of experimental design are flexible, to be employed only where appropriate. The fact is that *there are no rules of experimental design.*

Every experiment is unique. Experiments are made to find out something we do not yet know. If we knew the results beforehand, there would be no point in performing the experiment. In our search for new information we must be prepared at any point to alter our conception of what is desirable in experimental design. Nature does not yield its secrets easily, and each new problem of investigation requires its own techniques. Sometimes the appropriate techniques will be the same as those which have been employed elsewhere. Often the known methods will have to be modified, and, on occasion, new principles of experimental design and procedure will have to be devised. There is no rule to inform an experimenter which of these eventualities he will meet.

Once he encounters a problem of experimental design, the experimenter is on his own. If he finds that other investigators have encountered similar problems, he must then evaluate their solutions in the light of his own particular requirements. It may be possible to make an effective judgment on the combined basis of his own and others' experience. On the other hand, the problem may be resolvable only by empirical procedures. He may have to perform the experiment not once but several times, with major or minor modifications, before a satisfactory solution is available. Appropriate experimental design cannot be legislated, either by logical or by empirical principles.

Chapter 7

Pilot Studies

EXPERIMENTS preliminary to a major effort are often called pilot, or exploratory, studies. Out of the tradition in psychology that all experiments are designed to test some hypothesis, has come the conception that pilot studies must precede any definitive experiment. If exploratory work does not suggest confirmation of the hypothesis, the investigator typically will either revise his experimental plan of attack or drop the problem and go on to something else that seems more promising. Justification for these courses of action is simple. The current state of psychological theorizing being what it is, the investigator can always point out some ambiguity in his theory which excuses negative pilot results. Also, since psychological theories seldom specify with any rigor the means for testing them, it can usually be shown that a negative pilot study did not measure up to a number of *post hoc* specifications. Exploratory work is considered necessary because it serves to minimize the amount of time and effort that would otherwise be spent on tests of incorrect hypotheses, or on inadequate tests of correct hypotheses.

There is, however, a fundamental misconception involved in the use of pilot studies for the purpose of gaining an inexpensive preview, as it were, of more definitive experimental findings. In what way does such a pilot study differ from its more definitive successor? The pilot experiment, if it is the precursor of a statistical group-type study, may utilize only a small number of subjects. Or it may employ subjects with a previous experimental history, whereas the projected study calls for experimentally naive subjects. The apparatus in a pilot study may be subject to occasional failure, which would never be tolerated in a full-fledged experiment. The experimenter is loath to expend his best equipment, along with a significant portion of his time and attention, upon exploratory work that may never yield useful, or publishable, data.

Pilot studies conceived in this way possess a curious status. They are supposed to provide the investigator with an estimate of the probable success or failure of a subsequent well-designed experiment. But the defining feature of this type of pilot study is its lack of control over certain variables. Inadequate control is considered permissible in a pilot study because, after all, "We only want to get a rough notion of how our experiment will turn out. There is no sense in spending a great deal of time and effort until we are fairly sure it will pay off."

But if a pilot study is not run under exactly the same conditions as would be required in a full-scale experiment its predictive value is completely negated. If, for example, the subjects' experimental histories are not considered important factors in pilot work, why bother to control them in the major study? The same may be said of any other difference between exploratory and full-scale experiments. Pilot studies that are not carried out in as rigorous a fashion as possible have neither positive nor negative value as indicators of subsequent results. A sloppy experiment is a poor experiment, and can never be justified by labeling it "pilot."

Pilot Studies

All this leads us inevitably to ask what the differences are between a pilot study and a full-fledged experiment. If the same operations must be undertaken in each case, where is a distinction to be found? In answer, there is *no* distinction to be found under the terms with which I introduced this discussion.

An experiment is never deliberately designed as a pilot study. It is designated as such only after it has been performed, and even then only under certain conditions. One of these conditions is *not* a failure of the experiment to support a hypothesis. Nor is it permissible to classify an experiment as exploratory, and thereby to dismiss it, on the grounds of inadequacies in its theoretical development. If an experiment is technically adequate, its data must be accepted, regardless of whether or not they are appropriate to the investigator's purpose in carrying out the study. If, on the other hand, an experiment is technically inadequate, its data are unacceptable, even if they bolster the investigator's preconceptions.

The first step, therefore, in designing an experiment, is to evaluate its technical adequacy. The experimenter's eventual aim may be to prove, or to test, a hypothesis, or he may simply be in search of new and unpredictable information. Regardless of his eventual aim, his primary attention must be directed toward his experimental technique. He must decide what variables to control, and he must select appropriate methods for such control. What is to be the baseline from which changes are to be measured, and what measures are feasible and appropriate to the particular behavior that will be generated? Is it possible to generate the type of behavior that would be maximally useful in the investigation?

Problems such as these give rise to pilot studies. For the experimenter often does not know the answers, and he must proceed "by the seat of his pants." He makes his best possible estimate of the adequacy and appropriateness of his technique, and proceeds with the experiment. At some point along the way, it may become evident that the technique he selected has a serious fault. At that point, the experiment becomes a pilot study. Its data are useful only insofar as they have revealed the technical inadequacy, although they may also contain hints as to the means for rectifying the fault. After the necessary changes have been made, the experiment proceeds on its course. The investigator is continually optimistic. He proceeds watchfully on the assumption that his procedure is technically adequate and that his experiment will yield valid information. Since he employs his whole available skill and knowledge in setting up any experiment, he is always prepared to see the investigation through to a satisfactory conclusion. It becomes a pilot study only when some overlooked factor comes into play and reveals a technical fault in the procedure.

The following experimental procedure, described by Blough (8), is an excellent example of the initial stages of experimental design. I shall take up the procedure in considerable detail, for the solutions to many of its problems are of considerable practical interest to the student of experimental technique. In fairness to Blough, however, I must note that he did not simply wait for each of the problems to arise before devising their solutions. He is a competent and imaginative investigator, and many of the problems described below were anticipated and solved before he started the experiment. A few of them did not arise until he was well into the experiment, and this forced him to classify the preceding work as a pilot study. For expository purposes, however, it will be useful to describe each of the problems as if they belonged in that category. This might well have been the true case for an investigator of lesser stature.

Blough was initiating a program of research into a behavioral process known as "conditional discrimination." His first task was to devise a procedure by means of which he could generate and maintain an appropriate type of behavior. The appropriateness of this behavior had to undergo continual evaluation of its utility and its validity as a baseline from which to measure the participation of relevant variables in the process of conditional discrimination.

I shall pass over the problems that were encountered in selecting appropriate subjects, constructing the apparatus, and setting up the basic procedure. We may move directly to Figure 22, which provides a schematic illustration of the subject and apparatus.

The (hungry) pigeon confronts two recessed, semicircular translucent response keys separated by a vertical plastic partition. The visible edge of this partition forms a third stimulus element that I shall call the "bar." Either key may be lighted by the 6-watt lamp (left or right) behind it, and the vertical bar may be lighted by lamp B. The clear plastic partition conducts light from lamp B to the bar, but its sides are blackened to

FIGURE 22. A schematic illustration of the subject and apparatus in Blough's investigation. The "front" view shows one of four possible stimulus patterns. (*From Blough,* 8.)

restrict the light from each lamp to its own stimulus area. The front view shows the response keys and bar as they appear to the pigeon. One of several possible stimulus patterns is represented. Only one key is lighted at a time, and the bar may be lighted or dark. Thus there are 4 possible stimulus arrays.

To make reinforcements as immediate and effective as possible, the grain-filled magazine is placed directly below the response keys. It can be raised within reach by a solenoid. During reinforcement an overhead lamp goes on and the grain rises within reach for about two seconds (8, p. 335).

The pigeon can obtain food by pecking the lighted key when the bar is dark, and by pecking the dark key when the bar is lighted. Responding is therefore under the stimulus control of both the key light and the bar light. It is necessary to be certain that the bird makes the discrimination on the basis of these two stimuli only. If other cues are used by the subject, the baseline will not measure what the experimenter intends it to measure. In fact, the process then may not involve conditional discrimination at all.

Suppose, for example, the experiment was begun with the four possible stimulus combinations being presented in a fixed sequence. The bird might then base its discrimination upon the order in which the stimuli appear rather than upon the stimulus configurations. For example, a fixed sequence might be (1), left key dark, bar lighted; (2), right key dark, bar lighted; (3), left key lighted, bar dark; (4), right key lighted, bar dark. In the presence of stimulus pattern (1), responses on the left key would be reinforced. In pattern (2), reinforcement would shift to the right key. In pattern (3), responses on the left key would again be reinforced; and in pattern (4), it would again be the right key that would pay off. Thus with each stimulus presentation the animal could shift keys. The alternating pattern of responding would indicate a highly developed discrimination, but the behavior might not be based upon the pattern of bar and key lights at all.

If the experimenter were to change the sequence, so that the stimulus combinations appeared in the order (1), (3), (2), (4), he might well find that the pigeon, instead of making an immediate behavioral adjustment, would continue to alternate from one key to the other. When the experimenter discovered his technical error, he would have to classify his experiment as a pilot study, rectify the situation, and go on from there.

Even then, however, it might have turned out that the alternation behavior proved interesting in its own right, and the experimenter could have decided to postpone his initial objective in favor of this new development. In such a case, the original work would no longer constitute a pilot study, and it could be integrated into the research program.

Blough adopted the commonly accepted solution to the alternation problem. He simply presented the four stimulus arrays in a mixed sequence, so that alternation behavior could not consistently be reinforced. But other problems soon arose. When he reinforced every response on the correct key, the bird soon became satiated with food, and it was not possible to secure the five-hour baseline that was required for some planned studies on the time course of drug action. The difficulty was overcome by employing a reinforcement schedule according to which food could be obtained, on the average, no more frequently than once every minute and a half. With this technique, incorrect responses were never reinforced, and correct responses only occasionally produced reinforcement.

Reinforcement delivery introduced another problem. The apparatus was set up so that each stimulus presentation lasted for 15 seconds, with each presentation separated from the next by a 15-second "dark interval" during which all stimulus lights were off. But after one reinforcement had been received, the bird could then disregard the stimulus lights for the remainder of the 15-second stimulus period and simply continue to perform the response that had just proven to be the correct one. Reinforcement delivery, rather than the stimulus lights, became the basis for the discrimination under these circumstances. Pilot work again. The error was rectified by terminating the stimulus whenever a reinforcement was delivered. In order to prevent a temporal discrimination, reinforcements were scheduled to occur at various points within the presentation interval, for example, 1, 3, 6, or 13 seconds after the stimulus onset. In this way, a constant rate of response was generated and maintained throughout the stimulus duration.

In spite of all the pilot work that was necessitated by the above-mentioned technical difficulties, a number of additional problems remained to delay the initiation of full-scale experimentation. The next problem was revealed when, after long experimentation, it appeared impossible to reduce the number of incorrect responses to a level sufficiently low to indicate a well-developed discrimination. Blough's analysis of this problem, and his solution, are best described in his own words.

When two response keys are used, and the desired discrimination involves responding to only one of the keys at a time, there is danger that a so-called "superstitious" chaining of the two responses will occur. For example, it might frequently happen that the apparatus will ready a reinforcement just as the bird is pecking on the *incorrect* key. In that case the very first peck on the correct key that follows these incorrect responses would be reinforced. Instead of learning to make correct responses, the bird might learn to make one or more incorrect responses and *then* a correct response. It might even tend to obtain reinforcement by pecking the keys alternately instead of pecking only the correct key. To prevent these possibilities, incorrect responding is made to postpone reinforcement. Each incorrect response starts a one-second timer and, during this one second, no response is ever reinforced. Since at least one second intervenes between each incorrect response and reinforcement, incorrect responding is relatively depressed, and alternation is discouraged (8, p. 336).

Thus was another technical difficulty disposed of, but a progress report at this point would have stated that the experiment was still in the pilot stage. A number of additional problems still remained to be met and conquered, and a description of these may be found in Blough's paper. They are somewhat too complex to be taken up here.

Not every experiment involves as extended and as difficult an exploratory phase as did the one I have just described. On the other hand, some experiments involve a great deal more. It is, unfortunately, only the rare, technique-oriented publication that describes such exploratory work. The student can be assured that there is generally a certain amount of unwritten material between the introduction and the main body of any experimental report. Sometimes it is possible to see this material between the lines. In describing an avoidance experiment, for example, the experimenter may have written that his response lever was wired into the shock circuit. His experienced colleague will recognize, without further explanation, that he had run into the problem of lever holding by the subjects, and that making the lever one of the shocking electrodes was the solution to this problem.

A pilot study, then, is one in which technical problems are met. The investigator must be certain that the behavior with which he is working is appropriate to his experimental task. The initial phase of experimental design is concerned with this problem. But, contrary to popular impression, the experimenter does not say to himself, "I am now going to undertake Phase I, a pilot study. If the pilot experiment works out, I will then move on to Phase II, and do the experiment properly." Instead, he sets up his experiment, at the start, as if it were Phase II, and until some unforeseen difficulty crops up, he assumes that the experiment will go forward to a satisfactory conclusion. Only when such a difficulty appears does he classify the work up to that point as pilot. If the investigator is fortunate as well as skillful, that point will arise early before a great deal of time and effort have been expended. Sometimes, however, a problem may go unrecognized until the "final" report is being written, or even until after the paper has been published. In that case the completed experiment becomes a pilot study, an unfinished job. There is no neat point of demarcation at which an experiment is transformed from a pilot study into a substantial contribution.

If one is attempting to test a weak theory, or to demonstrate a specific behavioral phenomenon whose existence is very much in doubt, pilot studies are generally left unpublished. Their function is simply to sharpen up the experimental technique. But it should be remembered that if one's technique has a general utility beyond the specific purposes of the experiment at hand, a description of the pilot studies may be valuable to other workers. If they can learn in advance some of the difficulties they are likely to encounter, and the solutions to them, they will be spared a considerable amount of time and labor. Furthermore, other investigators might attempt to employ the technique without even recognizing all the problems involved, and the publication of pilot studies might raise the general level of scientific accomplishment in areas in which the technique is employed. If, of course, the technique is applicable only to a specific experiment, the pilot work might just as well remain buried.

In experiments performed simply for the purpose of satisfying one's curiosity, pilot studies can serve another function. An unforeseen technical difficulty may give rise to behavior that turns out to be of greater interest than that which the experiment was originally set up to investigate. The experimenter may then change his course and, instead of eliminating the technical "difficulty," follow it up more intensively. The experiment becomes an incomplete pilot study with respect to the original design, but forms a major steppingstone in the new investigation. I am particularly fond of the following illustration of how a pilot study can be transformed into the launching vehicle for a new investigation. Not only was a fresh orientation brought to my own research in this case, but the new investigations actually provided the key to the original problem that occasioned the pilot study.

The story actually begins back in 1941, with a paper by Estes and Skinner entitled "Some Quantitative Properties of Anxiety" (29). In this paper, the writers introduced their "conditioned suppression" technique. The subjects, hungry white rats, were first trained to press a lever, for which they occasionally received a small pellet of food. After the rate of lever pressing had become relatively stable, a new operation was introduced. While the animal was working for its food, a stimulus was presented for five minutes. During the stimulus, the animal could continue to press the lever and receive an occasional pellet. But after five minutes of the stimulus, a brief shock was delivered to the animal's feet, and, at the same time, the stimulus was terminated.

During the first stimulus presentation, the animal's rate of lever pressing did not change. After a few stimulus-shock pairings, however, the ongoing lever-pressing behavior was profoundly disturbed. Figure 5 (in Chapter 3) illustrates the effect. The stimulus, after several presentations with shock, completely suppresses the ongoing lever-pressing behavior. The response rate during the stimulus falls nearly to zero, and, upon gross observation, the animal appears profoundly disturbed.

During the ensuing ten years, little was done in the way of following up the conditioned suppression phenomenon experimentally. The procedure was eventually resurrected by Brady, Hunt, and their co-workers, who employed it to generate a behavioral baseline for the study of electro-convulsive shock "therapy," brain lesions, drugs, and other physiological operations (18). Largely because of its extensive use as a technique for studying relations between behavior and other biological phenomena, the conditioned suppression began, in recent years, to attract experimental attention as an interesting behavioral phenomenon in its own right. The pilot study, and its consequent elaboration which I am about to describe, formed one of the bypaths into which this resurgent experimental interest was channeled.

The question that started us off was a simple one. Would the conditioned suppression still occur if we employed shock-avoidance behavior as the baseline instead of food-reinforced behavior? What would happen if we introduced the stimulus-shock pairing while the animal was engaged in pressing a lever that served to postpone a shock? Our experimental answer to this question demonstrated that the subject, in this case a monkey, not only failed to show any suppression of its lever-pressing response during the preshock stimulus but actually increased its response rate (78).

Our procedure was the following. The monkey received a brief shock every time it permitted 20 seconds to elapse without a lever-pressing response. Each time it pressed the lever, however, the shock was postponed for 20 seconds. By pressing the lever often enough, the animal could completely avoid the shock. The procedure generated a relatively constant rate of lever pressing over a long period of time. When this baseline behavior stabilized, stimulus-shock pairings were introduced. A stimulus, five minutes in duration, was presented, at the end of which the animal received an *unavoidable* shock. The stimuli were presented at regular intervals, with five minutes intervening between each unavoidable shock and the onset of the next stimulus. The avoidance procedure was in effect throughout. Any time 20 seconds elapsed without a lever press, both in the presence and absence of the stimulus, the animal received a shock. As I have already indicated, this procedure resulted in a higher rate of responding, instead of suppression, during the preshock stimulus.

When the avoidance procedure was eliminated, the result was even more striking. With this modification, the only shocks the animal received were the unavoidable ones at the end of each stimulus presentation. Shock was no longer controlled by the animal's lever-pressing behavior. Figure 23 shows the typical result, a near-zero response rate in the absence of the stimulus and marked acceleration during the stimulus up to receipt of the unavoidable shock. The contrast with the Estes-Skinner finding is striking. We drew the tentative conclusion that a response which has had a

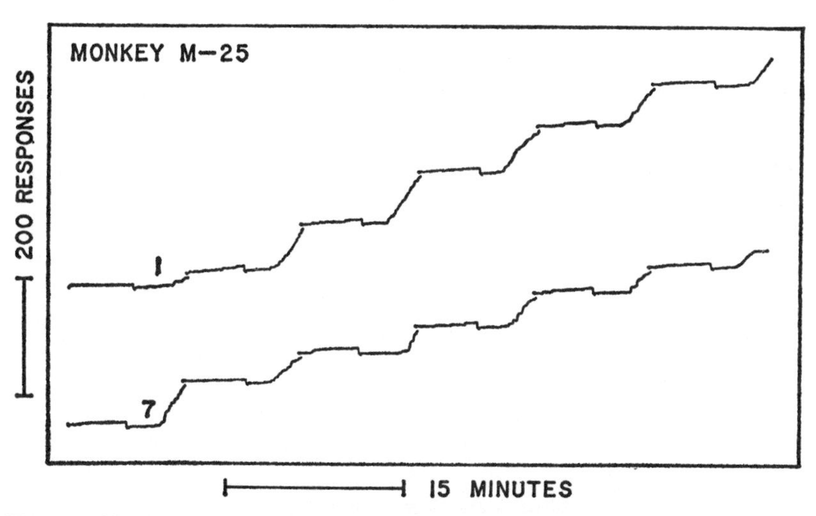

Figure 23. Cumulative response curve showing the nearly complete absence of lever pressing when the warning stimulus was off, and the accelerated responding when the stimulus was on. The pen is deflected downward at the onset of each stimulus and returns when the shock is delivered. The record is divided into one-hour segments for compact presentation, with the first and seventh stimulus presentations indicated by number. (*From Sidman, Herrnstein, and Conrad,* 78.)

history of avoidance conditioning will manifest an increased rate, or facilitation, rather than a suppression when exposed to the sequence of stimulus and unavoidable shock. This conclusion was strongly supported when we found that the pre-shock stimulus would facilitate even a food-reinforced response once we had given that response a prior history of avoidance conditioning (45).

Now we come to the heart of the affair, with respect to our discussion of pilot experiments. Our next step was to determine whether we could demonstrate, in one subject, a simultaneous suppression and increased rate during the pre-shock stimulus (74). If this could be accomplished, we would have great confidence in our ability to control the variables relevant to the two opposing phenomena. We first conditioned two responses concurrently. By pressing one lever, the monkey could postpone shock for 20 seconds. By pressing another lever, the monkey could produce a food reinforcement. Food delivery was programed according to a variable-interval schedule. The animal thus possessed an experimental repertoire of two concurrent responses, one of them maintained by occasional food reinforcement, the other by shock avoidance. Both of these responses were emitted frequently during each experimental session, and each was recorded separately.

What would happen now when we introduced the stimulus and unavoidable shock? To make the situation comparable to that which yielded the data of Figure 23, we again removed the shock from the animal's control. The only shocks delivered were the unavoidable ones at the end of each stimulus presentation. Would there be a suppression of the food-reinforced response and, *at the same time*, an increase in the rate of the response that had an avoidance history?

In fact, we found an increase in the frequency of both responses during the preshock stimulus. Figure 24 illustrates the beautiful identity in the nature of the control exercised by the stimulus over each response simultaneously. Both responses displayed a near-zero rate during the periods between stimuli and during the first few minutes of the stimuli themselves. In the minutes immediately prior to the unavoidable shocks, however, both responses began to occur at a relatively high rate, which continued until the shocks actually were delivered.

We had apparently failed to demonstrate the adequacy of our

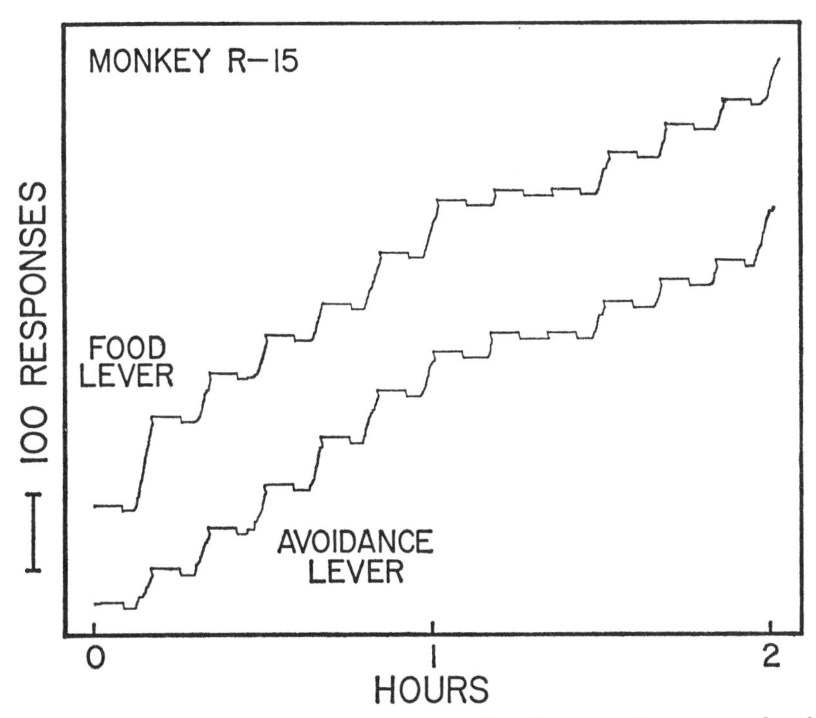

FIGURE 24. Concurrent cumulative records of responding on each of two levers. Each downward displacement of the record indicates the onset of a warning signal. (*From Sidman*, 74.)

original supposition. For here was a food-reinforced response which had not been given an avoidance history nonetheless displaying facilitation, instead of suppression, during the preshock stimulus.

One clue, however, led us to consider the possibility that our attempted demonstration had failed because of a technical inadequacy rather than an interpretive one. That clue, interestingly enough, was suggested to us by an apparatus breakdown. At one stage of the experiments, an electrical transformer in the shock power supply suddenly failed. Since this prevented any shocks from being delivered to the monkey, responding on the avoidance lever gradually declined in frequency. Much to our surprise, there was a corresponding decline in the frequency of the food-reinforced lever-pressing response. The changes in the two responses were almost perfectly synchronized.

Now why should the food-reinforced response extinguish, along with the avoidance behavior, when the shocks failed to occur? The experiment had been set up with the intention of generating two *independent* responses, one with, and one without, an avoidance history. Was the plan actually successful? If it were not, then the baseline was not adequate for the purpose at hand and the experiment would have to be classified as exploratory, at least with respect to the problem it was designed to investigate.

Our task, then, became one of determining whether we had performed a definitive experiment, or whether it was, in fact, only a pilot study. Was there something more than an avoidance history involved in the increased response rate during the preshock stimulus? Or was there some factor we had not taken into account in our experiment with two concurrent responses?

In experimental terms, the question was posed as follows: Was the food-reinforced response actually independent of the avoidance contingency? Or was it somehow being maintained, at least in part, by reinforcement from shock avoidance? It became necessary to perform another experiment to determine whether this possibility was, indeed, true. Meanwhile, we had to hold in abeyance our decision concerning the pilot status of the original two-response experiment.

The new manipulations were simple, and did not involve the stimulus and unavoidable shock combination. We simply recovered the condition in which one response was maintained by food reinforcement and the other, concurrently, by shock avoidance. Then we attempted to extinguish the food-reinforced response by disconnecting the food-delivery mechanism. The attempt was unsuccessful. The response with a food reinforcement history persisted as long as the avoidance contingency was in effect for the other response. It was not possible to demonstrate independence between the two responses. Our original two-response experiment had not, therefore, established an appropriate baseline to test the relevance of the behavioral history as a factor in determining the effects of the preshock stimulus. Although we had explicitly given an avoidance history only to one response, our procedure had, in some unknown manner, also given the food-reinforced response an avoidance component. The experiment was unequivocally a pilot study.

There are two lessons to be learned here. One of them is that the pilot status of an experiment may not be immediately obvious. Additional experimentation may be required before an adequate evaluation can be made. The second lesson is the one with which this discussion began, and derives its importance from the course taken by our experimental program after nonindependence of the two responses had been demonstrated. The nonindependence itself seemed to be a phenomenon worth following up in its own right. Experimental attention was therefore diverted from the Estes-Skinner paradigm to an investigation of the factors involved in the linkage of the two responses. A series of experiments was performed in which the two responses were conditioned and separately extinguished, or were both extinguished and separately reconditioned. A chain-pulling response was then substituted for the food-reinforced lever-pressing response. New measures were employed which took account of the sequences in which the two responses occurred. How often was a chain pull followed by a lever press, and how often by another chain pull, etc.? Other food-reinforcement schedules than variable interval were employed to maintain the chain-pulling response.

One consequence of this new program was to shed increased light upon the factors responsible for nonindependence of concurrently maintained behavior. With respect to this program, the initial two-response experiment could in no sense be considered a pilot study. Although it had not been designed to study response linkage, it turned out to be appropriate to this problem.

But, more important to our present purpose, the new research program provided the key to the solution of our original problem. In the course of studying response interdependence, we discovered a set of conditions through which we could maintain relatively independent concurrent avoidance and food-reinforced responses. Let me complete the picture simply by describing the resulting experiment, without going through all of the developments that led to it. Lever pressing, as in the initial experiment, was the response with an avoidance history. The other response, chain pulling, was reinforced according to a fixed ratio schedule of 15:1. Fifteen chain pulls were required for each reinforcement. Then the sequence of stimulus and unavoidable shock was reintroduced. The results may be seen in Figure 25. Now, in the presence of the stimulus, we see facilitation of the avoidance response and suppression of the food-reinforced chain-pulling response.

Our investigations of nonindependence had yielded a technique (whose critical aspect was the fixed-ratio reinforcement schedule) for increasing the independence of two concurrently maintained responses. Application of this technique made it possible to generate a baseline appropriate to the original problem. Experimental control over one of the critical factors responsible for behavior during the

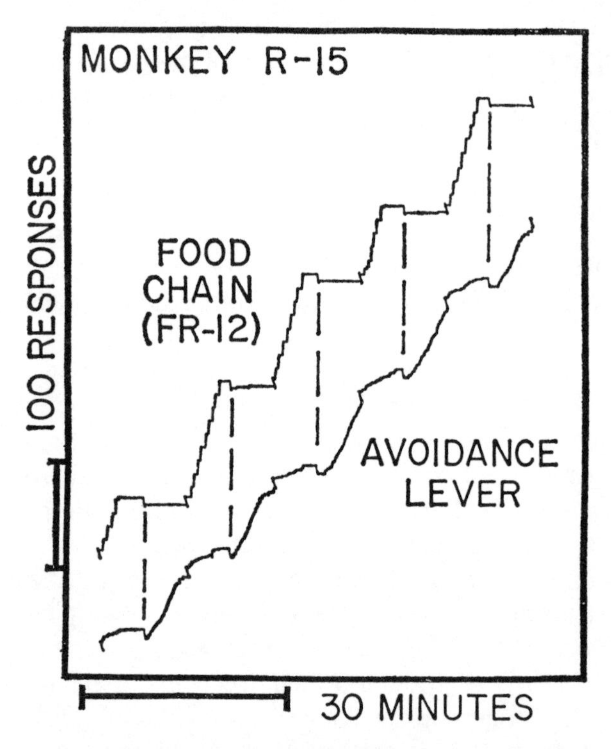

Figure 25. Concurrent cumulative records of responding on the chain and on the lever. The portions of the records displaced downward denote periods during which the warning stimulus was on. The broken lines connect temporally corresponding points (stimulus onset) on each curve. (*From Sidman*, 74.)

preshock stimulus was achieved. With respect to its original purpose, therefore, the first experiment in the series was a negative pilot study. Its technical inadequacy prevented us from drawing any valid conclusion about the factors that lead to suppression or facilitation of behavior during the preshock stimulus. With respect to the problem of response independence, however, the first experiment made a positive contribution. And when the positive finding was followed up for its own sake, a means was discovered for rectifying the original technical defect, thereby transforming the negative pilot study into a definitive experiment.

The pilot study, then, is not a necessary first step in experimental design. It is an unplanned consequence of experimentation that is carried out without sufficient knowledge of the important variables. Pilot experiments occur as frequently as they do because there are so many poorly understood factors involved, singly and in combination, in most behavioral research. But it is also because of our relative state of ignorance that pilot studies may often be turned to good use. The experimenter who is willing to follow his data and to accept the challenge of new variables as they arise can often use his pilot studies to advantage. But he will only be able to do this if every experiment is carried out under conditions which would make it definitive if no unexpected problem arose. A deliberate pilot experiment, in which the experimenter purposely fails to maintain the most rigorous conditions, can never rise above itself.

Chapter 8

Steady States

A DECISION TO STUDY BEHAVIOR in the stable state rather than in transition states, or vice versa, can greatly influence the design of a particular experiment. We may, for the moment, define a stable, or steady, state as one in which the behavior in question does not change its characteristics over a period of time. Behavior passes through a transition state in the process of change from one steady state to another. The two are thus not completely separate. In order to identify the beginning and end of a transition state, one must know something about the properties of the boundary stable states.

Two major types of experimental interest in steady-state behavior have developed. One of these may be termed "descriptive" and the other "manipulative." In the purely descriptive study, a set of experimental conditions is maintained over an extended period of time, providing an account of both stable and transitory aspects of the resulting behavior. This form of research is fundamental to the establishment of behavioral control techniques and of baselines from which to measure behavioral changes. The design of such purely descriptive steady-state experiments contrasts sharply with the traditional research plan in psychology.

Descriptive studies of steady-state behavior are set up according to a simple design. A fixed procedure is set into the automatic control apparatus, the subject is placed in his experimental environment, and a switch is thrown to start the experiment. From that point on, until the time comes to evaluate the data, the investigator does nothing but observe. He focuses his attention on the recording instruments and the subjects. He may add new recording devices as the experiment proceeds, in order to get a more complete description of the behavioral process he has generated, but he performs no new manipulation of the experimental conditions. Only in his original selection of the variables to be wired into the control apparatus does the investigator exercise his creative ingenuity, his knowledge of behavioral subtleties, and his manipulative skill. Once the procedure has begun, all the subtleties and manipulations appear in the behavior of the subject, not of the experimenter.

The data yielded by such an experiment do not relate an aspect of behavior to several values of a manipulated independent variable. Rather, the resulting curves show some aspect of behavior as a function of time in the experimental situation. It is the characteristics of behavior in time, under a constant set of maintaining conditions, which are of major interest. From experiments of this sort we have learned, for example, the major long-term properties of behavior as it is maintained by various reinforcement schedules. The experimenter sets up the desired schedule on the programing apparatus and does not alter it until he is satisfied that he can give a reliable description of the behavior the schedule generates.

An interesting example, out of many possible ones that could be selected, is the *mixed fixed-interval and fixed-ratio* schedule of reinforcement (34, pp. 620-629). Following each reinforcement on this procedure, the apparatus programs either a fixed-ratio or a fixed-interval schedule, in a mixed order. No stimulus is provided to inform the subject which of the two schedules is in effect at any time. Thus, the subject must either emit a fixed number of responses or allow a fixed period of time to elapse before the next reinforcement will become available, with no external indication as to which of these alternatives is currently appropriate. After many hours of exposure to the mixed schedule, the pigeon consistently produces a record of the sort shown in Figure 26. A high response rate, characteristic of behavior on a fixed-ratio schedule, follows each reinforcement. (Reinforcements are indicated by the oblique markers on the cumulative record.) If the current schedule happens to be fixed ratio, another reinforcement occurs when the required number of responses, 27, has been emitted. If reinforcement is not forthcoming after a number of responses approximating the ratio requirement, the high rate ceases abruptly and a "scallop," characteristic of fixed-interval behavior, appears. The fixed-ratio "count" serves as a behavior-produced stimulus which helps to inform the bird which of the two schedules is currently being programed.

The behavior generated by the mixed schedule is quite complex, but extremely orderly. It results from a precisely specified set of conditions which, when maintained unchanged over a long period of time, eventually produces a consistent behavioral pattern. The data of Figure 26 are a solid contribution to the analysis of behavior.

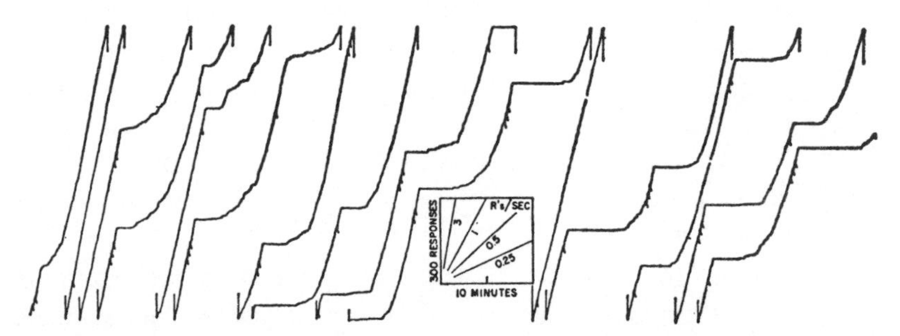

FIGURE 26. Cumulative record illustrating a well-developed performance by a pigeon on a mixed fixed-ratio and fixed-interval schedule of reinforcement. The oblique "pips" indicate reinforcement. (*From Ferster and Skinner*, 34, p. 622.)

But because the experimental design does not call for manipulation of any variables once the schedule has been set up, some would deny the status of an experiment to data such as those of Figure 26. They prefer, rather, to class such data as a demonstration. Figure 26 is, to be sure, a demonstration. It demonstrates a complex temporal pattern of behavior in the individual subject that can be reproduced by any investigator who observes the normal precautions of experimental control. The relation between the behavior and its controlling reinforcement schedule is sufficiently precise and consistent to require its inclusion in any comprehensive description or theory of behavior. It is certainly true that new questions are raised by the data, questions whose answers will require the manipulation of other variables. This is the mark of a more than ordinarily creative experiment. There is no textbook on the design of behavioral experiments that includes this highly productive design technique—the simple description of behavioral properties as they reveal themselves over a long period of time and under a constant set of conditions.

Experimental psychologists are accustomed, in designing their experiments, to securing control observations in each of their experiments. The same controls may actually be run time after time in company with different experimental operations. But the mixed-schedule experiment of Figure 26 does not seem to provide the usual control observations, and this, perhaps, is another reason for the reluctance to classify it as an experiment. For example, one might want to see a comparison with behavior under the fixed-ratio schedule alone, and similarly, under the fixed-interval schedule. Are the brief periods of high response rate following each reinforcement really a consequence of the ratio component in the mixed schedule, or would they also occur if the fixed-interval were programed alone, without any added complications? Or perhaps the desirable comparison would be a multiple schedule (see Chapter 11), which differs from the mixed schedule only in the provision of an exteroceptive stimulus to "tell" the subject which schedule is currently being programed. With an external stimulus to indicate the prevailing schedule, would the bird still display ratio behavior after each reinforcement? If it did, the mixed schedule would not tell us anything new.

Such controls were not omitted by accident. Experiments that serve to reveal and to describe orderliness in behavior under a constant set of controlling conditions do not necessarily stand off by themselves as isolated pieces of work. The data of Figure 26, for example, derive much of their significance from a comparison with other experiments in which fixed-ratio, fixed-interval, and other schedules, singly and in various types of combination, have been similarly investigated. The control observations have been made in independent experiments. But it is possible to use such independently obtained control observations, without the necessity of repeating them in every experiment, only in areas in which a high order of experimental control and replicability has been achieved. In such areas, experiments may be designed so as to utilize information which has been solidly established in previous experiments.

The descriptive investigation of steady-state behavior must precede any manipulative study. Manipulation of new variables will often produce behavioral changes, but in order to describe the changes we must be able to specify the baseline from which they occurred; otherwise we face insoluble problems of control, measurement, and generality.

The control problem is a basic one. I discussed it earlier in connection with variability, but amplification will be relevant now. When an experimental design calls for manipulation of some independent variable, a steady-state baseline prior to the experimental operation tells us whether extraneous variables are likely to play an important role in determining the results of our experiment. If, before beginning the manipulative phase of the experiment, we maintain the behavior in a steady state of known characteristics, we can attribute any consistent deviations from the typical stable performance to unwanted variables that are creeping into the picture. Unusual departures from the typical stable performance will require further refinement of our technique before we introduce the experimental operations. But unless the steady-state behavior has first been descriptively investigated, we will not be able to judge whether the performance is typical or is contaminated by extraneous factors.

As a general application of descriptively investigated steady-state behavior, I may cite the fixed-interval reinforcement schedule as a screening technique for inadequate experimental control. It will be recalled that the fixed-interval schedule makes reinforcement available only after a fixed period of time has elapsed from some well-defined starting point, such as a previous reinforcement. An example of typical fixed-interval behavior was shown in Figure 18 (see pp. 174-175). Reinforcements are followed first by a period of no response and then usually by a gradual rise in the response curve up to the next reinforcement. But the curvature in this cumulative record is typical only in a restricted sense. There are some experimenters working with fixed-interval schedules who have never seen such pronounced curvature in their data. Experience has shown that the degree of curvature in fixed-interval records is a sensitive indicator of the degree of experimental control, particularly with intervals of 10 or 15 minutes, or longer.

Under well-controlled conditions, it is possible to maintain, say, a consistent ten-minute fixed-interval performance in which the subject takes more than five minutes (50 per cent of the interval) to emit the first 25 per cent of the total responses in each interval. This measure has been termed the "quarter-life" (44). If the curve were linear, the first 25 per cent of the responses would be emitted in the first quarter of the interval, and the quarter life, in our example, would be 2.5 minutes. If the curve were negatively accelerated, the quarter-life would be less than 2.5 minutes. With positive curvature, the quarter-life is greater than 2.5 minutes.

Descriptive studies of steady-state fixed-interval behavior have demonstrated that a quarter-life less than 50 per cent of a long fixed interval reflects poor control over certain variables, such as deprivation, type of reinforcement, magnitude of reinforcement, etc. Such variables are common to a great number of experimental procedures, and their adequate control is a matter of general concern. It is an increasingly common practice, therefore, before beginning an experimental program, for experimenters to calibrate the adequacy of their reinforcement variables against a 10- or 15-minute fixed-interval schedule. When they can maintain a ten-minute fixed-interval performance with a quarter-life greater than five minutes, along with a high terminal rate, they can proceed to manipulate variables of major interest, in a context of procedures other than fixed interval, with confidence that their reinforcement variables are under adequate control for most purposes. In general, the greater the deprivation, the larger the magnitude of the reinforcement, and the more adequate a food reinforcement is as a maintaining diet, the more likely the experimenter is to achieve maximal control.

Steady-state behavior also provides an indication of the rigor of experimental control in more restricted situations. In the preceding example, a stable state of fixed-interval behavior was employed to check the adequacy of control over variables that are common to a great many different procedures. If the proposed experiment were to be one that involved the manipulation of variables specific to the context of fixed-interval behavior, the demonstration of control over the fixed-interval curvature would be even more directly relevant. Suppose, for example, we wish to investigate the effects of a drug upon behavior that is maintained by a fixed-interval reinforcement schedule. If we do not first establish a baseline in which the degree of curvature assures us of rigorous control, our drug effects are likely to prove embarrassingly variable. The poor workman will attribute the variability to inherent factors in the drug or in the behavior, when the true fault lies in his own disregard of fundamental descriptive information.

The same is true of other types of procedure than fixed interval. Without an adequate prior descriptive account of avoidance behavior, for example, an experimenter may manipulate variables in steady-state avoidance experiments indefinitely, but he will never know whether his data are typical or whether they result from a combination of factors that are simply irrelevant to the main issues.

A steady-state baseline, obtained before instituting any experimental manipulations, also makes possible a relatively refined type of measurement of behavioral changes. It permits the effects of the manipulated variables to be evaluated with reference to the individual's own behavior. The classical psychological experiment uses, as its measure of behavioral change, the difference between a group that has been exposed to the experimental variable and a control group that has not been so exposed. One immediate virtue of the stable state as a substitute for the control group is the elimination of intersubject variability. This enormously increases the sensitivity of the behavioral measurements. Variables that might be dismissed as having little or no effect, when group comparisons are made, may prove to be extremely powerful when evaluated against a stable individual baseline. Intersubject variability is not a feature of behavioral processes in the individual organism, and when such variability is included in the measurement of presumed individual processes, the resolving power of the measures is inevitably sacrificed.

The more rigorous the experimental control, and the more precise and sensitive the measurement technique, the greater will be the generality possessed by the experimental findings. Insofar as steady-state behavioral baselines can contribute, in these ways, to generality, they should be built into an experimental design wherever possible. The remainder of this chapter will include a number of examples of the manipulation of steady states in behavioral investigations: these should dramatize the utility of such experimental designs.

REVERSIBILITY

If we manipulate a subject's behavior from one stable state to another, it is important to know whether we produce any irreversible changes that make it impossible to recover an earlier state of the behavior. Suppose, for example, we wish to investigate lever-pressing behavior on a variable-interval reinforcement schedule as it is affected by a number of doses of a certain drug. We want to obtain a "dose-response" curve. Our first step might be to expose the subject to the variable-interval schedule, without the drug, until a stable response rate is attained. At that point we would administer the first dose of the drug, which we call Dose 1. Let us suppose that the response rate increases following the administration of Dose 1.

We now have two points on our dose-response curve. We know the response rate with no drug and with Dose 1. A problem now arises with respect to Dose 2. Has the initial drug administration altered the response rate in such a way as to make it impossible to recover the original variable-interval baseline performance? If this were the case, we could not legitimately add the third point to our curve, for the response to the second dose of the drug would reflect, in addition, the influence of the first dose. The third, and possibly the succeeding, values on the curve would not represent the same process as the second. It is necessary, therefore, to determine whether the original response rate can be recovered after each drug administration. Additional doses should not be given until the original rate has been reproduced within some tolerable range of variability. The experimental design will then involve alternating determinations of drug effects and recovery of the steady-state behavior. The same design is, of course, applicable to other variables than drugs.

There are additional methods for evaluating reversibility, but before describing these, it should be pointed out that irreversibility does not necessarily negate data that arise from the manipulation of steady states in the individual organism. Functional relations obtained in the face of irreversibility can still provide useful information, although they will also require a certain amount of additional qualification. The most satisfactory type of qualification will take the form of an explanation of the nonreversibility.

In one experiment, for example, Boren studied the rate of responding under a fixed-ratio reinforcement schedule as a function of the size of the required ratio (11). He found that as he increased the ratio of responses per reinforcement, in an ascending series, the response rate increased in an orderly fashion up to a limiting value. After the maximal rate had been reached, Boren then reduced the ratio. He found, with some of his subjects, that he could not quantitatively reproduce the function he had obtained in the original ascending series. Here was a clear case of partial irreversibility (see Figure 28).

Both Boren and other experimenters, however, had made observations corollary to the response rate in experiments that involved high fixed ratios. They noted that as the ratio was increased, the topography of the animal's response changed markedly. A rat, for example, might stand on the floor of the chamber and press the lever with its forepaws when the reinforcement schedule is a low fixed ratio. At a higher ratio, the animal might lean against the wall of the chamber, with its forepaws at the height of the lever, thus eliminating the necessity of rising up to the lever and supporting its full weight on its hind legs. When the ratio is increased still further, the rat may grasp the lever with its teeth and vibrate it at a near maximal rate. Then, when the ratio is again reduced, some of these later forms of behavior persist, and the original low rates are not recovered.

In the light of these auxiliary observations, the finding that response rate increases with progressively higher values of a fixed-ratio schedule is not invalidated by nonreversibility. What is required, however, is a concomitant description of other aspects of the behavior, in addition to its rate of occurrence. The additional description helps to explain the rate increase and at the same time reveals the source of the irreversibility.

The student may wonder whether the situation could not have been rectified simply by mixing the order in which the ratios were originally programed, instead of using an ascending series. A little experience, however, would soon demonstrate that this design will not avoid the problem. For one thing, too large a jump in the size of the ratio would cause the behavior to disappear, rather than to increase in rate. High ratios must be approached gradually if the behavior is to be maintained. Secondly, even if the jumps were not too large, the topography of the behavior would still change when the ratio was increased. Upon programing a subsequent smaller fixed ratio, the effects of the change in topography would be reflected in the response rate. Irreversibility, therefore, would still be encountered. In addition, the rate data would probably appear chaotic, since the effects of topographical changes would be distributed unequally throughout the whole function relating ratio size and rate. The curve would be an almost unevaluable mixture of Boren's ascending and descending functions. Increasing the ratio gradually was, then, the only method of bringing out the orderly relation that Boren found.

Do these restrictions upon the interpretation of the experimental findings lower their generality? The relation Boren found between response rate and ratio size can be observed only when the ratio is gradually increased. Mixing the order in which the ratio is changed will not yield the relation, nor will increasing the ratio in larger steps. Decreasing the ratio from a high value will not reproduce the function. In the light of these qualifications, does the function possess any generality, or is it trivial?

The answer to this question goes in favor of generality. As we identify more precisely the conditions under which a phenomenon will occur, we automatically increase its generality. No correlation between two variables exists, as it were, in a vacuum, unaffected by other conditions. As long as other contributory factors remain unknown, we are unable to state with any assurance the conditions under which the relation will hold true. Ignorance of which variables are relevant, and which irrelevant, makes generality specious. We are likely to ascribe a general importance to the finding which is not justified by fact, and its reproducibility will be greatly diminished. Every additional contributory factor that we discover will place greater restriction upon our interpretation of the phenomenon. A given functional relation may be found to stand up only, for example, when a particular reinforcement schedule is employed, when the subject is deprived of food for 24 to 48 hours, when the temperature does not exceed 90 degrees, when the independent variable is manipulated in an ascending order, when the subject has had a history of avoidance conditioning, etc. But when these important restrictions are known, the function can then be reproduced at will. So long as we control the known, important factors, the function will stand up in the face of all other possible variations in the surrounding conditions.

Knowledgeable reproducibility of this sort is the basic defining feature of generality, and should not be confused with simple reliability. A phenomenon may be reproducible, and therefore reliable, in the absence of precise knowledge of its important determining variables. It is possible to keep conditions constant without knowing exactly which ones, out of all of the constant factors, are necessary for the reproducibility of the phenomenon. When the conditions for its reproducibility can be specified, however, generality is added to reliability.

Schoenfeld and Cumming, who encountered a case of irreversibility, or "inelasticity," similar to Boren's, summarized its implications for experimental design very neatly:

> Behavioral functions like the present ones, obtained from single organisms, each serving as its own control and brought to response equilibrium or "steady state" under systematically changing and successive values of an experimental independent variable, are not, of course, invalidated by any such "inelasticity." The phenomenon does impose, however, an added condition upon the interpretation of such functions; further, it carries several implications for the design of behavioral experiments, for example, the desirability in cases like the present of avoiding the randomly ordered use of independent variable values, in favor of such

systematic exploration of the continuum as would not contaminate the primary effect of the variable with any irreversibility. Aside from such considerations, however, any "inelasticity" demonstrable in a behavioral function is as important in its own right as the function itself (66, p. 352).

THE EVALUATION OF REVERSIBILITY. Reversibility can be evaluated in other ways than by direct replication, e.g., by systematic replication. As one case—instead of replicating a function with the same subject, additional subjects may be exposed to the same values of the experimental variable, but in a different order. If the functional relation is the same in all cases, it may safely be concluded that there is no order effect. A case that illustrates both this technique and a more refined variation of it, may be found in an experiment I reported several years ago (70).

The experiment dealt with shock-avoidance behavior, with three rats as subjects, and investigated two major variables. The first of these was the *shock-shock* interval, defined as the time between successive shocks if the animal did not make an avoidance response. As long as no response occurred, shocks were delivered at a rate specified by the shock-shock interval. Whenever the avoidance response (lever pressing) occurred, however, the next shock was postponed. Each avoidance response put off the next due shock for a given period of time. The interval by which each response postponed the shock, *i.e.*, the *response-shock interval,* was the other manipulated variable. Curves relating the rate of avoidance responding to each of the independent variables were obtained.

The general design was as follows: Keeping the shock-shock interval constant for a given animal, the rate of avoidance responding in the steady state was measured for a variety of response-shock intervals. The sequence in which the response-shock intervals were programed was different for each of the three subjects. For example, Subject #1 was exposed to response-shock intervals of 20, 15, 30, 10, 50, 7, 4, 90, and 150 seconds, in that order; Subject #2 went through the series in the following order: 10, 30, 15, 50, 7, 90, 20, 4, 150, and 2.5 seconds. With Subject #3, a third sequence was employed.

After the first series of response-shock intervals was completed a new shock-shock interval was programed, and again a sequence of response-shock intervals was investigated. The order of exposure to the response-shock intervals again varied among the three animals. The sequences were also different from the first three that had been employed. The same procedure was then followed several more times for each animal. All in all, there were 14 replications of the function relating rate of avoidance responding to response-shock interval, each replication accomplished with a different sequence of response-shock intervals.

Not only did the sequence of response-shock intervals vary among the three animals for every value of shock-shock interval but the order of exposure to the several values of shock-shock interval was also different. With Subject #1, for example, the first series of response-shock intervals was accompanied by a shock-shock interval of 10 seconds. Succeeding response-shock sequences were run off with shock-shock values of 30, 5, 2.5, and 15 seconds, in that order. The order of exposure to the shock-shock intervals for Subject #2 was 5, 20, 10, 2.5, 50, and zero seconds. Still another sequence was used with Subject #3.

Each of the 14 functions thus obtained constituted a systematic replication, since the order of exposure to the critical variables was different in every case. A portion of the resulting data may be seen in Figure 27, in which the rate of avoidance responding, in logarithmic form, is plotted against the logarithm of the response-shock interval. The shock-shock values are indicated to the left of each curve. We note that the functions for all animals take the same form, in spite of the fact that both the shock-shock and response-shock intervals were programed in a different sequence in each case. The order of presentation was therefore not critical, and the processes involved are apparently reversible.

The replication of the form of the function for a given animal was systematic rather than direct. Instead of replicating the function under exactly the same conditions, one of the major variables, the shock-shock interval, was changed in value for each replication. Also, the sequence of response-shock intervals was varied in each replication. The repeatability of the functional relation in a single subject, with new sequences of response-shock intervals and new shock-shock intervals, gives us another confirmation of reversibility.

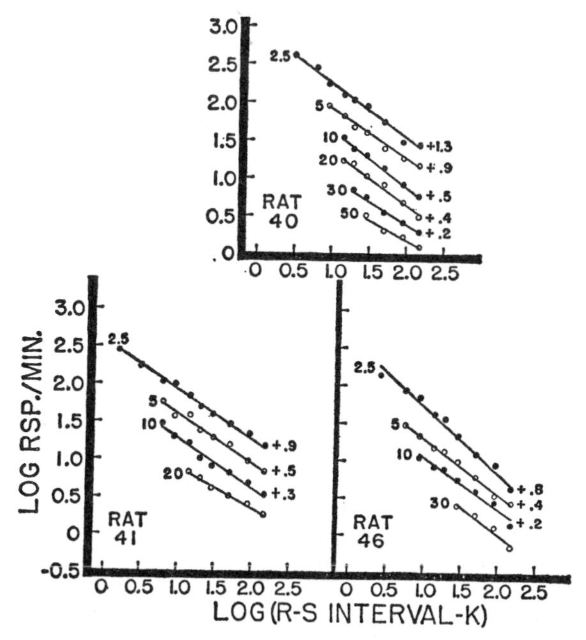

FIGURE 27. Logarithm of response rate plotted against logarithm of response-shock interval for each of three animals. Numbers at the left of each curve identify shock-shock intervals. For ease of comparison, the curves have been displaced upward on the ordinate; the amount of displacement, in log units, is indicated by the numbers at the right. (*From Sidman*, 70.)

The experiment thus illustrates two variants of systematic replication as a method for evaluating reversibility. One method involved the individual subject only, with different sequences of manipulation of one variable (response-shock interval), along with each successive value of the second variable (shock-shock interval). The second method involved the use of additional subjects, with both independent variables being manipulated in different orders. Consistency of the data in the face of these variations indicates that the behavioral processes are truly reversible. In addition to demonstrating reversibility, there is also the dividend, common to all types of systematic replication, of additional data. We were able, for example, to examine the relations between rate of avoidance responding and shock-shock interval for each of several values of response-shock interval. Other more detailed analyses were also possible. Direct replication of the functions would have been a most uneconomical procedure.

Experiments in which steady states are manipulated usually take a relatively long period of time to accomplish. The process of change from one state to another is often prolonged, and the steady state itself must be observed over an extended interval in order to determine that stability has, in fact, been achieved. Nonreversibility may arise, in such long-term experiments, from processes that require an extensive period of time before they can exert any major effect. When such a process is suspected, a very simple check is often possible. An example was involved in the experiment whose data were presented in Figure 3 (see Chapter 3). The points on these curves were obtained in order, from left to right, consecutively. A relatively sudden drop in response rate occurs at some low value of the shock percentage, to which the animals were exposed late in the experiment. The independent variable in this experiment is of such a nature as to make one suspect that the sudden drop may have occurred as the result of a long-term extinction process rather than as a function of any particular value of the independent variable. The implication is that the sudden decline in rate might have occurred at that particular temporal stage of the experiment even if the shock percentage had been maintained at, say, a value of 50 per cent throughout. If that were the case, then the process would turn out to be irreversible.

The possibility was checked simply by returning the subjects to the shock percentage to which they had been exposed just prior to the drop in rate. If the response rate recovered, then a long-term process was ruled out as a determiner of the rate decline. It was not necessary to replicate additional points on the curve when such "single-point" replication was successful.

Reversibility can thus sometimes be evaluated by a simple spot check rather than by a more extensive type of replication. Economy in experimental design may be enhanced if the investigator is alert to this possibility.

When order effects are observed to preclude reversibility, they cannot, as Schoenfeld and Cumming pointed out, be ignored (66). Nor can they be eliminated. Irreversible changes in behavior, induced by prior exposure of the organism to some variable, cannot simply be accepted without further analysis. The order of presentation of variables is not, in itself, a basic variable. Every instance in which the sequence is shown to be critical must be analyzed in terms of the behavioral processes generated by the sequence. These will not be the same in every case. Different values of a fixed ratio, for example, may generate different response topographies; different values of a variable-interval schedule may produce adventitious reinforcement of high rates; some values of response-shock interval are more likely than others to produce efficient timing behavior, etc. These are interesting and important behavioral processes in their own right. Investigation of them will often prove more profitable than continued attention to a function which they make irreversible.

Any preconceived experimental design will then fall by the wayside as order effects suggest new paths to explore. Such a diversion is not necessarily irrelevant to the original design. For the functional relation of initial interest will require, for its complete description, an account of the processes responsible for its inelasticity.

Irreversibility can and should be accounted for in any description or theory of behavior. It cannot, contrary to some prevalent notions of experimental design, be eliminated by the "balancing" of experimental conditions. A prototype balanced design is illustrated in Table 1. In this experiment there are two values of an independent

TABLE 1
An Illustration of Balanced Design

	Phase I	Phase II	Phase III
Subject #1	Condition A	Condition B	Condition A
Subject #2	Condition B	Condition A	Condition B

variable, labeled "Condition A" and "Condition B." Subject #1 is exposed to Condition A in the first phase of the experiment, and to Condition B in the second phase. The reverse order is employed for Subject #2, with Condition B prevailing in Phase I and Condition A in Phase II.

Let us suppose that the behavioral measure in the experiment is latency of response. It is found that for Subject #1, Condition B yields the shorter latency, whereas Subject #2 shows a shorter latency under Condition A. The finding then stands up under replication with other subjects. It is apparent that the latency is a function not simply of the two experimental conditions but also of the order in which the subjects were exposed to the two conditions.

After additional controls demonstrate that the latency does not change merely as a function of time, Phase III is added to the experiment, with each subject being returned to the same condition as in Phase I. It is found that the response latencies for both subjects remain short and do not return to the level observed in Phase I. The phenomenon appears irreversible.

How, then, does the investigator go about solving his original problem, which was to determine the relation between latency and the two experimental conditions, independently of their presentation sequence? The sequence variable has ordinarily been treated as a methodological nuisance, to be circumvented whenever possible. Our hypothetical investigator goes back to his original two-phase experiment, which was designed to take care of just such an eventuality. He has a neat trick up his sleeve. By averaging together the data for both subjects under Condition A, and again under Condition B, he "cancels out" the order effect and completely bypasses the problem of irreversibility. By a simple arithmetical operation, two subjects have become one, and a variable has been eliminated.

The performance resembles that of a magician who makes a rabbit disappear from a hat. Everyone in the audience, except, perhaps, the children, knows that the rabbit is still around, but wonders where it has gone and how the magician got it there. In the present case, the magician has made the numbers that describe the behavior disappear, but we all know that the behavior really did take place, and we wonder where it has gone.

It has not, in fact, gone anywhere. Numbers may be made to disappear by adding and subtracting them from each other. Five apples minus three apples are two apples. The numbers are easily changed by a few strokes of the pen, but some eating has to be done before the apples themselves will vanish. In our illustration, the only operation analogous to eating the apples would be elimination of the order effect by some experimental manipulation. This can only be accomplished by identifying the processes responsible for the irreversible order effect, and by gaining experimental control over such processes. The sequence variable is not eliminated by averaging, for the average contains the effects of both variables.

Suppose the average latency for Condition A turns out to be higher than the average for Condition B. The conclusion would be that, with sequence effects canceled out, Condition A produces longer latencies than does Condition B. This finding could come about if the Condition A latencies in each separate phase of the experiment are higher than the corresponding Condition B latencies. But it could also come about if Condition A produces a much higher latency than B in Phase I, and only a slightly lower latency in Phase II. Or the latencies may be equal in Phase I, with Condition B producing a much greater decline than A in Phase II. Similar averages, then, might result from quantitatively different sequence effects. The generalization about the relative effects of Conditions A and B would not, in actuality, be independent of the sequence. Sequential effects would be present in the numbers, but hidden from view.

Underwood, who discusses the counterbalanced design in some detail, points out that, "Counterbalancing does not eliminate [sequence] effects; counterbalancing only distributes these . . . effects equally over all conditions when the effects are considered for all subjects combined" (91, p. 325). In line with our own discussion, he also recognizes that, "If the experimenter has reason to believe that the effect of going from A to B is quite different from the effect of going from B to A, the method should not be used since it would give a distorted picture of the influence of the experimental conditions as such" (91, p. 326).

We may go even further than this. Unless the intersubject variability has been reduced to negligible proportions, there will inevitably be large individual differences in the effects of the A-to-B and B-to-A sequences. That is to say, not only may the effect of going from A to B differ from the effect of going from B to A, but this difference itself is likely to vary both in direction and in magnitude from one subject to another. To assume that the differences are the effects of uncontrolled variability, and will therefore average out, would be gratuitous and dangerous. With the degree of inter-subject variability customarily tolerated in behavioral experiments, the most reasonable assumption is that the A-to-B and B-to-A sequences *do* produce different effects from one subject to another, and that the counterbalanced design should be distrusted.

There is, in fact, no experimental design that can nullify true irreversibility. It cannot be done by statistical control, nor can it be done by experimental control. If a change from one value of an experimental variable to another generates a behavioral process which then prevents recovery of the original behavioral state, that process must be included in our descriptions. If this means that a simple functional relation will not serve to encompass the results of our experiment, then so be it. Behavior, or any other subject matter, cannot be forced into a simple descriptive scheme just because we, as scientists, have found that simple laws are preferable to complex ones. A descriptive scheme can be no simpler than the subject matter it encompasses. The investigator, therefore, must be prepared to deal with irreversibility when he encounters it.

There are, currently, almost no data available which describe irreversible behavioral processes. The experimental designs which would be required for such description seem tedious, and this, perhaps, accounts for the void. But an experimental design is tedious only when the potential data are of little interest to the investigator. Let us, therefore, outline some experimental designs, both to bring them to the student's attention and to see just how interesting the potential data might be.

Suppose we select, as our first case, the experiment by Boren, to which I have already referred. This experiment, it will be recalled, dealt with behavior which was maintained by a fixed-ratio reinforcement schedule. Boren manipulated the size of the fixed ratio, *i.e.*, the number of responses required for reinforcement, and measured response rate as a function of ratio size. He started with a low ratio and gradually shifted the ratio upward, in an ascending series. The solid curve of Figure 28 shows one animal's level of steady-state responding at each value of the fixed ratio.

The next phase of Boren's design was actually the first step toward a description of irreversibility. He attempted to replicate the function, in the same animal, by starting with the highest ratio and

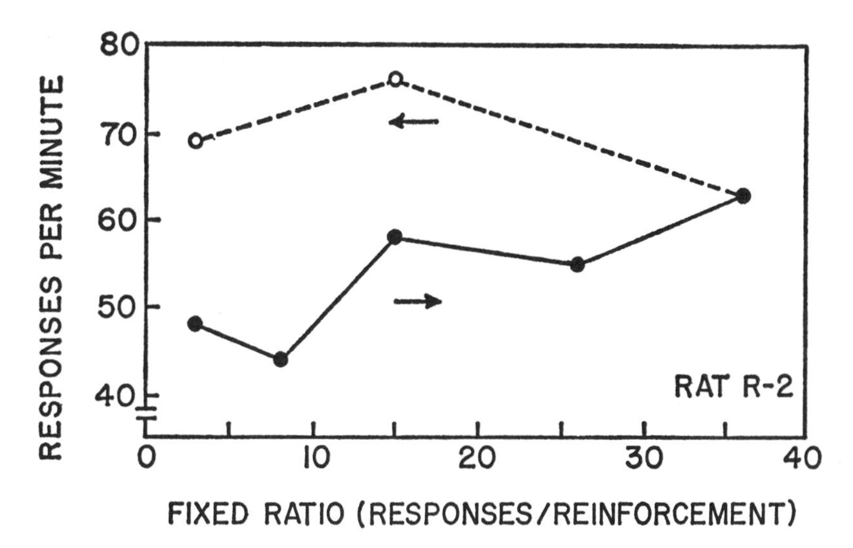

FIGURE 28. Curve relating an animal's response rate to the number of responses required per reinforcement. The points on the solid curve were obtained in order of ascending ratio size; the points on the dashed curve in order of decreasing ratio size. (*Curves drawn from data of Boren, 11.*)

working back down to the lowest. The results appear in the dashed curve. Replication was not achieved.

The investigation stopped at this point, for the problem of irreversibility was not Boren's concern at the time. A more complete description of the function's irreversibility would have required several additional stages. The animals might have been exposed a second time to the ascending series of ratio sizes, and again to the descending series. Perhaps several more repetitions would be necessary.

This might seem a tedious and uninspiring set of manipulations. But new and interesting data do not have to come only from creatively different experimental designs. In the present case, the resulting data would be the first of their kind. We would have a picture of the process of irreversibility itself, as it developed and perhaps as it waned. What would this picture be like? The variety of possibilities, and the uncertainty of prediction, provide these potential data with much of their fascination.

For example, would the second ascending series replicate the first descending one? Or would it, too, reveal irreversibility? Would we get a family of curves, each successive one rising higher on the ordinate, until the function finally became stable? Would all the curves pivot about the same maximal rate, or would the maximal rate itself change systematically? Sooner or later the factors which cause the irreversibility would, themselves, reach an end point, and from there on, subsequent replications would demonstrate reversibility. Where would that point be? Would the stable function still be an increasing one, or would it take some other form?

Data such as these would open up an entirely new area of behavioral research. The experimental design is a simple one, applicable to a wide variety of situations and procedures. The data, however, would be complex. But they would be clean data, evaluable in the same fashion as any others that I have described. Irreversibility would be shown up for what it is, a behavioral phenomenon worthy and capable of study, not something to be hidden in a closet.

A second experimental design for evaluating irreversibility can be illustrated in the context of some data provided by Findley (35). He was actually using another approach to the problem we have just been discussing, that of response rate as a function of ratio size. (I will have more to say about this approach in Chapter 11.) Findley attempted to circumvent the irreversibility problem encountered by Boren. He did this by correlating each ratio size with a different stimulus, and programing the whole series of ratio sizes during each single experimental period. The procedure went as follows:

With monkey as subject, Findley programed five different ratio sizes, the lowest calling for 33 responses per reinforcement. The experimental period was divided into two-hour cycles, with the first 30 minutes of each cycle further subdivided into six-minute periods. The animal could obtain a single reinforcement during each six-minute period. During the first six-minute period, stimulus #1 was on, and a single reinforcement was delivered when the animal emitted 33 responses. During the next six minutes, in the presence of stimulus #2, 66 responses were required to produce the reinforcement. In each successive six-minute period the stimulus changed, and the number of responses required to produce the reinforcement was doubled. Following the fifth period, all stimulus lights went off for the remainder of the two-hour cycle, and then a new cycle began again with stimulus #1.

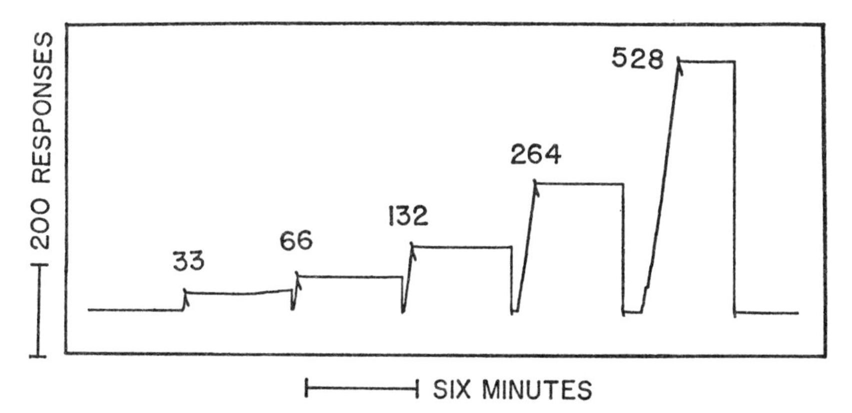

FIGURE 29. Record of a monkey's lever-pressing behavior on a fixed-ratio reinforcement schedule in which the ratio requirement doubled after each reinforcement. (*Data generously supplied by Findley,* 35.)

A record of the steady-state behavior resulting from this procedure may be seen in Figure 29. The figure begins with a run of 33 responses, which produces a reinforcement. There are only a few additional responses until Stimulus #2 appears, where the pen resets to the baseline. Then there is a run of 66 responses before the next reinforcement. The record continues in this way until the final run of 528 responses. The remainder of the two-hour cycle is not shown.

Using this technique, Findley replicated the shape of Boren's original function. Response rate increased along with ratio size. The reversibility problem, however, is not the same here as it was in Boren's experiment. There is no doubt that the function is recoverable, for it is, in fact, recovered several times within each experimental session. By the time a stable state is achieved, the subject will have experienced each ratio size a great number of times. Findley was, essentially, working at the stage Boren would have reached if he had continued to repeat his ascending series until the processes which generated irreversibility had reached their limit.

The problem in Findley's case may be expressed as follows: Would he obtain the same function if he programed the largest ratio during the first six-minute period, and then decreased the ratio by one half during the succeeding periods? Would the original function be recoverable if the ratios were programed in order of decreasing, rather than increasing, size?

At present the answer to this question is unknown. But let us assume, for the purpose of illustration, that the function would not be replicable if the ratios were presented in reverse order. According to classical conceptions of experimental design in psychology, Findley's data would be considered to have only limited generality. The commonly accepted solution would be to adopt a different experimental design, one in which the sequence of ratios would vary from cycle to cycle. In such a design, it would be argued, there would be no sequence effects, and the data would possess the greatest possible generality.

But if, indeed, order effects were present, mixing the sequence from cycle to cycle would be a most undesirable procedure. The effects of various sequences would still be present in the data, but they would be hopelessly confounded with each other, and, thus, unevaluable.

Only the deliberate and systematic manipulation of the sequences will provide an adequate solution to the problem. The experimental design which is called for in this case requires that the behavior be brought to a steady state under a number of possible presentation sequences of the ratio sizes. Comparisons should be made, for example, among the functions obtained with ascending sequences, with descending sequences, with sequences in which the ratio size first increases and then decreases, etc. In this way, a precise description of the sequence effects will become available. The factors that prevent reversibility can be accounted for and included among the determiners of the function which relates response rate to ratio size.

Again we see that the proper experimental design in a case that involves irreversibility is not necessarily the simplest one. Perhaps when we know more about irreversibility in general, simple experimental designs will become available. Until then, however, there is no short cut.

Chapter 9

Steady States (Continued)

THE STABILITY CRITERION

In experiments involving the manipulation of steady states, how does the experimenter decide whether the behavior in question has stabilized? How is a steady state to be identified? Let me state first that, regardless of the stability criterion one may employ, there is no assuredly final answer. The utility of data will depend not on whether ultimate stability has been achieved, but rather on the reliability and validity of the criterion. That is to say, does the criterion select a reproducible and generalizable state of behavior? If it does, experimental manipulation of steady states, as defined by the criterion, will yield data that are orderly and generalizable to other situations. If the steady-state criterion is inadequate, failures to reproduce and to replicate systematically the experimental findings will reveal this fact.

How does one select a steady-state criterion? There is, again, no rule to follow, for the criterion will depend upon the phenomenon being investigated and upon the level of experimental control that can be maintained. Here, descriptive long-term studies of steady-state behavior are extremely useful. By following behavior over an extended period of time, with no change in the experimental conditions, it is possible to make an estimate of the degree of stability that can eventually be maintained; a criterion can then be selected on the basis of these observations.

I have already described, in some detail, an experiment in which the rate of avoidance responding was manipulated from one stable state to another by means of experimental variations in shock-shock and response-shock intervals (Chapter 8, pp. 245-248). The criterion of stability was derived from prior descriptive studies of avoidance behavior under fixed, unchanging values of the two temporal parameters. As a result of these long-term descriptive studies, it seemed possible to make a generalization about the stable state. When the rate of responding settled down to a particular level of stability, there was unlikely to be any further systematic change. This level was selected as the stability criterion. A particular combination of shock-shock and response-shock intervals was maintained until the response rate met the criterion. The criterion of stability required, before changing from one shock schedule to another, was a difference in rate not greater than 0.1 responses per minute between any two out of three consecutive experimental periods.

That the criterion in this particular experimental situation was adequate could be confirmed by the orderliness of the resulting data. There were a few marked deviations in the obtained functions, however, and it is likely that these occurred because the stability criterion was not stringent enough. A small amount of variability of this sort can be tolerated if the remaining data are sufficiently extensive and consistent to make it clear that the deviant points do not reflect a major, unevaluated variable.

Further extensive investigations of avoidance behavior gave rise to a more serious objection to the particular stability criterion employed here. It became clear that, under some conditions, the criterion did not represent a valid stable state. For example, when monkeys, instead of rats, are used as subjects, lengthening the response-shock interval produces only a very slow and long-delayed decline in the rate of avoidance responding. The criterion of a difference no greater than 0.1 response per minute in two out of three consecutive sessions is met many times over in the slow process of change from the high to the low response rate. Each time the criterion is met, it specifies a progressively lower response rate.

The original findings, with rats as subjects, are still generalizable to the monkey, but the stability criterion must be modified in experiments with monkeys. This does not detract from the generality of the data. If the same criterion were to be used for both species, it would not specify equivalent states of behavior in each animal. The ability of the criterion to select a reproducible state is its important defining feature.

If the steady-state criterion yields orderly and replicable functional relations, it may be accepted as adequate. It need not, in fact, represent the ultimate stable state of the behavior in question. It is possible that more extended exposure of the subject to a set of experimental conditions will produce further behavioral modification beyond the level that is arbitrarily selected as the stable state. But if the state selected by the criterion is one through which the behavior must inevitably pass on its way to the final steady state, then the data will be orderly and meaningful.

Since it is necessary, in steady-state experiments, to adopt some stability criterion, and since experiments rarely duplicate each other exactly in all respects, there must be a considerable amount of experience and intuition involved in the selection of an appropriate criterion. An inadequate selection may well transform an experiment into a pilot study. The investigator's experience will be a compound of his own observations of stability in related experiments, the results of long-term descriptive studies, the amount of variability to which he is accustomed in his own laboratory, his systematic knowledge of the area in which he is working, and the reported experience of other investigators. This last source of information must be carefully evaluated. Stability criteria will be transferable from one laboratory to another only if the two are matched with respect to the general level of experimental control which they have achieved. For example, the stability criterion adopted by one laboratory in its program of research into certain types of reinforcement schedules has been defined as follows:

> The first seven days on any schedule are not considered in computing stability. For the next six days the mean of the first three days of the six is compared with that of the last three days; if the difference between these means is less than 5 per cent of the six days' mean, the bird is considered to have stabilized and is shifted to the next schedule. If the difference between submeans is greater than 5 per cent of the grand mean, another experimental day is added and similar calculations are made for that day and the five immediately preceding it. Such extensions of the experiment and calculations of stability are continued daily until the bird reaches the aforementioned 5 per cent criterion (67, p. 567).

This criterion is a relatively stringent one, though its authors are not convinced of its general validity. The point I emphasize is that only those experimenters whose laboratories are characterized by meticulous attention to details of experimental control will be able to employ the same stability criterion. The variability which they observe will otherwise be so great as to cause them to spend a lifetime, if they are that stubborn, on the same uncompleted experiment. Even if the criterion were occasionally met by chance, in the course of uncontrolled variability, the data would be chaotic. As a result, either the experiment will be abandoned (with an attendant loss of time and effort), or the data will be invalid (with an attendant systematic confusion).

The two stability criteria described thus far have been, in a naive way, statistical in nature. This is an inevitable characteristic of such criteria, for they must involve comparisons among several sets of observations. High-powered statistical techniques, however, are not required and may even be inappropriate. The degree of variability to be tolerated in the definition of a steady state will be determined by the consistency of the functional relations so obtained and by the degree of experimental control that can be achieved. Statistical theory is no help in these matters.

This is a case, furthermore, in which experimental and statistical significance not only are different but may even be in opposition. A stable state that is defined by statistically insignificant differences in performance over a period of time may be completely useless experimentally if a high level of variability contributes to the statistical evaluation. A statistical *description* of the stable state may be appropriate, but statistical *evaluation* of stability should be replaced by experimental evaluation. If the experimenter's experience, however gathered, in designing and carrying out steady-state experiments is not enough to permit him to select a useful stability criterion, no amount of statistical manipulation will lift him out of his hole.

Accumulated experience and good experimental judgment enter into the selection of stability criteria in yet another way. The particular criterion chosen may depend in part on the economics of the laboratory setup. For example, the criterion described above, which demands the daily calculation and comparison of means and submeans, perhaps for several subjects, involves considerable labor. An alternative method would be to expose all subjects to each value of the independent variable for the same length of time and to define the final set of observations as the stable state.

For example, each subject might be exposed to a given schedule for 100 hours, with the average performance during the final 30 hours being accepted as the steady state. Such a procedure, to be maximally effective, will depend upon prior observations of the range of time periods within which a population of subjects is likely to achieve stability. One must select an exposure period long enough to encompass the slowest case. The stability criterion in this instance must also select the final steady state, and not an intermediate one; otherwise, individual subjects may be halted at different stages in their approach to ultimate stability.

Whereas the first type of criterion involves computational labor, normally performed by laboratory workers, a criterion based upon a fixed period of time is likely to lengthen the duration of an experiment and tie up the control and programing equipment. A choice between the two methods of defining stability will depend in part upon the relative availability of personnel-hours and apparatus-hours. The laboratory with a small personnel investment and a large automatic equipment investment is likely to develop fixed time-interval criteria. The reverse case is likely to produce stability criteria that involve more or less complex human computation.

The three stability criteria described thus far have all included one or more restrictions designed to eliminate from the measures the confounding effects of initial transition states. In two of the cases, evaluation of the stable state does not even begin until a predetermined number of experimental hours have elapsed after introduction of a new value of the independent variable. A certain amount of data is, therefore, arbitrarily ignored. This "precriterion" phase serves an important function. A transition from one behavioral state to another may take place slowly, particularly if the change in the experimental condition is a slight one. In such a circumstance, a stability criterion might be met before the transition has even begun, and the conclusion mistakenly drawn that two successive values of the independent variable produce identical states of behavior. An attempt is usually made, therefore, to adopt a precriterion phase of sufficient duration to ensure that the behavioral change, if one is going to occur, will at least have begun before the criterion data are examined.

The rapidity of a transition from one state to another may be a function of the magnitude of the difference between the two values of the experimental variable. Or it may even be a function of the direction of the change. For example, a change in the response-shock interval from 20 to 15 seconds may be followed only slowly by the appropriate increase in response rate. A change from 30 to 15 seconds, however, may produce a rapid transition. Furthermore, while a change from 30 to 15 seconds, which is likely to produce an almost immediate increase in shock frequency, will probably result in a rapid behavioral adjustment, a change in response-shock interval in the other direction, say, from 30 to 60 seconds, is likely to result in a more gradual behavioral adaptation. The precriterion phase must be of sufficiently long duration to encompass all such eventualities. Otherwise the criterion may be met before the transition has even begun, and attempts to recover a given behavioral state from different baselines will be frustrated.

A similar precaution of a more local nature must often be taken in evaluating a steady state. Not only are there long-term transition effects from one behavioral state to another, but there also appear, in many cases, transition stages at the beginning of each experimental session. It is often observed, for example, that the response rate at the start of a session differs from the rate at the end of the session, and from the rate at the end of the preceding session. White rats, on an avoidance procedure, often take a number of closely spaced shocks at the start of a session before they settle into an efficient pattern of responding. Monkeys, on a fixed-interval reinforcement schedule, may display little curvature in their cumulative response record during the initial intervals of the session. Such local transition states are often given the name "warm-up effect."

We have little information of an experimental nature concerning warm-up effects. In evaluating steady states, such effects are usually either absorbed into the criterion data or explicitly excluded from the stability criterion. For example, the criterion data may be taken from only the final portion of each experimental session.

A major problem is raised by the exclusion of data, either from the precriterion phase or from the warm-up. Transition states are of potential interest as important behavioral phenomena in their own right. It is likely also that the transition state, whether long term or local, contains some of the keys to an understanding of the subsequent steady state. Variability in the warm-up phases may account for some of the variability in the terminal stages of the experimental sessions. The duration of the warm-up period in an avoidance procedure may well be an important determiner of the final response rate. Spiraling behavioral processes during the precriterion transition phase may determine the final state. Such effects do not invalidate functional relations that describe steady-state behavior, but ignoring them may postpone more complete understanding of the function.

The investigator is thus faced with a dilemma in designing manipulative steady-state experiments. He is forced to adopt a stability criterion, but in doing so he eliminates from consideration some possibly important aspects of the behavioral processes in which he is interested. It is important to recognize that the problem involves two requirements. One of these is the description of the steady state, in terms of its functional relation to the independent variable. The other is the search for a systematic account within which the function may take its place in relation to other behavioral processes.

Stability criteria, with all their defects, are necessary for the first task. A different experimental approach may be required for the second, when the systematically related processes involve transition, rather than stable, states. I shall have more to say about this in Chapter 10.

Evidently, there are many possibilities for error in selecting a valid stability criterion. Sometimes an error may not be detected until the experiment has proceeded far enough for the data to make it clear that the criterion is unsatisfactory. The investigation must then be scrapped and redesigned. Even with a generally satisfactory criterion, however, a small number of exceptions may appear, showing up, perhaps, as deviant points in the functional relations. When the deviant points are few in number relative to the total covered by the experiment, it is legitimate to redetermine their values experimentally. The deviations, in addition to being few, must also be of an unsystematic nature; otherwise it would be more reasonable to suppose that they represent a real behavioral process, to be investigated rather than eliminated. The avoidance experiment whose stability criterion was described above yielded a total of 138 experimental points comprising the empirical functions. Of these, five were markedly deviant from the general trend of the data. Since these five points seemed to occur at values of shock-shock and response-shock intervals which had no systematic relation to each other, they were all determined a second time, after which they did, indeed, fall into line with the other data.

An occasional inadequacy in the criterion may show itself before all the data have been obtained, and in such cases a certain elasticity in the experimental design is not only permissible but desirable. It is possible for the subject sometimes to meet a criterion, if his behavior settles within the tolerable limits of variability, but still to show a continuing, uncompleted trend of change in his behavior. Such cases are most easily detectable, and most likely to occur, when a fixed time period defines the stability criterion. One hundred hours, for example, may be sufficient for the attainment of a predefined stable state in most instances in a given experiment, but occasionally the behavior may be observed to be still changing systematically at the end of this period. It is unwise, in such a case, to stick blindly to the criterion. The experimental conditions should be maintained, without any change, for an additional number of hours. The purpose of the experiment is, after all, to investigate steady-state behavior, and if a choice has to be made between stability and an occasionally inadequate criterion, the criterion must be modified.

There is, of course, considerable risk entailed in *ad hoc* modifications of the stability criterion. An important reason for adhering to a predetermined criterion is to prevent the arbitrary and unconscious selection of only those data that the experimenter wants to see. Without a specified criterion the experimenter may decide, on insufficient grounds, that a steady state has been reached when the behavior conforms to his expectations. Therefore, exceptions to the stability criterion must be only occasional in relation to the total amount of data collected. If they become frequent, the safest course is to begin the experiment anew, with a more stringent criterion. The experimenter must not lay himself open to the charge that he halts the transition states at points calculated to give him the data he wants.

Incidentally, the experimenter, in publishing his findings, should note any exceptions he has made to the stability criterion.

VARIABILITY AND THE STABILITY CRITERION. Stability criteria contain within themselves a specification of the amount of variability which an experimenter considers permissible in the definition of a steady state. But an important concern must precede any such specification: If the data are extremely variable, either because of poor experimental technique or because of inadequate understanding of the processes involved, no specification of permissible variability will yield orderly functional relations. The utility of a steady-state criterion is an inverse function of the level of uncontrolled variability. This is simply another way of saying that steady states cannot be investigated experimentally unless steady states can actually be observed. The first task, before any parametric study of steady-state behavior can begin, is to refine the techniques of control till all major fluctuations in the data are removed. Only then will a stability criterion be experimentally meaningful.

Certain types of fluctuations, particularly those of a systematic nature, cannot be eliminated by technical refinement. They may, in fact, become more prominent as the general "noise" level is reduced. I shall have more to say about such cases below. At this point, I should like to take note of systematic changes that may occur in variability itself as a function of the experimental operations. The likelihood of such changes must be considered in selecting a stability criterion. It might, for example, be expected that behavior which occurs at a low rate will be characterized by a low level of absolute variability as compared with behavior that occurs at a high rate. An adjusting stability criterion might then be used. The experimenter can build into the criterion a mechanism to take account of systematic changes in variability.

One of the criteria already described is of this nature. The difference between the average response rates in two successive blocks of three sessions was required to be 5 per cent of the average rate of the whole six days before stability would be accepted. This criterion permits a wider latitude in absolute variability when the response rate is high than when it is low.

If variability itself changes as a function of the experimental operations, an adjusting criterion of some sort should be used. Otherwise, misleading data may result. Suppose, for example, that instead of specifying the permissible variability in percentage terms, we use a criterion based upon the absolute response rate. Let us say that we will accept stability when the range of response rates over six consecutive days does not exceed 0.5 responses per minute. This fixed criterion, independent of systematic changes in variability, would actually impose a more stringent requirement upon states that are characterized by greater absolute variability, even though the relative variability may be quite stable. If, in a given experiment, high response rates do, indeed, show greater variability than low rates, then a fixed stability criterion will take a longer time to be met when high rates prevail. The eventual steady state achieved by high response rates may represent a functionally different stage of behavior than that at which a low rate meets the criterion. The obtained functional relation will not in these circumstances represent a unitary behavioral process.

An adjusting criterion also has its pitfalls, however. It, too, may yield misleading data if the method of adjustment does not correspond to the realities of the behavior. On fixed-ratio reinforcement schedules, for example, low response rates may be characterized by a higher level of absolute variability than are high response rates. If the stability criterion permits greater variability at high rates, a distorted picture of the steady states may result. The criterion in this case will be too severe at the low end of the scale, and too relaxed at the upper end. One way of getting around this problem is to employ a criterion of such severity that even in its loosest application it will still suffice to carry the behavior out to its final steady state.

A second alternative is to precede the main experiment with a series of studies designed to evaluate variability *per se,* and then to devise a stability criterion based upon the results of these studies. For example, instead of expressing the permissible variability as a percentage of the over-all rate during the criterion period, one might select a percentage of some function of the reciprocal of the over-all rate. That criterion would take account of higher variability at low rates.

The third alternative is to have the criterion adjust, not to some predetermined estimate of the variability, but rather (geared empirically as the experiment proceeds) to the observed variability. The permissible difference, for example, between the mean rates of two successive blocks of five sessions might be allowed to vary from one state to another, not as a function of the over-all rate, but rather as a function of the over-all variability. For example, if the variability is high we might accept a difference of 15 per cent between the two means, whereas if the variability is low we might accept only a 3 per cent difference. This method involves no prior assumptions about the relation between variability and the experimental manipulations.

There is one final type of stability criterion that is particularly difficult to specify: the criterion based on simple visual inspection of the data. Such a stability criterion is not generally employed in parametric studies in which quantitative values assumed by the behavioral measures are critically important. Many experiments, however, are directed simply at explorations of relevant variables, with little or no concern as to their exact quantitative effects. Ferster and Skinner, in their book *Schedules of Reinforcement,* have presented the results of a magnificent six-year research program devoted largely to experiments of this sort. Their investigations involved a survey of a number of variables relevant to performance on several reinforcement schedules. Where their concern was with steady-state behavior, stability criteria were based largely on inspection of cumulative records. This practice, arbitrary though it may seem, produced data of wide generality.

One of the basic requirements for the success of "criterion-by-inspection" is that the experimental manipulations produce large behavioral changes. If the changes are of such magnitude as to be easily apparent by visual inspection, then such inspection automatically assumes greater validity as a stability criterion. A more quantitative criterion might show that the behavior in question is still undergoing development, and a more precise evaluation of the independent variable's effect might require a stricter behavioral specification. But the demonstration that a variable is effective does not require the attainment of a stringently defined stable state as long as the demonstrated change is large enough to override the baseline "noise."

A good example is provided by Ferster and Skinner's demonstration of the effectiveness of a "time-out" in developing and maintaining curvature in the cumulative record of performance on long fixed-interval reinforcement schedules. In one type of experiment, the fixed-interval was programed in the classical fashion, with reinforcement being made available to a response that occurred 45 minutes after the preceding reinforcement. Following extended observation of this baseline performance, the time-out was introduced after alternate reinforcements. Simply, this involved shutting down the experiment for 20 minutes after each alternate reinforcement. The programing apparatus was turned off during this 20-minute time-out, and the lights in the experimental chamber were extinguished (34, pp. 185-226). Under the time-out condition, the behavior which was being recorded ceased completely. During the fixed-intervals following time-out, however, the behavior changed radically, as may be seen in Figure 30. It is apparent that insertion of the time-out after reinforcement produced a marked increase in the fixed-interval curvature.

It is likely that neither of the records in Figure 30 represents a final stable state, within the limits of variability that might be defined by a rigorous criterion. In spite of this, it is also apparent that

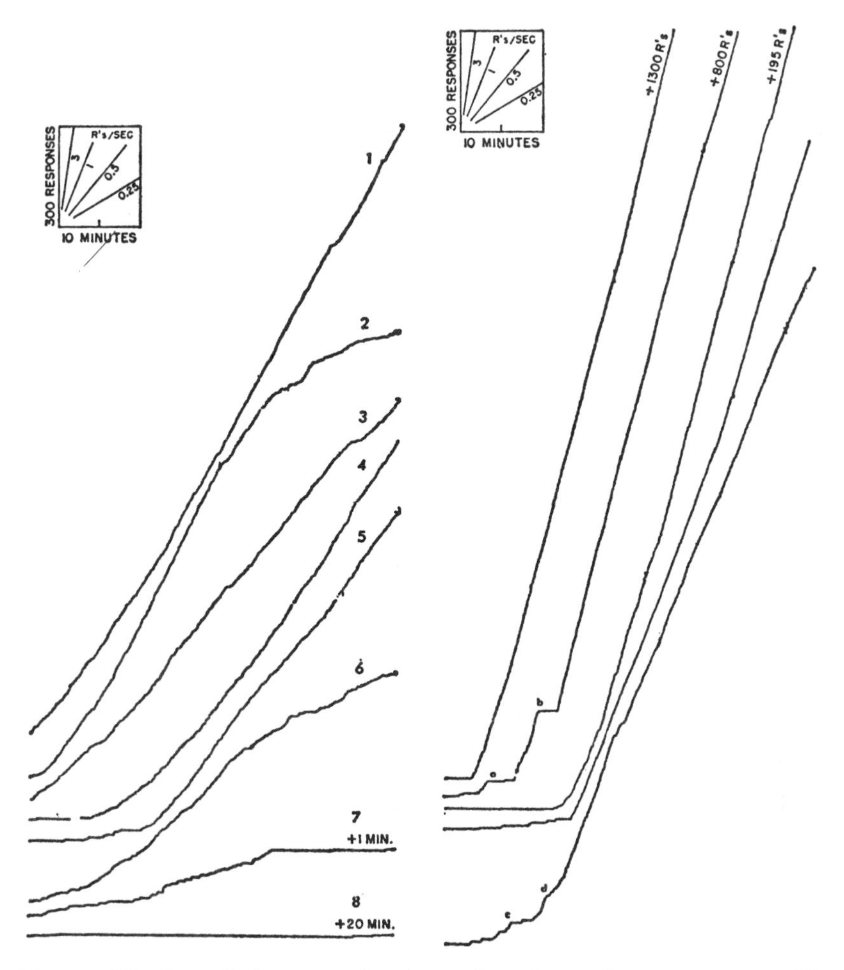

FIGURE 30. Cumulative records of a pigeon's performance on a 45-minute fixed-interval schedule of reinforcement, in which a 20-minute time-out occurred after every alternate reinforcement. The curves at the left depict typical behavior during intervals not preceded by a time-out; the curves at the right show the behavior during intervals that were preceded by a 20-minute time-out period. (*From Ferster and Skinner,* 34, p. 195.)

the time-out is a powerful variable. Its effect is great enough to be clearly visible in the cumulative record. A more precise specification of stability might be required if one were interested, say, in the quantitative relation between curvature and the duration of the time-out, but the Ferster and Skinner experiment serves its purpose more than adequately.

Criterion-by-inspection is not, of course, a wholly arbitrary matter. The experimenter must be backed up by considerable experience, both from his own laboratory and from related work in other laboratories. The first record in Figure 30, for example, showing the fixed-interval baseline without the time-out, represents the end point of many experimental hours. Based on their experience with this and other procedures, the investigators had reason to expect no further major changes in the subject's performance within the time normally spanned by their experiments. Their cut-off point was not predetermined according to a quantitatively specifiable stability criterion, but neither was it capricious.

Another type of supporting data arises from a demonstration of reversibility. In a third phase of the experiment represented in Figure 30, the time-out was removed, and the original baseline performance recovered. Such reversibility, by itself, justifies the inspection criterion. While the baseline behavior may not be recovered in precisely its original form, its characteristics are such as to demonstrate conclusively the importance of the time-out. A return to the original condition should always be included in the design of experiments that explore the relevance of a variable in steady-state behavior, whether stability is evaluated by inspection or by a quantitative criterion.

The experimenter's confidence in a visual inspection stability criterion may be further enhanced by collateral data of the sort which arise from an intensive, long-term research program. Replicability, both direct and systematic, will enhance the validity of the criterion. Additional justification of the criterion employed in the experiment I just cited comes from systematic replication of the effect in other experimental situations (34, pp. 422-429). The time-out, for example, was shown to exercise a similar control over curvature when fixed-interval and fixed-ratio schedules were programed in tandem. That is to say, reinforcement occurs only when a fixed number of responses have been emitted following the termination of the fixed interval. The number requirement, added to the fixed interval, produces marked changes in the behavior, but the effect of the time-out remains essentially the same. Evaluation of the visual inspection criterion must take such replications into account. Generality of the findings is the ultimate test of the validity of any stability criterion.

While an investigator may grant the validity of particular steady-state experiments whose design involves inspection criteria of stability, he may be disturbed by the problem of reproducing the data in his own laboratory. How does he know that the steady states which he evaluates by inspection, in the light of his own experience, are the same as the states that have been observed by another experimenter? The problem is a real one, and is faced by workers in many fields. In order to avoid such difficulties, an experimenter should make public the data upon which he bases his estimate of stability. When this estimate is made by simple inspection, the records must be available for others to carry out the same inspection. Sometimes it is possible to conserve valuable publication space by referring to prototypical data that have appeared previously, but when the stable state is an original discovery, it is necessary to present it so that it may be replicated by other workers.

UNSTABLE BEHAVIOR. Stability criteria can neither be selected blindly nor slavishly adhered to; for behavior in some situations is not stable at all. Methods for dealing with unstable behavior will differ according to the type and degree of instability in any particular case.

When an experimental procedure yields unstable behavior, the first task of the experimenter is to assure himself, within reasonable limits, that the observed variability does not arise from poor control of conditions extraneous to the procedure itself. That is to say, he must rule out such factors as disturbing noises, failures of the reinforcing mechanism, uncontrolled variations in shock intensity, artifacts in the programing circuits, wide temperature fluctuations, etc. With the elimination of these and similar variables, he can be reasonably certain that instability is a characteristic product of his experimental manipulations. His next task, then, is to examine the instability and to describe it as fully as his available methods will allow. It is only after such description that he and others will be able to determine how to deal with the instability when it appears in subsequent experiments.

One form of instability is characterized by cyclic fluctuations in the behavior. The cycles may range from those with an easily recognizable periodicity to those which seem to have no consistent pattern. In the simplest cases, as in fixed-interval and fixed-ratio reinforcement schedules, some dimension of the cycle is determined by a well-defined experimental operation. In the fixed-interval schedule, the period of the cycle is constant, being defined as the minimum time between reinforcements. Each reinforcement initiates a new cycle of pausing and accelerated responding. In the fixed-ratio schedule, each reinforcement again initiates a new cycle, but in this case the amplitude is fixed. The required ratio of responses to reinforcement determines the height of each cycle, but the periodicity can vary. At the other extreme, the cyclic fluctuations in response rate during extinction, for example, do not have any boundaries of amplitude or periodicity that are marked by specifiable changes in the experimental conditions.

When some dimension of a cyclic fluctuation is operationally fixed, it is relatively easy to describe the characteristics of the cycles. The behavior may even be treated as a steady-state phenomenon. For example, a fixed-ratio schedule of intermediate size will generate cyclic changes in response rate. But, from cycle to cycle, the pause following reinforcement will be relatively constant; the local rates will be invariant; and, of course, the number of responses in each cycle is fixed by the procedure. Certain experimental variables will produce changes only, say, in the pause after reinforcement, and the duration of this pause may characterize the steady state as a function of changes in the experimental variable.

Selection of those aspects of behavior which are stable is, then, one method of handling otherwise unstable forms. A second technique often employed to deal with cyclic instability is to take measurements only over large samples of behavior. The samples must be large enough so that the cyclic variability is equally distributed throughout each. For example, in the differential reinforcement of low rates (DRL), it has often been noted that reinforcements occur in clusters, separated by periods of relatively high response rates. An extreme example appears in Figure 31. On this procedure, a thirsty rat was required to space its responses at least 20 seconds apart in order to secure a drop of water. The small diagonal marks on the cumulative response record of Figure 31 indicate reinforce-

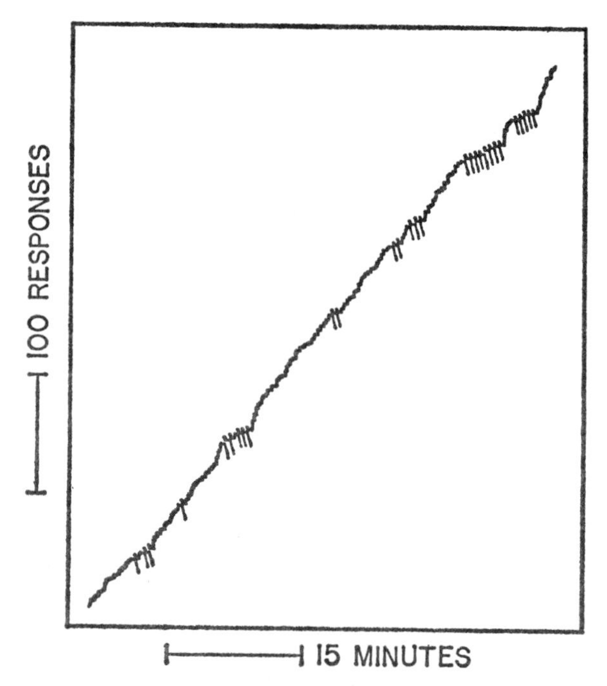

FIGURE 31. Cumulative record of a rat's performance when reinforcements were procured only by responses spaced at least 20 seconds apart. The small diagonal marks, indicating reinforcements, illustrate the cyclic nature of the performance.

ments, which occurred only when the low-rate criterion was met. The tendency of two or more reinforcements to occur in closely spaced groups is fairly evident. The curve, therefore, fluctuates in an irregular cyclic fashion between relatively high, unreinforced response rates and low rates approximately equal to the minimum requirement of one response per 20 seconds.

A description of the response rate in Figure 31 would suffer from gross variability if the rates were measured over successive periods as short as ten minutes. Some of the ten-minute periods would be occupied by a trough in the cycle. Others might contain only the high-rate portions of the record. Still other ten-minute intervals would contain varied proportions of high- and low-rate segments of the performance. A description of the effects of some independent variable in terms of ten-minute segments of the curve would be hampered by gross, unsystematic-appearing variability. One method of dealing with this problem is simply to increase the size of the behavior sample over which the rate is measured. In the DRL situation, a two-hour sample has proved adequate. In spite of the local cyclic variations, the response rate over successive two-hour periods is relatively constant, and long-term performance is characterized by stability.

The use of large behavior samples to "smooth out" cyclic instability is similar, at another level, to the practice of combining data from a large group of subjects in order to average out individual variability, and it suffers from similar limitations. With a single subject there are, of course, none of the problems that arise from the lumping together of individual differences. In this respect, the method of using large behavior samples from the individual marks an advance over group data. We are, however, now lumping together those behavioral variations which occur within the individual subject. The rate averaged over two hours does not eliminate local fluctuations any more than a group average eliminates individual differences. All that we accomplish by the averaging process is to hide the cyclic variations from view. The effects are still present in the behavior and we cannot presume that they are irrelevant, particularly when they are systematic.

Before pursuing this matter further, it should be noted that data obtained from the averaging of behavior within the individual are, in at least two respects, preferable to data obtained from the averaged behavior of a large number of subjects. One advantage, which I have already noted, is the elimination of a major source of variability. Group averages are contaminated both by intra- and intersubject variability. Individual averages are free from the latter. The second advantage arises from a consideration of the behavioral processes actually described by the data. Group data may often describe a process, or a functional relation, that has no validity for any individual. The validity of a behavioral description obtained from group data will be related inversely to the amount of intersubject variability. But, most important of all, we often have no way of evaluating whether or not a given example of group data actually does provide a true picture of individual behavioral processes.

As I have noted earlier, reproducible group data describe some kind of order in the universe and, as such, may well form the basis of a science. It cannot, however, be a science of individual behavior except of the crudest sort. And it is not a science of group behavior in the sense that the term "group" is employed by the social psychologist. It is a science of averaged behavior of individuals who are linked together only by the averaging process itself. Where this science fits in the scheme of natural phenomena is a matter for conjecture. My own feeling is that it belongs to the actuarial statistician, and not to the investigator of behavioral processes.

Averaged data within the individual, on the other hand, do at least provide a true description of the behavior of the individual within the limits of the measure employed. In spite of local fluctuations, a response rate averaged over two hours is a true description of the performance by an individual subject. We may be unable to describe the behavior at particular points in time, but we can state, without qualification, that the subject has emitted a particular number of responses in a two-hour period under certain experimental conditions; and that under other conditions, a different average rate was recorded. Although the description is not precise, it is valid for the individual.

The major problem associated with the use of large samples of individual data to smooth out cyclic fluctuations is not, then, a matter of representativeness of the data. It is, rather, a problem concerned with the precision and completeness that such data permit us to attain in our understanding of behavioral processes. By lumping cyclic fluctuations into a single, over-all measure, such as average response rate, we may lose important information about the characteristics of the behavior under study. One of the greatest virtues of the recording technique devised by Skinner, exemplified by the cumulative response records I have employed here as illustrations, is the quickly visible, continuous picture it yields of the subject's moment-to-moment behavior. Such a record permits us to evaluate the contribution of local fluctuations to a summary measure. For a more concrete illustration, let us examine Figures 32 and 33.

Figure 32 represents the performance of one monkey and one rat whose lever-pressing behavior was reinforced with liquid on a fixed-ratio schedule that required 25 responses per reinforcement. The behavior possesses characteristics normally generated by this sched-

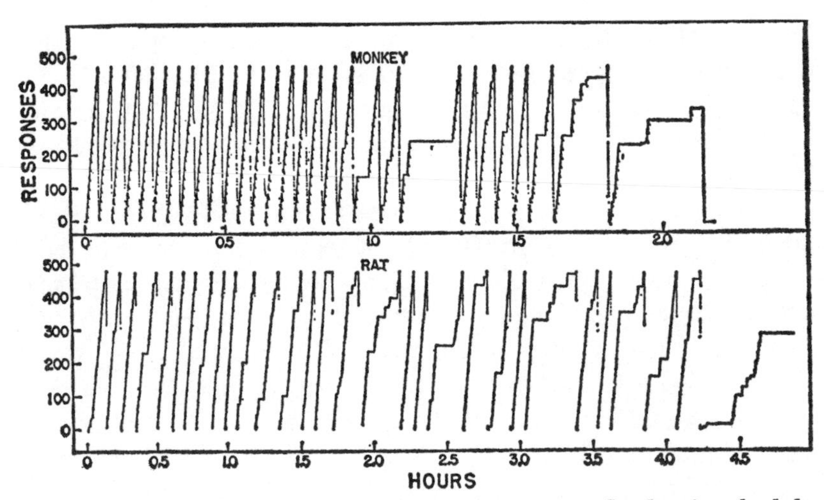

FIGURE 32. Performance of a monkey and a rat on a fixed-ratio schedule requiring 25 responses per reinforcement. (*Adapted from Sidman and Stebbins,* 79.)

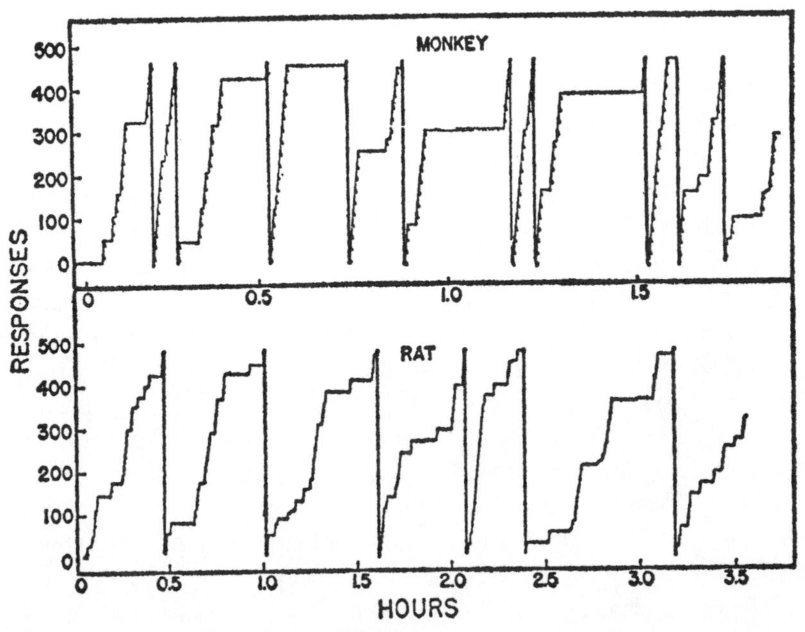

FIGURE 33. Fixed-ratio performance of the same subjects as in Figure 32, after they had been pre-fed a large quantity of the reinforcing agent. (*From Sidman and Stebbins,* 79.)

ule. At the start of the session, high, sustained response rates are observed. As the animals become satiated, pauses following reinforcement become more frequent.

Figure 33 shows the performance of the same animals after they had been fed a large quantity of the reinforcing substance just before the experimental session. The average response rate after pre-feeding is considerably less than that recorded in Figure 32. The effect of the pre-feeding operation could be described as a lowered output over the whole experimental session. This description would be perfectly accurate, but it hardly tells the whole story. For, when the animals do respond, their rates are the same both with and without pre-feeding. The chief effect of pre-feeding was to alter the cyclic pattern of zero and maximal response rates. After pre-feeding, the pauses following reinforcement appear more frequently and earlier in the session. But when the animals respond at all, they immediately assume their characteristic high, constant rate. This gives us a quite different picture of the effects of satiation upon fixed-ratio behavior than we could obtain by considering only the average response rate over the whole session.

Sometimes the fact of cyclicity itself may be the critical datum. In that event, it will be necessary to devise measures to indicate the amount and type of fluctuation. There are only a small number of published experiments in which cyclicity *per se* has been examined in any detailed fashion. Most measurements of behavioral fluctuation have been derived from simple inspection of the data or have been of a summary nature, taken over a relatively large sample of behavior. In the former category are the observations of fluctuations in response rate during the experimental extinction of a response. The cumulative extinction curve, recorded after continuous reinforcement, displays prominent fluctuations, with irregular cycles of pausing and rapid responding. The extinction process after intermittent reinforcement, however, is relatively smooth and undisturbed by pronounced fluctuations in response rate. This difference, which I regard as potentially one of the most fruitful observations in the study of behavior, has not been exploited much beyond the original observation (81). No investigator has yet devised a descriptive tool sufficiently precise to capture, in quantitative fashion, the type of irregular fluctuation in response rate that occurs during extinction.

Until an adequate measure of cyclicity *per se* is developed, phenomena such as this will remain challenging but untapped problems. Experiments whose design encompasses such data will suffer from our present state of technical inadequacy.

Techniques are available for handling certain types of behavioral oscillation, particularly those in which the behavior fluctuates between two or more easily identifiable states. For example, the subject may display some manner of alternation between two responses. It is possible, by measuring the sequences in which the two responses occur, to characterize the response fluctuation in terms of its frequency and pattern. If we denote the responses as A and B, we may measure the probability of occurrence of each of the four possible double sequences, AA, BB, AB, and BA. How often is response A followed by another A response, and how often by a B response, etc.? This will give us some indication of the amount of oscillation between the two responses.

Similar measurements may be taken over sequences of three, four, or more responses, the analysis stopping at the point where orderliness ceases. That point will, itself, provide another measure of the cyclicity of response alternation. From such measurements as these, we may even derive a summary statement which describes the overall cyclicity in terms of the "uncertainty" with which we can predict the next response in a sequence (37, 56). While measurement techniques of this sort, derived from an area popularly called "information theory," are proving increasingly useful, they still suffer from the fact that they require a large sample of data. The statistical description they provide is similar, in this respect, to an average response rate. Both types of measure ignore local fluctuations that may be of great functional importance.

Cyclic fluctuations, then, are a serious challenge to the study of steady-state behavior. As we continue to refine our methods of experimental control, the challenge is likely to become increasingly pressing. We are undoubtedly missing a great deal of lawful cyclicity because it is covered up by the variability our present techniques force us to accept. This is not completely a measurement problem, however. If we can gain greater understanding of the factors underlying behavioral cyclicity, it may be possible to design our experimental procedures so as to increase the orderliness of the cycles. It is when fluctuations are irregular that serious measurement problems arise. Stable cycles, as we have seen, may be followed instance by instance throughout the course of an experiment, with no loss of detail through averaging.

How do we achieve a degree of understanding of cyclic processes that will permit us to design experiments to study them in detail? Each case will, of course, demand its own approach, but there is a general orienting principle to serve as a guide. When behavioral cycles are observed in an experiment, and there are no external stimuli correlated with the cycles, the sources of the cyclicity can often be found in the behavior itself. If we have maintained a high degree of constancy in the environmental conditions, a likely place to search for oscillating variables is in the very behavior we are examining. There are already several known instances in which behavior generates the conditions that produce its own oscillation (23), and appropriately designed experiments may be expected to uncover more. It has been shown, for example, that behavior during any segment of a long fixed-interval reinforcement schedule is strongly influenced by the number of responses that were emitted in the immediately and more remotely preceding segments. I have outlined the cyclic nature of this process in Chapter 5, page 175. By means of Ferster and Skinner's time-out technique, it is possible to minimize the effects of variables that arise from preceding behavior, and thus to regularize fixed-interval curvature to a remarkably high degree (34).

The time-out technique, however, may not always be appropriate to the problem at hand. It may be desirable, instead of eliminating the control arising from prior behavior, to maximize it in order that its components may be studied. The experimenter may then be able to decrease the variability of the cyclic process itself and, consequently, to include it within a systematic and quantitative account. Earlier, for example, I discussed the cyclicity of fixed-interval "scalloping" in terms of changes in the number of responses emitted per reinforcement. If the analysis is correct, a fundamental connection between fixed-interval and fixed-ratio behavior is thereby established. But number of responses may not be the only variable. Rate of responding may also be critical, as may acceleration, duration of pause at the start of the interval, and the length of time over which the terminal rate is maintained. Experiments designed to isolate these features may increase the regularity of the cyclic variations in the fixed-interval scallop, making it more amenable to experimental manipulation and measurement.

The tentative nature of my discussion indicates that cyclic instability in behavior is a relatively unexplored area. The implications for experimental design cannot be outlined with any great assurance. Experimental efforts have, until now, been directed at the elimination of cyclic instability. As we become more secure with respect to the technical adequacy of our control procedures, perhaps we will return to study further the unstable states we have succeeded in eliminating. The major path at which I have pointed is to stabilize the instability. When variability can be made to conform to a pattern, we can be assured that we have an adequate baseline from which to measure the effects of relevant operations. Whether the experimenter wishes to eliminate or to study cyclic instability will depend upon the type of problem he has under investigation. If he chooses to *study* cyclic changes in behavior, traditional techniques may prove to be of little help, and may even be a hindrance. The work will demand innovations, and the innovator cannot afford to accept any "established" findings or techniques at their face value.

Chapter 10

Transition States

WE HAVE SEEN some of the problems that arise in investigations of steady-state behavior: problems of cyclic and irregular variability, long-term trends, size of the behavior sample, stability criteria, and reversibility. The same difficulties will be met in studies of transition states, some of them intensified. The first problem in studying a transition state is to determine the boundaries of the state in question. When does the transition begin and when does it end? The answer will require some knowledge of the boundary stable states. Unless the experimental conditions are changed before it is complete, a transition state will always involve a change from one stable state of behavior to another. For this reason, the study of transition states cannot easily be divorced from the study of steady states.

In many procedures, the start of a transition can be identified operationally as the point at which we change the experimental conditions. The beginning of extinction can be identified, for example, by noting the point at which the reinforcement magazine was disconnected. Even this apparently simple definition, however, gives rise to problems. Let us suppose that the initial stable state was maintained by a fixed-interval reinforcement schedule, and that the food magazine was disconnected immediately after a reinforcement. From the subject's point of view, extinction does not begin until the next fixed-interval has elapsed and a reinforcement fails to appear. We are treading on dangerous ground here. Any time the experimenter assumes the subject's point of view he runs the risk of biasing his data in the direction of his assumptions. In the present example, however, there is little to fear. The point at which reinforcement fails to appear is slightly more complicated to define, operationally, than is the point at which the magazine is disconnected, but it is capable of being so defined. Complications arise from the fact that we must take into account not simply a change in the environment but a change, as well, in the relations between that environment and behavior.

The advantages and disadvantages of such a definition are of a practical nature. There is one immediate advantage of defining the beginning of a transition in terms of operations that involve behavioral contingencies. It is possible then to eliminate from the measures of transition those aspects of the behavior that are completely under the control of the preceding steady-state variables. Suppose, for example, we want to investigate extinction as a function of the length of the fixed interval. We carry out extinction after achieving stable states at fixed-interval schedules, say, of one, 5, 10, 20, and 40 minutes, and we define the beginning of extinction by the operation of disconnecting the magazine immediately following a reinforcement. Our measures of extinction after fixed-interval schedules of various lengths will then include differing amounts of behavior which had no opportunity to "feel" the effects of the changed conditions. After a ten-minute fixed interval, for example, the first ten minutes of extinction behavior will be wholly under the control of the schedule. Only after ten minutes have elapsed can the fact that the magazine is inoperative make contact with the behavior.

If the fixed interval is one minute, however, the critical change in the contingency will occur very soon after the magazine has been disconnected. Such a difference will loom very large in our comparison of extinction after one- and 40-minute fixed intervals, and will be present to a lesser extent in our comparisons of intermediate points. On the other hand, if we define the beginning of extinction as the point at which the first reinforcement fails to occur, our measures will be free of such complications.

A change in the type of contact that behavior makes with its environment does not always define the initiation of a transition quite so satisfactorily. Suppose, for example, the baseline behavior from which we initiate a change is maintained by a variable contingency, such as a variable-interval reinforcement schedule. It would be difficult, and probably meaningless behaviorally, to specify as the start of the transition the first point at which a scheduled reinforcement was not delivered. The best solution here would appear to be an operational criterion, with the transition being measured from the point at which the schedule was changed on the programing apparatus. The degree of error introduced by this criterion could be specified in terms of the distribution of inter-reinforcement intervals that had been punched into the programing tape.

We may look forward, however, to the development of more rational techniques for identifying the start of a transition state. As the variables maintaining a given sample of behavior are more precisely identified, it will become possible to measure a transition state from the point at which such variables first make contact with the behavior. As a hypothetical case in point, let us wishfully assume that the response rate generated by a variable-interval schedule has been discovered to be solely under the control of reinforcement frequency. If we shift to a new value of the schedule, we could then measure the transition from the point at which reinforcement frequency changes, since this is known to be the critical variable.

The example is, perhaps, not a particularly apt one, but I have selected it because of the additional difficulty that it introduces.

A change in a variable such as reinforcement frequency will, under many conditions, require a long period of time before its effects are observed in behavior. This will be especially true if the frequency is characterized by short-term variability, with constancy being maintained only over extended periods, as in a variable-interval schedule. How, then, can we determine precisely when a change in reinforcement frequency makes contact with the behavior and initiates a transition phase?

We might measure the distribution of reinforcement frequencies over successive small segments of the steady-state behavior, and then select as the beginning of the transition that point in the new schedule at which reinforcement frequency falls significantly outside the original distribution. But there is no guarantee, or even any reason to expect, that a statistically significant change in reinforcement frequency will correspond to a behaviorally significant change. A criterion of this sort must be based upon an empirical determination, and probably a rational one as well, of the amount and consistency of change that must take place in the variable before its effects begin to show up in behavior.

The student may already have recognized, from the above discussion, that a behavioral transition state can contain two segments. One of these is the time it takes for a new variable to initiate a change; the other is the behavioral transition that occurs once the new variable has begun to take hold. Both of these stages are of interest but they are, more often than not, confounded in experiments that involve transition states.

Studies of learning, in which the two phases are ordinarily combined in a single measure, are prime examples. How long does it take an animal to reach a final stable performance in running to a dish of food at the end of a runway? The initial phase of the transition, in this case from a presumed zero level of performance, may not be under the control of the food reinforcement at all. Identification of the point at which the reinforcement begins to have an effect upon the measured behavior may almost be thought of as a psychophysical problem. At what point in the procedure does the reinforcement operation have a just-noticeable effect? Once this initial effect is felt, the remainder of the transition phase may take an entirely independent course, or it may, indeed, be a function of the initial phase. Both phases are worth studying, and it is to be hoped that methodological refinement will permit the two to be evaluated independently.

The difficulties involved in identifying the start of a transitional state of behavior are minor compared to those we meet in attempting to determine where a transition ends. What are the criteria by which we can mark the dividing line between the end of a transition and the beginning of the subsequent stable state? In the traditional learning experiment, for example, how do we decide when the learning is complete? Depending upon the aspect of behavior which is measured, the answer to this question may be a strong determiner of the conclusions to be drawn from a given experiment.

Figure 34 illustrates two transition phases; both start from the same behavioral level and reach similar steady states. But each arrives at the end state via a different route. One question that may be asked is which of the two transitions takes place more rapidly. The student will recognize this as the question that is usually asked

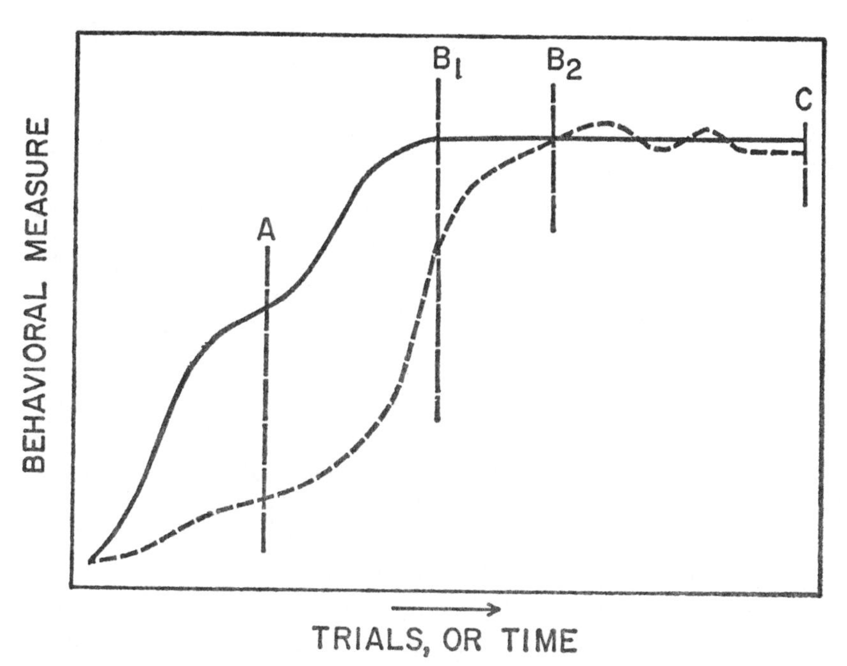

FIGURE 34. Two hypothetical learning curves.

in experimental studies of learning. The answer will depend upon the point at which the transition is judged complete. If the investigator cuts off his experiment at A, he will report that transition I takes place more rapidly than does transition II. This is by no means an uncommon procedure. Experiments on the acquisition of behavior are often not continued long enough for the final level of performance to be reached.

If, on the other hand, the experiment were terminated at C, in Figure 34, another conclusion might well be drawn. By the time C has been reached, the two curves have been indistinguishable over a large portion of the experiment. If C were taken as the stopping point, it might be concluded that both transitions took place equally rapidly. If fact, the curves have been similar over such a wide range of abscissa values that some statistical tests might yield the conclusion that there is no difference at all between the two transitions. In this case, the error would be caused by a failure to stop the experiment soon enough. The final stable states here are inextricably confounded with the transition phases.

Visual inspection of the curves of Figure 1 suggests that transition I ended at B_1, and that transition II ended at B_2. If this were correct, we would have to conclude that transition I was the more rapid of the two. By what quantitative criterion could we legitimately draw such a conclusion? The problem is essentially that of defining the beginning of the final steady state. The point at which the steady state begins also marks the end of the transition.

In our previous discussion of stability criteria, we noted that the usual course was to adopt a criterion more stringent than necessary. We were interested in a relatively unequivocal identification of the final steady state, and were not concerned with the point at which stability began. We saw, therefore, that most stability criteria discarded the data with which we are now concerned. A certain amount of data was thrown away because it was unclear whether it belonged to the transition or to the stable state.

Not only would a solution to this problem be important in principle; it would also have convenient practical consequences. If the end point of a transition could be identified unequivocally, the problem of the stability criterion would automatically disappear. There would be a saving of countless hours of experimental labor now devoted to carrying behavior out to some overly rigorous stability criterion. For the termination of a transition state and the start of a steady state are one and the same point.

Since the solution to this problem has, as yet, not even been approached, we may raise the question of its feasibility. Will it ever be possible to mark, with any precision, a point at which transition ends and stability begins? Current methodology may well yield a negative answer. Behavioral processes take place in time and must therefore be observed over some temporal span. The concept of a behavioral state is sometimes employed as if it were something momentary, but our actual observations always occupy a period of time. There have been attempts to circumvent this problem, for example by arranging experiments in discrete trials. But we cannot escape from the continuous temporal properties of a behavioral state by arbitrarily selecting discrete observation points.

Transition and stable states are extremes along a continuum of behavioral change, one representing a maximum degree of change, and the other, a minimum. At least two temporally separated observations must be employed to measure any change. Once a change has been detected, at least one additional observation must be made to determine when the change has ceased. A minimum of three measurements must be made, then, to identify the end of a transition state.

In actual practice, of course, many more than three measurements will be required. One of the fundamental problems in identifying the termination of a transition state is how frequently to make the measurements. Continuous measurement in time would be most desirable, but present methodologies are not well suited to this. Skinner's cumulative record, which permits continuous visual appraisal of a behavioral process, does not lend itself conveniently to a continuous numerical evaluation. Even if we were to apply some mathematical sophistication in the form, say, of the calculus, we would first have to make a large number of discrete quantitative observations. The observations would have to be sufficiently close in time to make them equivalent, in a practical sense, to a continuous measure. The closer we make our measurements in time, the greater will be the precision with which we can mark the boundaries of the transition. On the other hand, the closer together our measurements are, the less will be our confidence that a true boundary point has been identified unless we extend the measurements well past the boundaries. If, for example, a subject's behavior has been changing steadily for several hours, with measurements being made once every second, we are not likely to accept invariance in two successive measurements as an indication that the change is complete. Here we are, then, right back where we started.

Perhaps, however, something has been gained, for we can now state part of the problem with somewhat greater precision. Behavioral processes occur in time and must be measured over time. To identify the precise boundaries of a process, frequent measurements are necessary. As we space our observations closer together, however, we must utilize a greater number of them to identify the boundary points. The end point of a transition becomes fuzzy, therefore, as we space our measurements closer together or farther apart. In the former case we will be required to take a large number of measurements into account and to perform some sort of statistical evaluation; in the latter case, we leave a larger area of uncertainty with respect to the exact point of termination.

Is statistical evaluation the answer? The problem may be viewed as one that requires the identification of a point at which change ceases. We must be able to state that there is no difference between the values on either side of this point. Can we, by some sort of sequence or trend analysis, evaluate the end point of a transition in relatively unequivocal terms? This certainly is one way to approach the problem, but, unfortunately, statistical methodology does not eliminate the basic difficulties. Statistical evaluation must always utilize samples of at least several values of the behavior in question in order to permit a judgment of no significant difference. How far apart must the items of each sample be located? How large must the sample be, and how great a change can be tolerated within the range of no significant difference? The latter two questions are generally considered to be answerable in terms of the statistical theory, but this is not true. The questions are empirical ones. A difference that is significant within any particular statistical method for handling variability may well be inconsequential as far as any experimental manipulations are concerned. And, in the opposite direction, a statistically inconsequential difference may be of the greatest importance behaviorally.

Statistical evaluation contains no weaknesses that are not present as well in any other currently utilized approach to the problem. The chief factor that underlies the poor methodological quality and lack of precision in most modern research into behavioral transition states is the failure of the experimenters themselves to face up to the problems involved.

A curious situation exists today. In terms of quantity of work, experimental psychology in this country is dominated by research on transition states. Experiments on learning in many species, under many different conditions, and often with a background of ingenious theorizing occupy the bulk of our journal pages—all this with little or no attempt to solve the basic technical problems attendant upon the study of behavioral transitions. It might be an interesting historical exercise to discover whether similar situations have existed in other sciences; situations in which a given problem has occupied the experimental and theoretical attention of a majority of the workers without even lip service being paid to unsolved technical problems. Psychologists are busy studying the transition state called learning without being able to identify, with any reasonable degree of precision, either the beginning or the end of the process. They handle variability by treating a group of subjects as if it represents a single ideal subject. Reversibility is a term that has been forced upon their attention by workers concerned with steady-state behavior, but there has, as yet, been only token experimental acknowledgment of this problem. The illusion that learning and other behavioral transitions are continuous processes, a view fostered by the almost exclusive utilization of group averages and inadequate experimental control, remains almost unchallenged, in spite of a few outstanding demonstrations that discontinuous change is often to be expected.

When such difficulties are faced squarely, we may expect that the study of behavioral transitions will take its place as a solid scientific endeavor. The task is a difficult one, and demands the painstaking type of experimental labor that must accompany any unexplored problem. I have no way of predicting where such research will lead, but it is certainly possible to point out the kind of initial steps that will have to be taken. The first requirement will be a reorientation in experimental rationale. The student must no longer formulate his problem in general terms. He will not be studying learning or, even more generally, behavioral transitions. He must first select a specific example of a transition state, and, even further, he must select a specific aspect of that transition for detailed study. At this stage of the game he must study the selected property of the transition as a phenomenon of interest in its own right, and not as an example of some more general class. Generalizations will come in time, after the properties of a number of individual transition states have been studied. Similarities will begin to emerge, and connections to other phenomena will become evident to the alert observer. An area of study (perhaps to be called transition states, perhaps not) will gradually be defined. It is unlikely that the resulting science will even remotely resemble what passes today as the study of learning.

To make the discussion more concrete, let me suggest a specific example and follow through its hypothetical development. For relative simplicity, I will utilize a transition that is reproducible in a single organism—the warm-up effect that is often observed in avoidance behavior with rats at the start of each experimental session. The phenomenon is illustrated in Figure 35, which depicts a seven-hour session of avoidance behavior for a single rat. For convenience in reproduction, the record has been cut into seven approximately one-hour segments, numbered in consecutive order from beginning to end. The session depicted here was the fifteenth for this animal.

The warm-up transition is most clearly to be visualized in terms of the relatively greater shock density at the beginning of the session. There is also a gradual increase in the response rate during the early part of the record. Now we must find some useful way of describing the transition so that we may then go on to determine its controlling variables. Let us take the beginning of the session as an arbitrary starting point and give our attention to the problem of identifying the end of the transition.

As noted before, an outstanding feature of the transition is the decrease in shock density as the experiment proceeds. Can we make use of the shocks to determine the transition boundary? Visual inspection of the record suggests that shock density may have become relatively stable following the fortieth shock, indicated by A in Figure 35. Does this point mark the end of the transition?

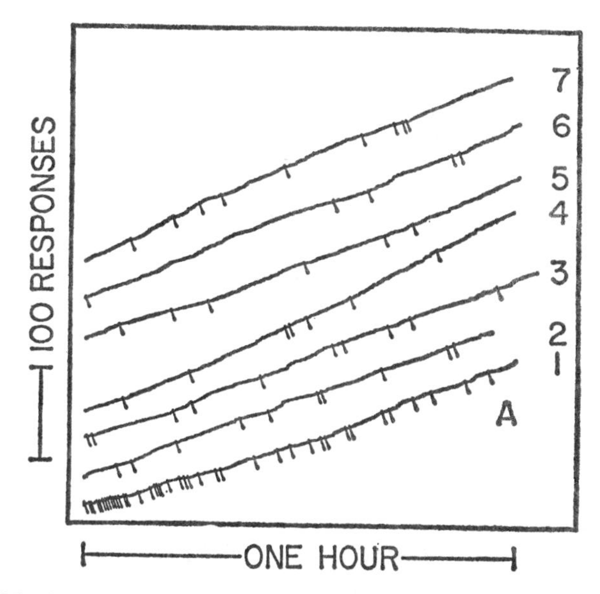

FIGURE 35. Cumulative record of a rat's avoidance behavior during a seven-hour experimental session. The oblique "pips" indicate shocks, and are most closely spaced at the start of the session.

TABLE 2

Number of Shocks

CONSECUTIVE HOURS	SESSIONS I	II	III
1	40	39	48
2	12	12	14
3	8	8	19
4	7	6	10
5	6	7	8
6	5	14	9
7	9	8	11

We can obtain a rough notion of the changes in shock density by counting the number of shocks that occurred in each successive hour. Table 2 presents the results of this count for the session shown in Figure 35 and for the two following sessions. It is apparent from this table that the end of the warm-up cannot be said to occur after a constant number of shocks has been received. In sessions I and II, the shock density became relatively constant after approximately 50 shocks had been delivered, whereas in session III, approximately 80 shocks were required. Similarly, we cannot mark the end of the transition in terms of a constant amount of time since the beginning of the session. The time required for the shock density to become constant varies considerably, even with the gross division of the session into one-hour periods. A simple data analysis, then, does not yield uniformity of the sort that will permit us to generalize about the end point of the warm-up transition.

The next step is to attempt an experimental identification of the end point. From here on, the procedures are highly speculative, but they will serve to indicate the type of research that may be expected to yield a solution to our problem. One should not be surprised, however, if the answer turns out to consist of a simple disappearance of the problem, for the method of attack is of such a nature as to produce new data. Whenever new data appear, one should be prepared for the possibility that they will permit, or even force, a fresh orientation toward old problems.

One method of experimental attack upon the warm-up phenomenon would be deliberately to manipulate some of the suspected variables. We might, for example, turn off the experiment during alternate 15-minute periods. This would tell us whether the simple factor of time in the experimental chamber contributes to the warm-up. A possible result of such an experiment is shown in Figure 36. We first plot the normal course of the warm-up as it is revealed in the number of shocks received by the subject during successive 15-minute segments of the session. The solid line pictures this control data, obtained when the avoidance procedure is programed without interruption.

In the experimental phase, let us turn off the shock during alternate 15-minute periods. The animal may continue to respond during these periods, but no shock will be received. If this procedure alters the warm-up, we will know that the shocks which would normally have been received during the shock-off periods are essential.

Hypothetical data from the second phase of the experiment are shown in the open circles of Figure 36. These indicate the number of shocks received during the alternate 15-minute periods. We see

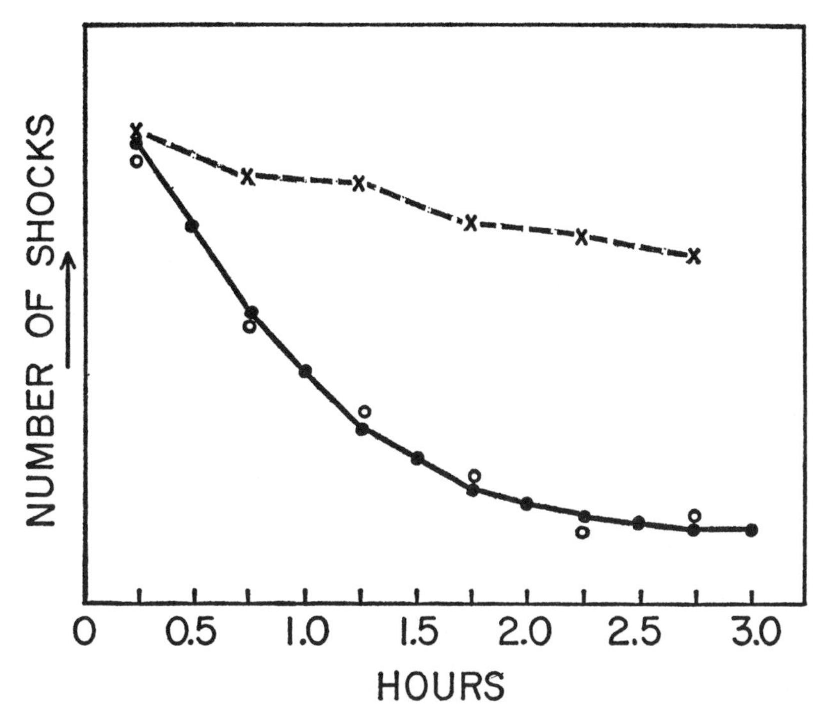

FIGURE 36. Data from a hypothetical experiment on avoidance behavior. The solid curve indicates the number of shocks received by an animal during successive 15-minute periods of a session. The open circles show the number of shocks received when the shock was turned off during alternate 15-minute periods. The dashed curve shows the number of shocks received when the animal was removed from the experimental chamber during alternate 15-minute periods.

that the decline in shock frequency follows approximately the same temporal course as before, in spite of the 15-minute shock-off periods. Because of the shock-off periods, the shock frequency was cut in half, yet the warm-up proceeded normally. It would appear, from these imaginary data, as though time in the chamber is a critical factor in the warm-up, even though shocks are not delivered.

We might, in order to refine this observation even further, actually remove the subject from the chamber during alternate 15-minute periods, and the broken-line curve of Figure 36 illustrates a possible result of this manipulation. We see that when the animal is removed periodically from the experimental space, there is a marked diminution of the warm-up. Shock frequency no longer declines in the same way as it had previously. Accompanying the diminution of the warm-up is a loss of efficiency in the avoidance behavior itself, as indicated by the larger number of shocks.

Findings such as the above would be of great interest in themselves and would normally be followed up for their own sake. The investigator is even likely to forget, at least temporarily, about the original problem of identifying the end point of behavioral transition states. He will, instead, accomplish a more immediate objective. By delving deeply into the characteristics of this particular type of transition, he is likely to bring out properties that were hitherto not known or even suspected. Subsequent detailed study of other transitions may reveal generalizable characteristics that will permit a more inclusive set of specifications for identifying the limits of transition states. In our limited, and hypothetical, example, the investigator will have identified one of the chief controlling factors in the warm-up. Perhaps other kinds of transition will be found to be under similar control. This will tell the experimenter that the transition is to be measured not in terms of shock frequency, but rather in terms of some other variable correlated with duration of exposure to the experimental situation. Perhaps an independently measurable emotional process will answer the requirements. Or we may have to look no further than the number of responses emitted by the organism in the experimental situation. Completion of the transition may simply require a certain number of responses from the subject.

The student will undoubtedly realize that I have not given him the answer to the problem of identifying the end point of a behavioral transition. The problem still lies out at the frontiers of experimentation, and I do not know the answer. What I have tried to do is to present a general method—not an experimental design, but rather a design of experimentation—by means of which the interested student may be able to find the answer himself. The course I have suggested is essentially that of eliminating variability through knowledge of and control of relevant variables. When the factors that govern the occurrence and time course of a transition state become known, the end point of the transition will become more precisely specifiable. As a general rule, whenever a problem seems as ill-defined as the one we have been discussing, the root of the trouble will usually be found to be lack of information. Until the basic properties of a behavioral process are made known, little can be accomplished in the way of answering more subtle questions.

QUANTIFICATION OF TRANSITION STATES

In view of the long discussion, above, of the great difficulties involved in identifying the beginning and end of behavioral transitions, the student might consider it thoroughly gratuitous on my part to discuss the quantification of such transitions. I shall, in fact, not go into this aspect very deeply. But the study of transitions is not completely hopeless, even with today's inadequate methodology. With the possible exception of the rare innovator who is able to discard past methodology and start afresh, most experimental contributors to this area will take current practice as their starting point. In addition to acquainting the student with current measurement practice, I may also be able to call to his attention some additional procedures whose fruitfulness remains to be tested.

The traditional measure of a transition is the speed, or rate, of the behavioral change. How long, or how many trials, does an organism take to reach a given arbitrary level of performance? Many psychologists have devoted their major effort to investigating learning curves under a multitude of experimental conditions. Curves of nearly all conceivable shapes and sizes have been reported, and as a result one seldom sees reference any more to the once prevalent concept of *the* Learning Curve. Psychologists now modestly qualify their particular learning curves with a statement of the experimental conditions within which they appear. The possibility exists that we have been barking up the wrong tree. Rapidity of change may not be the most appropriate aspect of transition states for effective systematization.

In fact—and this brings us back to methodological problems—the one large generalization that appears possible is that any non-instantaneous behavioral transition is a product of special conditions. It is highly likely that curvature in a learning curve is simply an indirect reflection of the interaction of processes other than those under direct experimental control. In most experiments on learning, the subject is actually learning more than he is being taught. That is to say, more is being learned than the experimenter is deliberately trying to teach. Just as curvature may result from the averaging of a number of discontinuous curves in a group of individuals, it may also result from the combination of a number of discontinuous curves for individual responses within a single subject.

What, for example, is reflected in the acquisition curve for the simple response of pressing a lever for food reinforcement? We only measure lever pressing, but the animal is also learning other behavior which is reflected only indirectly in the lever-pressing curve. The animal must learn that the pellet is edible, that it is to be found in a particular place, that it only appears there following the sound of the food magazine, that the sound comes after the lever has been depressed, that the lever must be depressed at least a certain distance and with a certain force, that the lever is located in a particular spot and at a fixed height, etc. There is a long chain of behavior involved here, and each element may be presumed to possess its own learning curve. The lever-pressing response we measure is only an intermediate link in the chain and is, therefore, an indirect reflection of all the learning that is taking place in the situation. By teaching the subject as many as possible of the other members of the chain before introducing the lever, the shape of the learning curve will more closely approach a discontinuous function (81, pp. 66-74).

There are many other possible instances of the same type, most of them not so thoroughly explored. They lead to the promising generalization that whenever gradual curvature is observed in a behavioral transition, one should suspect uncontrolled processes. The study of transition states will reach a new status when such processes are identified. Once they have been identified they can either be eliminated, corrected for, or deliberately studied. The major effect will be to lay bare the particular transition in which one may be interested, so that properties other than its rapidity can be studied directly.

In the lever-pressing experiment described above, the elimination of ancillary processes will involve a preliminary period of thorough magazine training; habituation to the experimental chamber in order to permit extinction of irrelevant behavior; pilot experimentation to determine the most appropriate location for the lever, to adjust its sensitivity, its excursion, and the most effective means of providing feedback; and the provision of an effective magazine stimulus. There is, in fact, some evidence that the lever-pressing response itself is too complex for this purpose. Its awkwardness, for an organism such as the rat, produces wide variations in response topography. The resulting enlargement of the response class that is reinforced undoubtedly increases the likelihood of a gradual acquisition curve. The adequate study of such curves may well require the utilization of a response that is more congenial to the organism, and topographically more consistent.

Other types of response and apparatus commonly employed in behavioral experiments will require similar attention to technical detail if transition states are to be investigated adequately. But what about other kinds of transitions than those involved in learning a new response? Are the transition curves that characterize, for example, the learning of a discrimination, subject to similar kinds of limitations? Again, let us take a simple example. The subject has already learned to press a lever, but now we want to teach him to press it only in the presence of a light. We arrange a situation, then, in which the lever-pressing response produces reinforcement only when the light is on, and never when it is off. The customary result in such a situation is a gradual learning curve. Responses in the absence of the light, though they are no longer reinforced, continue to occur for some time at a gradually decelerating rate.

The same complicating factors that entered into the original learning of the response are also present here. In the absence of the light, the subject has to unlearn more than the lever-pressing response. All of the behaviors that were conditioned along with the lever-pressing response contribute to the discrimination learning curve. If discrimination training is begun along with the original learning of the response, the process is considerably accelerated.

In addition, other factors may enter the picture. Lever-pressing responses that occur just prior to the onset of the light will be accidentally reinforced. The discrimination will proceed more rapidly if such responses are made to postpone the positive stimulus, so that accidental correlations can never occur. There is also the problem of stimulus generalization. While the presence and absence of the light are readily distinguishable from each other, all the rest of the stimuli in the situation are common to both the positive and the negative stimulus. If the subject is actually placed in a different apparatus during the negative stimulus, the discrimination can be made to form abruptly, with no gradual transition.

All of the above discussion leads to the conclusion that measurements of the speed of a behavioral transition may hide more than they reveal. The most adequate and complete description of a transition state is to be accomplished in terms of the variables and processes that control the behavior during the transition. Gradual transition states are second-order phenomena and their rapidity should be derivable from more basic observations.

This conclusion has two consequences for experimental design. First, if the investigator's primary concern is the speed of a behavioral transition, he should make every effort to refine his experimental conditions to the point where the transition occurs abruptly. He may then manipulate variables, singly and in combination, and observe the changes that take place in the reference curve. There is a lifetime of work—several lifetimes, in fact—condensed in the last two sentences, and perhaps this explains why it has never been done. The field is wide open, though, and there are rich pickings for the student who ventures in.

A second consequence for experimental design is that a more fundamental characterization of transitions may be possible in terms other than their speed of occurrence. Let us return to the warm-up effect as our example of a transition and treat the warm-up as a *changing state* of behavior. What are the properties of the changing state other than its rate of change? We may suspect that the behavior will offer varying resistance to extinction at different phases of the transition. To check this suspicion, we can simply disconnect the shock at various points during the warm-up.

If we find that there is, indeed, a lawful function, we may be able to characterize the warm-up transition by means of an extinction scale. We will then have to design experiments to determine whether such a scale is related in an orderly fashion to other variables in the situation. At a more advanced stage of our progress, we can try to determine whether other types of behavioral transition can be described in the same manner. If resistance to extinction does not do the job, either wholly or in part, we will have to start again with another possibility. The attempt here is to describe transition states in terms of their interaction with variables whose effect is to alter the course of the transition.

TRANSITIONS AS A FUNCTION OF THE PRECEDING STATE OF THE BEHAVIOR

ANY CURRENT BEHAVIOR IS, to a large extent, determined by historical factors. Variables to which the organism has been exposed in the past continue to exert an influence even after they are no longer physically present. This consideration has colored much of our discussion up to this point, and becomes particularly relevant in experimental investigations of transition states. For behavioral transitions are always a function not only of the new variables that produce the transition but also of the variables that have been maintaining the behavior up to that point. Transition states cannot be studied in isolation from their history.

It has often been argued that techniques that produce rapid transitions are not suitable for the study of such processes as the acquisition of behavior. If our experimental situation produces rapid learning, it is sometimes held, we are defeating our own purpose because the relevant processes are not available for study. Only when acquisition is slow are we supposed to be able to get a good look at the process. But I have suggested strongly that slow transition states represent special cases; that a gradual transition comes about through the action of contributory factors that are not, in principle, intrinsic to the transition. Slow transitions, then, far from providing the reference experiments upon which to base a systematic account, impose upon us the obligation to examine the historical and current factors that are responsible for their gradual appearance. In the preceding section, I have already touched upon some of the current variables relevant to the problem. What special implications for experimental design are carried by historical factors?

The first implication comes from a simple experimental observation such as the following: The behavioral transition that takes place when the value of a fixed-ratio reinforcement schedule is increased from, for example, five to one hundred, is a function of the method by which the ratio is raised. If the number of responses required per reinforcement is increased slowly, the behavior may develop some strain—*i.e.*, longer pauses following reinforcement—but will be maintained at the ratio of one hundred. If the ratio is increased abruptly, however, from five directly to one hundred, the transition is likely to go in the opposite direction. The strain will increase to the point where the behavior disappears completely.

To achieve some transitions, then, a specific behavioral history must be built into the organism. In shifting from a low to a high fixed ratio, certain variables must be given the opportunity to take hold before the transition can become available for study. It will not do to argue that the transition is artifactitious simply because experimental manipulations are taking place during the change. The manipulations are specifiable and are no more arbitrary than is the gradual addition of heat in studying the course of a chemical reaction.

It is not sufficient, however, from a systematic point of view, to specify our experimental operations simply as "gradual vs. sudden change" in a fixed-ratio schedule. We must go on to ask how such operations alter the relations between the behavior and its immediate controlling variables. What has happened to the behavior, as a result of the gradual change in the ratio, that permits its continued maintenance under a high ratio requirement? Has our operation permitted the "count" to become a conditioned reinforcer? The possibilities have been ably discussed by others (34) and need not be gone into here. The important point to which our discussion has led is that historical factors are likely to be relevant not because of some type of action at a temporal distance, but because of some residue of their effect that is self-sustaining into the present. Dietary deficiency produced by excessive drinking may result in liver damage that is irreversible even after the drinking has been forsworn. Similarly, a particular behavioral history may change the relation between behavior and its controlling variables in such a way that the new relation persists even after the originating conditions are no longer present.

We have seen, then, two related implications of historical factors for the study of transition states: (*a*) A transition may require deliberate experimental manipulation in order to establish a history of control that makes the transition possible; and (*b*) the thorough understanding of the processes involved in a transition may require investigation of the connecting links between such a history and the current variables.

The above observations lead back to a conclusion that I have stated before; but it is worth emphasizing again. Adequate study of transition states requires a knowledge of the behavioral history, certainly the immediate history and probably the more remote also. There is no such condition as the absence of a behavioral history, and ignorance is no substitute for specification. The best way for an experimenter to specify an organism's behavioral history, insofar as it is relevant to a given problem, is to build that history into the organism deliberately. Of course, different histories will exercise differential effects upon subsequent transition states, but this is a fact of behavior, not something from which to try to escape. The lack of systematic information describing transitions as a function of behavioral history leaves a major void in the data of experimental psychology, and in the area of learning in particular. Specification of the state of behavior prior to a transition is, therefore, both a methodological problem in any particular experiment and a general problem worthy of study in its own right.

On the methodological side, there is an interesting problem that must inevitably be faced. A behavioral transition can be studied either as it develops from a preceding stable state or as it emerges from another uncompleted transition. The second alternative has received even less experimental attention than the first, yet it holds greater promise of revealing the properties of transition states. The method involves a change in the experimental conditions while the behavior is still in transition from one stable state to another. This is a tricky procedure, for it involves all the uncertainties of measurement and control that are attendant upon current techniques for studying behavioral transitions. We have the problem not simply of identifying the beginning and end of the first transition but also of specifying intermediate stages in a manner that will permit meaningful replication. The problem of how to characterize a transition is here doubled in magnitude, for we are dealing with two transitions almost simultaneously.

In spite of such problems, the technique is worth trying. Although the difficulties may be doubled, the potential yield may be multiplied even more. If a second transition can be shown to vary as a function of the stage of a prior transition from which it originates, then we will find ourselves in possession of valuable information about *both* transition states. This is the sort of information that is likely to change some of our traditional notions about transition states, for it describes transitions in terms of their interrelations with each other. It emphasizes those properties of a transition which extend out to, and are derived from, other aspects of an organism's behavior.

In addition to the implications this technique carries for original experimental designs, its very difficulties also require a precautionary note to those investigators who will prefer using other experimental approaches to transition states. Unless one designs his experiment deliberately for the examination of transitions as they develop from a baseline of other transitions, it would be fatal to permit such a complication to creep inadvertently into the picture. A steady state is the only alternative to a baseline of transition. If a transition state is not desired as a baseline from which to initiate a second transition, the experimenter must take every precaution to ensure that his baseline behavior is maintained in the steady state. If he ignores this control, he is likely to find that his data are not replicable.

To take a simple example, suppose we wish to examine the transition that takes place when we shift from a discriminated to a nondiscriminated avoidance procedure. In discriminated avoidance, the subject postpones a shock for, say, 20 seconds every time he presses a lever. In addition, a warning signal appears five seconds before a shock is due to be delivered if no lever press has occurred to postpone the signal. It has been found, with this procedure, that the white rat will eventually come to wait for the warning stimulus before pressing the lever, with very few responses at other times. Following the development of such waiting behavior, suppose we disconnect the warning stimulus, keeping all other aspects of the procedure unchanged. Our interest is in the course of the behavioral change that takes place after the signal has been eliminated.

In one such experiment, elimination of the warning stimulus was found to result in an increased rate of avoidance responding. The animals no longer waited till a shock was imminent before pressing the lever, but responded much more rapidly than was necessary. The course of this rate increase could be followed nicely on a cumulative response record. With other subjects, however, no transition took place at all. Although the stimulus had been eliminated, the animals continued to behave as though it were still part of the procedure. They refrained from pressing the lever until five seconds or less remained before the next shock, just as they had when the five-second period was marked by a signal (71).

Subsequent experimentation demonstrated that the different results were explainable in terms of the state of the baseline. With long exposure of the subjects to the discriminated avoidance baseline procedure, temporal control over the behavior developed, and the signal became superfluous. The animals responded at the appropriate time, but no longer used our warning stimulus as a signal. They developed some other technique for telling time. Small wonder, then, that their behavior did not change when we eliminated the warning stimulus.

Here, then, we have an extreme example of the difficulties that may beset replication when the baseline behavior has not been brought to a steady state, but is still in transition. Those animals whose baseline behavior was still in transition from stimulus to temporal control displayed a change in behavior when we removed the warning signal. But this operation produced no change at all in the animals who had completed the transition from stimulus to temporal control.

It may be noted that the transition from stimulus to temporal control which was taking place during the discriminated avoidance procedure was not even suspected until a change was made in the experimental conditions. Our example, then, serves a second function in that it illustrates how some aspects of a transition—even the very existence of the transition—may be revealed only through their relations with other aspects of behavior.

RECOVERABILITY OF TRANSITION STATES

A BEHAVIORAL HISTORY may continue to exert control even after a different set of variables has been introduced. The characteristics of a transition may then change systematically with each repetition in a single subject. Is intrasubject replication of a transition possible in such a situation?

Before dismissing intrasubject replication in cases where history is important, we should ask the question I have discussed before: "With what aspects of the transition are we concerned?" If we are satisfied to go no more deeply into a transition than its speed, we might conclude that an original observation is not recoverable. But if our concern is with the behavioral processes involved in the transition, we may be able to accomplish systematic individual replication even if the rapidity of the transition changes with each successive repetition.

For example, let us take as our model a transition described in great experimental detail by Ferster and Skinner. Their description of the behavioral development that follows a change from continuous reinforcement to a fixed-interval schedule is a classic account of a behavioral transition. Let Figure 37 constitute our reference curve, illustrating the important features of the analysis. I have paraphrased the text of Ferster and Skinner in describing the transition.

1. When the fixed-interval schedule begins, the preceding continuous reinforcement first produces a negatively accelerated extinction curve, suggested by the first segment *b* and the dashed curve at *a*. The rate usually reaches a low level, as at *c*, which is considerably below the rate

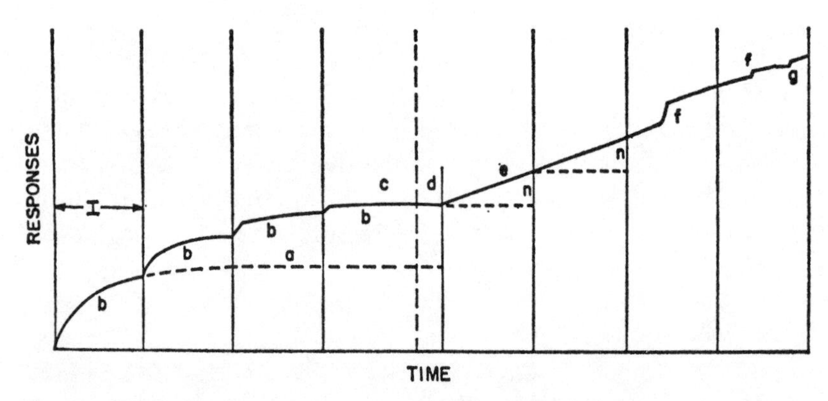

FIGURE 37. Stylized curve of the transition from continuous reinforcement to a fixed-interval reinforcement schedule. (*From Ferster and Skinner*, 34, p. 135.)

which will eventually be maintained by the fixed-interval schedule of reinforcement. Each reinforcement, indicated by the solid vertical lines, is followed by an increase in rate, and the interval is usually marked by a small negatively accelerated segment. The larger negative acceleration attributed to extinction is combined with these smaller curves.

2. A fairly uniform rate of responding then emerges during an interval and from interval to interval, as at e. This constant rate seems to develop regardless of the size of the interval, and is presumably due to the special probability of reinforcement at low rates arising from the contingencies up to this point. The high rate of responding early in the segments labeled *b* is correlated with nonreinforcement, while the low rate toward the end of these segments constitutes a favorable stimulus. The negatively accelerated fixed-interval segments, therefore, generate low rates, and the relation between the low rate and the reinforcement is the most important difference between transitions from continuous reinforcement to fixed-ratio and fixed-interval schedules.

3. Because of the uniformity of rate which develops, the number of responses at reinforcement becomes fairly constant. This condition appears to produce occasional brief runs at higher rates, as at *f*. No instances of rates this high have been observed up to this point, nor, of course, have such rates ever been reinforced. The brief runs appear, therefore, to be caused by the automatic reinforcement resulting from progress toward the number of responses characteristically prevailing at reinforcement. Since such a run destroys the constancy of this number, the situation is unstable.

4. In the last stage of the transition, not illustrated in Figure 37, pauses develop after a reinforcement and are followed by a smooth acceleration to a terminal rate, which is maintained until the next reinforcement (See Figure 18) (34, pp. 135 ff.).

This description of a behavioral transition, which is only a portion of the whole story, is notable for its lack of emphasis upon the speed of the transition. The account could have been presented in the form of traditional learning curves, but this would only have obscured the richness and complexity of the process. Also, it would have precluded intrasubject replication.

Ferster and Skinner, however, did accomplish a large number of intrasubject replications. By paying analytic and experimental attention to the multiple processes involved in the fixed-interval transition, they were not only able to replicate systematically their initial observations but, in addition, were able to shed considerable light on the variables that control the several aspects of the transition. By such manipulations as changing from a small to a large fixed interval and vice versa, programing a time-out following each reinforcement on both small and large intervals, inserting a time-out as a probe during the interval, adding exteroceptive clocks and counters, and programing other schedules in tandem with the fixed interval, they were able to emphasize or to eliminate selectively the various aspects of the transition. The experimental control achieved in this way will now permit any experimenter who is so inclined to generate nearly as rapid or as slow a transition from continuous reinforcement to a fixed-interval reinforcement schedule as he pleases.

With the information Ferster and Skinner have provided, however, the rapidity of the transition has become a superficial characteristic. For an experimenter to become discouraged, at this stage of the game, because of the difficulty of replicating the rate of transition implies that his interest in the behavior is, likewise, only a superficial one. The *processes* involved in the transition can be placed under experimental control and can be replicated within individual subjects.

There are, unfortunately, too few similar examples available for citation. The student should regard this fact not as a barrier but as a challenge. The task of analyzing the components of behavioral transitions will be a rewarding one, in terms both of new data and of technical advance.

An interesting case in which repetition produces a progressively more rapid transition is the phenomenon sometimes called "learning set," or "learning how to learn," extensively investigated by Harlow and his associates. Harlow's summary of the experiment goes as follows:

> [Eight rhesus monkeys were trained] on a series of 344 object discrimination problems utilizing a different stimulus pair for every discrimination. Each of the first 32 problems was 50 trials long; the next 200 problems, 6 trials; and the last 112 problems, an average of 9 trials. Learning curves showing the percentages of correct responses are presented in Fig. 38. These data demonstrate that the animals' ability to

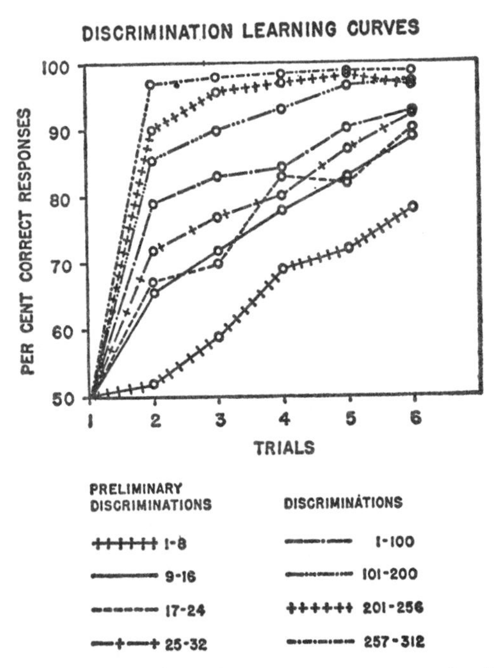

FIGURE 38. Discrimination learning curves on successive blocks of problems. (*From Harlow*, 40, p. 201.)

solve discrimination problems progressively improved. The monkeys gradually learned how to learn individual problems with a minimum of errors, a process designated by the term *learning set*. The animals attained such mastery that if they chose the correct object on the first trial, they rarely made on error on subsequent trials. If they chose the incorrect object on the first trial, they immediately shifted to the correct object and subsequently responded almost perfectly (40, p. 200).

The increase in the initial slope of the learning curves with successive blocks of problems provides an indication of progressively faster transitions. Many workers have accepted this changing transition at its face value, and have employed it to measure differences among species. Harlow writes: "The rigidity of fixed and relatively unchangeable habits so characteristic of some of the lower animals gives way to the plasticity of behavior and the ability to shift set that are typical of the primates (40, p. 208).

Others, however, have been led to inquire into the nature of the changes in behavioral control that are responsible for the more rapid transitions. Harlow, himself, noted that "The only cue for problem shifts was the failure of reward of a previously correct response" (40, p. 207). Other investigators have studied this more basic phenomenon, sometimes called "discrimination of extinction." In the course of demonstrating it even in an organism as lowly as the white rat, they have succeeded both in illuminating the process by which the nonreinforcement of behavior acquires discriminative control and in raising new problems about the nature of such control.

The basic design of such experiments has been to alternately reinforce and extinguish a response, with no exteroceptive cue correlated with the beginning of extinction other than the omission of the food reinforcement. The changing transition is reflected in a declining number of responses during successive extinction periods (20, 62). When the behavior is only intermittently reinforced, the decline in extinction responding is retarded (93), a result to be expected if the transition is controlled by stimuli associated with the omission of reinforcement.

On the other hand, it has been found that a similar progressive change in the transition occurs when shock-avoidance behavior is alternately conditioned and extinguished (12). How does an organism come to discriminate the fact that shock no longer threatens when there is no external event to mark the omission of a shock? There are still unsolved problems here, problems which observations of learning sets pose for us but do not solve. Our understanding of learning sets will depend upon functional investigations of the controlling variables. Premature use of the technique as a tool for studying comparative aspects of behavior can only give us misleading generalizations about the behavioral differences among organisms.

Systematic changes, then, that prevent us from replicating the speed of an initial transition with a single subject can be attributed to corresponding changes in the relations between the behavior and one or more of its controlling variables. When such changes interfere with an investigation of a transition state, the experimental design should be altered to reveal the nature of the controlling relations. The information so gained will either make it possible to return to the original problem with a more effective degree of experimental control, or will show up the weaknesses in the original statement of the problem and thus permit a re-evaluation.

WHEN TO INITIATE A TRANSITION?

A SUBJECT'S BEHAVIOR is usually placed under experimental control for limited and discrete periods of time. In experimental reports, one often finds graphs in which some measure of behavior is plotted as a function of "days," "trials," "hours," "sessions," etc. Those familiar with the typical methodology will realize that the days, trials, hours, sessions, etc., do not usually represent continuous periods of time. More often than not, there are intervening periods during which the subject has been removed from the experimental environment and during which his behavior is neither manipulated nor observed. Animal subjects are returned to their home cages during these intervening periods, college freshman subjects return to the outside world, and the military trainee returns to his routine.

Discrete observation periods have probably become the rule in behavioral experiments because of the practical problems that would otherwise be raised by continuous programing, recording, and data analysis. Such problems are real ones, though methods for their solution are being developed. At this point I wish to consider only the influence which the customary discrete observation periods have exercised over the point at which we usually initiate behavioral transitions.

Transitions are generally initiated by altering the controlling variables immediately at the start of the observation period. This practice probably has its origin in two sources. One of these is the common acceptance of intersubject variability, and the consequent use of group data. Experimenters have been unwilling to change experimental conditions at some fixed point *after* the behavior has been in progress because not all the subjects of the group will have attained the same state of performance. The second consideration mitigating against changes during the observation period has been the relative difficulty of altering the programing equipment sufficiently rapidly as not to disturb the behavior currently in progress.

Although in recent years control techniques suitable for use with individual subjects and programing apparatus which permits automatic and almost instantaneous changes in the experimental conditions have been developed, the practice of instituting such changes at the start of an experimental period is still the prevalent one. I believe that this is, in the main, simple inertia. The advanced control and programing techniques were developed with other aims in view than the study of transition states, and all but a few of those employing the techniques have simply not recognized this application.

What are the pros and cons of initiating a behavioral transition at the start and during the middle of an experimental session? In spite of the fact that I have employed the former method almost exclusively in my own work, I can find little to say in its favor. Behavioral transitions instituted by changing a controlling variable at the beginning of a session are contaminated by the uncontrolled and usually unobserved behavior that has been taking place prior to the session.

There is, in addition, the loss of experimental control that often takes place during the period between sessions, a loss manifested in the various warm-up phenomena and about which little is known. These problems can be avoided by delaying the transition until the behavior has been in progress for a while. In this way, one will have a specifiable immediate baseline from which to assess the behavioral changes that take place. Even more important, the baseline will, by displaying known and characteristic properties, demonstrate whether the behavior is actually under the control of the current experimental conditions.

Here, then, is an opportunity for the new experimenter to make a considerable advance over the work of many of his predecessors. If he is interested in studying the transitions from one stable state to another, he will gain more reliable and useful information by designing his experiments in such a way as to initiate the transitions only after the baseline behavior assumes stability *within* an experimental session. Even the investigator whose chief interest is in the final steady state will reap a bonus if he follows this rule of experimental design. For he is then likely to gain useful information about the transitions as well as the boundary stable states. Such information, though it is so easily obtained, has been all too rare up to the present.

TRANSITORY STATES

TRANSITION STATES may also be thought of as transitory states, since the behavioral changes which are involved eventually cease with the attainment of a stable state of some sort. There is, however, another class of transitory states which is most usefully considered separately from transitions, though the two may occur in conjunction. A transition involves a change from one state of behavior to another, whereas the completion of a transitory phase is marked by a return to the same behavior that would have been observed if the transitory effect had never taken place. Figure 39 illustrates the difference. In curve I, Phase B forms a transition between one steady state, A, and a new steady state, C. In curve II, Phase B constitutes a transitory state followed by a return to steady state A.

In the study of such transitory states, one will encounter all the difficulties that I discussed in connection with behavioral transitions. Transitory phases, however, raise some additional problems. One source of complication is the fact that transitory changes in behavior often occur in an apparently spontaneous fashion. That is to say, they may be observed even though the experimenter has not manipulated any of the experimental conditions. Such instances

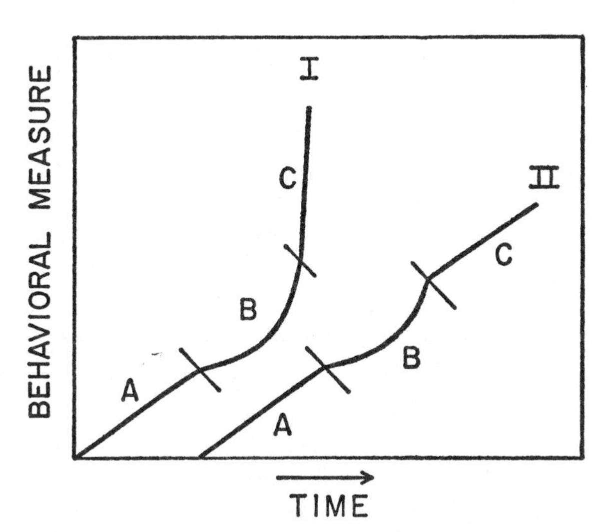

FIGURE 39. An illustration of transition and transitory states.

can often be traced to the subject's behavioral history and/or to interactions that take place between the ongoing behavior and its current controlling variables.

An instance in which a particular behavioral history may interact with current variables to produce transitory changes is provided by an animal subject whose reinforcement schedule has been changed from FR (fixed ratio) to DRL (differential reinforcement of low rates). The ratio schedule requires a fixed number of responses to produce each reinforcement, and generates a high response rate. The subsequent DRL schedule, however, requires the subject to space its responses at least 20 seconds apart to produce the reinforcement. Although the DRL schedule eventually generates its characteristic low, steady response rate, instances occur in which the older ratio behavior "breaks through." Occasional transitory phases of high rates, characteristic of the former ratio schedule, interrupt the smooth DRL performance. The historical origin of these transitory periods of high response rates is clear, and serves to point up the lesson that the subject's history must be taken into account when planning an experiment and when interpreting its data. But there is more to be learned from this example. A given history does not exert its effects in a behavioral vacuum, as becomes evident when we ask why the transitory changes took place at particular times.

The answer to this question, in our specific example, requires an acquaintance with some of the detailed characteristics of spaced responding as it is generated by the DRL schedule. Interspersed among the efficiently spaced responses, we usually observe small bursts of rapid responses. In an organism without a fixed-ratio history, the size of these bursts remains small. But for the subject who has had ratio experience, a rapid burst of responses reinstates one of the conditions which had prevailed prior to reinforcement under the ratio schedule. Rapid responding then generates additional rapid responding, and ratio-like behavior emerges from the small initial burst. This behavior eventually ceases because no reinforcement is forthcoming, and the subsequent pause reinstates the low DRL rate.

Transitory phases, then, do not imply spontaneity or capriciousness in behavior, even though they may appear without deliberate experimental manipulation. In order to eliminate such transitory changes, it will be necessary to inquire into their determinants, for experimental control will provide the only sure methods for preventing them.

If one wishes deliberately to study a particular transitory state, rather than to prevent it, then one is faced with a major problem: the usually short-lived nature of transitory states. If a behavioral phenomenon is a fleeting one, it will be extremely difficult to examine it in great detail. When we have the additional complication of "spontaneity" and must wait for the appearance of the transitory phase without being able to produce it at will, the problems are multiplied. It should not be surprising that, as a class of behavioral processes, transitory phenomena have been the least often and least adequately investigated.

A necessary first stage in the investigation of a transitory state is the simple observation of its occurrence. The first observations are not usually the result of an experiment deliberately designed for the purpose. Transitory states are usually observed in conjunction with experimental procedures that were designed with some other end in view. A well-known class of transitory states embraces the temporary behavioral changes that often occur when an experimental procedure is first altered, or when a new stimulus or other variable is introduced for the first time. An organism's initial exposure to electric shock, for example, may produce profound behavioral changes that are never again observed in that organism. Such transitory phenomena are often termed "emotional" both because of their widespread generalized manifestations and because of the adaptation that takes place. Similar transitory effects may be generated by novel stimuli.

The classification of such effects as emotional does not help to control them experimentally. The magnitude and duration of the changes, are, however, important properties to be gleaned from the initial observations. Additional studies which seek to determine the relevant properties of the initiating events, of the behavioral history, of the current behavior, etc., will be required before tight experimental control becomes possible. When such information has been secured, it may then permit one to make some educated guesses about other transitory states in which the initiating events are not so easily observable.

For example, transitory increases in response rate are often observed in avoidance experiments when the subject's response terminates a warning stimulus. The phenomenon is analogous, at an observational level, to an "after-discharge." This observation leads one to suspect a similar process in those cases of transitory rate increases that occur, seemingly spontaneously, when no exteroceptive warning stimulus is terminated. (See the points marked A and B in Figure 17, Chapter 5.) Perhaps, in such cases, the warning stimuli are provided by the subject's own behavior. This notion could be checked by deliberately making some aspect of the subject's ongoing behavior function as a warning signal. If the relevant aspect of behavior is then itself placed under stimulus control, one may achieve a behavioral preparation which permits intensive investigation of the transitory changes that take place.

Sometimes a transitory change may occur because of accidental contingencies between a reinforcing event and some aspect of behavior. Such changes are often observed during the initial acquisition of a response. If a hungry animal is required to press a pedal to obtain food, the first pedal press might be accomplished when the animal happens to lie down on the pedal. Similar responses may subsequently be made in the same manner but in the wrong place, so that no food is forthcoming. The next reinforcement may occur when the animal happens to fall on the pedal after leaping to the top of the chamber. A transitory stage of leaping behavior may then be observed. Such transitory states, when they occur prior to the development of relatively efficient, stereotyped behavior, are often termed "trial-and-error" behavior. There are some who never go beyond these initial observations and classify trial-and-error behavior as a basic learning process. The transitory phases then receive no further investigation.

Such transitory aspects of behavior seem to be completely beyond experimental control. They take place in an experimental setting in which all conditions are presumably constant. The transitory stages themselves occur with frequencies and patterns that are highly variable from subject to subject. How can one come to experimental grips with such transient and variable phenomena? Again, I have no final answer to this problem. Experimental design will have to be oriented around the specific questions being asked, and I am not sure that anyone has yet asked the right questions about transitory states. In the case of transitory changes that occur within a constant environmental setting, it might be profitable to look for accidental contingencies arising from variations in the behavior. Such contingencies could then be duplicated experimentally, and variables of suspected relevance could be manipulated. Additional information of this sort will permit eventual experimental control over the transitory phenomena.

Transitory behavioral changes may sometimes occur because the behavior under observation is being maintained in what may be termed a "borderline state." An example has already been presented in our discussion of the variability that results from weak behavioral control (Chapter 5, p. 168). This situation is particularly likely to exist if the function that describes the relation between the behavior and a major controlling variable is a discontinuous one, or if the function changes rapidly over a small range of values of the controlling variable. Let us take the following example.

Figure 40 illustrates a relation between the rate of avoidance responding and the time interval by which each avoidance response postpones an electric shock (response-shock interval). It may be seen that the response rate displays a sharp peak in the neighborhood of seven seconds for the particular conditions under which this curve was obtained. Small variations in the response-shock interval on either side of the maximum produce relatively large behavioral changes. These data tell us that a borderline state is likely to exist for this subject if we attempt to maintain the avoidance behavior with a response-shock interval of seven seconds. While the characteristic rate will be a high one, controlled by the seven-second interval, there will probably be transitory occurrences of low response rates.

One factor that will determine the frequency and duration of these transitory rate changes will be the degree of variability in the programing apparatus. The more variable the timer that programs the response-shock interval, the more likely we are to observe transient periods of low response rate. Variations in other contributing factors will have the same result. In the present example, shock intensity would be an obvious suspect, since this variable is notoriously difficult to control. Any factor which produces vari-

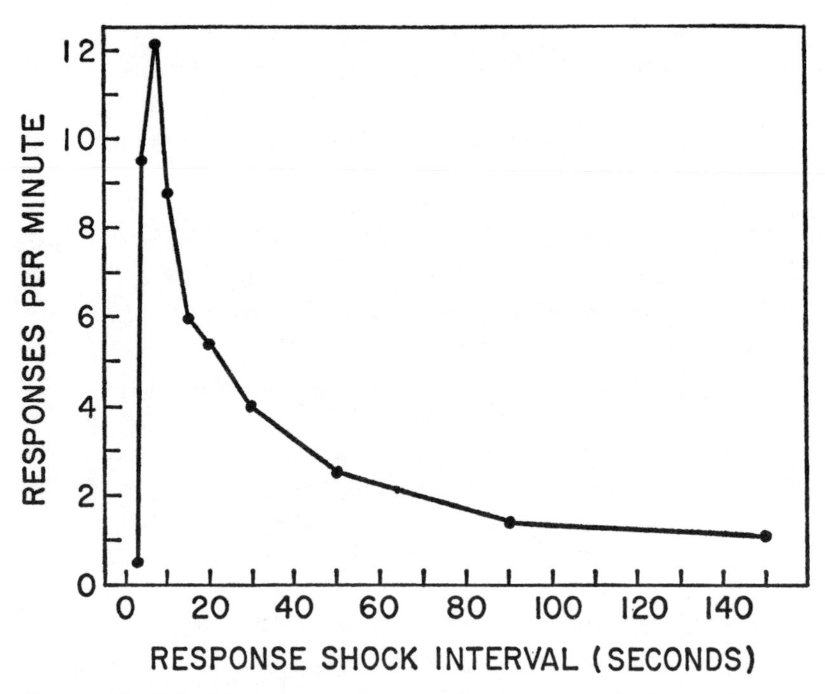

FIGURE 40. Relation between response-shock interval and rate of avoidance responding. (*Adapted from Sidman*, 70.)

ability in the temporal properties of the response will also increase the likelihood of transitory changes. To state this latter point loosely, a seven-second interval may sometimes seem to the subject more like a five- or a ten-second period, and such instances may have a marked effect upon the response rate.

The example illustrates again the need for thorough acquaintance with the characteristics of any baseline behavior one plans to use experimentally. An experiment designed around a poorly understood baseline may be plagued by transitory variability which might otherwise have been prevented by more appropriate selection of values of the controlling parameters. This leads us directly into our next problem of experimental design.

Chapter 11

Selection of an Appropriate Baseline

SOME INVESTIGATIONS have as their aim the study of relations between various types of baseline and specific experimental operations. The baselines themselves will constitute parameters of the phenomenon in question, and will be selected on the basis of considerations peculiar to the problem at hand.

When the baseline itself is not to be manipulated as an independent variable, its selection becomes a critical step in the design of an experiment. An injudicious choice may turn an otherwise well-conceived study into a failure, either by preventing a phenomenon from being observed or by leading to a misinterpretation of the findings. The ideal baseline should possess three major virtues if it is not to obscure either the data or their interpretation. These are stability, sensitivity, and built-in controls for processes extraneous to the purpose at hand.

STABILITY

THE FIRST REQUIREMENT is fairly obvious. If the baseline behavior is excessively variable, any changes brought about by the major experimental operations will be obscured. In consequence, one may decide incorrectly, by statistical or other criteria, that the manipulation in question has no effect upon behavior.

Stability over an extended period of time will often permit the investigator to evaluate his experimental manipulation by means of intrasubject replication. If the baseline is a reversible one, he will be able to apply the experimental operation many times during the course of an experimental period, and thus obtain an economical estimate of the reproducibility of the observed behavioral changes. The experimental operation may consist of a change in the reinforcement contingency with or without stimulus control, alteration in the subject's external or internal environment, the application of punishment, or any of a number of other possibilities. If the operation does turn out to exercise a considerable degree of behavioral control, there is no more exquisite way to demonstrate this than by turning it on and off several times during an experiment. To accomplish such a demonstration, however, the experimenter must select a baseline that remains consistent throughout.

SENSITIVITY

STABILITY, then, is the first requirement of a baseline. Failures to observe a behavioral change may also result, however, from a stable but insensitive baseline. To make a judicious selection on the basis of sensitivity, one must have an intimate acquaintance with the known properties of available baselines. Suppose, for example, one wants to investigate the effects of food deprivation upon response rate. What baseline will best reflect the variations in deprivation? Fixed-ratio reinforcement schedules are known to generate extremely stable behavior, and it might be tempting to maintain the baseline behavior with this schedule. The fixed-ratio reinforcement schedule, however, generates what may be thought of as a very tight form of internal cohesion. Responses early in the count act as discriminative stimuli for the following responses; and later responses act as reinforcers for the earlier ones. This powerful internal control would have to be overcome before changes in deprivation could show up in the response rate. It has, indeed, been shown that fixed-ratio response rates are relatively insensitive to a number of variables, although other aspects of the fixed-ratio performance may be responsive. Therefore, unless one is specifically interested in the effects of deprivation on fixed-ratio behavior, it will be well to use some other type of baseline.

Insensitivity in a behavioral baseline can sometimes be brought about through the experimental operations themselves. Some operations by nature preclude a comprehensive description of their effects unless special precautions are taken. A situation of this sort might be encountered, for example, if we interrupted an experiment for ten minutes each time the subject, working on a variable-interval reinforcement schedule, paused for less than two seconds. That is to say, each pause less than two seconds would produce a ten-minute period, marked by a stimulus, during which no reinforcement would be available.

One method of assessing the effects of such an operation would be to record the time intervals between successive responses (inter-response times) while the variable-interval schedule was in effect. However, the operation of cutting off the experiment after each brief pause would artifactually eliminate most of the inter-response times less than two seconds, since the subject does not respond during the time-out period. Our baseline would, therefore, be insensitive to changes that might otherwise be occurring in the frequency of inter-response times less than two seconds.

The solution to such a problem is relatively simple, for the insensitivity is a product, not of the variable-interval baseline, but rather of our method of scheduling the experimental operation. We can regain all but a negligible degree of sensitivity simply by administering the time-out, not for every pause less than two seconds, but only for occasional such pauses (33). The time-out may itself be produced according to a variable-interval schedule, or any other program that seems appropriate. There will then be minimal constraint on our observations of the baseline behavior.

An ideal baseline would be one in which there is as little interference as possible from other variables. There should be a minimal number of factors tending to oppose any shift in behavior that might result from experimental manipulation. A variable-interval schedule, if skillfully programed, comes close to meeting this requirement. When reinforcements are programed at varying and unpredictable time intervals, there is minimal opportunity for the response to come under specific temporal control, as in fixed-interval and spaced-responding schedules, or under the control of the behavior itself, as in ratio schedules.

Even here, however, one must have an intimate acquaintance with the properties of variable-interval schedules if one is to generate a maximally sensitive baseline. It is very easy to build into a variable-interval programing tape a few sequences that will give the behavior ratio- or interval-like properties, or that will permit other discriminations to form. If the tape has a relatively large number of long intervals, the behavior may come to show the scallops characteristic of fixed-interval performance. An excessive number of short intervals may result in extinction-like negative curvature during the longer periods between scheduled reinforcements. A preponderance of sequences in which a number of consecutive short intervals are followed by a very long interval will produce abrupt declines in rate whenever a short period elapses without a reinforcement. Contingencies of this sort are likely to be extraneous to the variables of major interest, and will act to reduce the sensitivity of the baseline to changes in the manipulated variables.

CONTROL OF EXTRANEOUS PROCESSES

I HAVE SELECTED the above example because it also contains elements relevant to the third criterion of a good behavioral baseline. This criterion requires that the baseline be one that permits the control, or elimination, of undesired behavioral processes. Such a criterion is necessary not simply because extraneous processes may reduce the sensitivity of the baseline but because they also prevent unambiguous evaluation of the data. A variable-interval programing tape, for example, which generates some of the characteristics of fixed-interval behavior also introduces the complex processes involved in fixed-interval behavior. These processes are interesting in their own right, but they only serve to complicate a simple description of behavior that is supposed to be under minimal temporal control. More important, the fixed-interval processes in such a situation will not themselves be under experimental control, and their interaction with the variables of major interest will be difficult to assess. If one is interested in studying such interactions, it would be more appropriate to design an experiment specifically for that purpose.

There are a number of other ways in which particular baselines may generate processes that complicate or obscure experimental findings. One potential source of difficulty may arise from baselines that are characterized by cyclicity of some sort. Suppose, for example, we wish to evaluate a behavioral transition against an ongoing baseline of fixed-interval behavior. The course of the transition may well be a function of the point in the fixed-interval scallop at which we initiate the change in the experimental conditions. A similar situation may hold for fixed-ratio behavior. If one's primary interest is such interactions between the experimental operation and the baseline, one will deliberately introduce the operation at various points in the ratio or interval cycles, and will then go on to compare the resulting transitions. But if such interactions are extraneous to the problem at hand, the experimenter will do well to respect the cycle by breaking into it at the same point each time he introduces a new operation, or to select a baseline that is not characterized by cyclicity at all.

Fixed-ratio and fixed-interval schedules are characterized by relatively clear behavioral cycles, but these and other baselines may also have less obvious cyclic fluctuations, some of which are less obvious because they take place over long periods of time. An intermediate case is that of the warm-up, in which behavior may not reach its stable state for as long as several hours after the start of each experimental session. If it is desirable to eliminate any interaction of the phenomenon under investigation with the variables responsible for the warm-up, the experimenter has three courses open to him. He can employ a baseline that is not characterized by a warm-up; he can wait until the baseline has reached its stable state before introducing a change in the experimental conditions; or he can set his main problem aside temporarily and plunge into an investigation of the warm-up itself, with the hope of getting enough experimental control to be able to eliminate it from the baseline.

Cyclic changes in behavior may also be hidden from view simply because they are not being recorded. In any experiment there is much that our recording instruments do not take into account, and we must be alert to the possibility that unrecorded aspects of the baseline performance will interact with our experimental manipulations. In the DRL schedule, for example, where the reinforcement contingency requires the subject to refrain from emitting the recorded response for a period of time, the state of the behavior during the waiting period undergoes a progressive change that does not show up until we institute specific probe techniques. If such a schedule is employed as a baseline, the introduction of a new variable early in the waiting period is likely to have a different effect than if it were introduced later (72).

Another source of unrecorded activity is the behavior involved in ingesting the food that is commonly employed as a reinforcer in animal experiments. Unless the baseline behavior is maintained by an intermittent reinforcement schedule, eating time is likely to occupy a considerable portion of the observation period. Even more serious is the interference from such behavior when it has not been placed under strict stimulus control. Unless an effective magazine stimulus is provided, and the animal is taught to approach the food magazine only in the presence of such a stimulus, abortive ingestion behavior will occupy a prominent, though unrecorded, segment of the baseline activity. It will then be unclear whether any changes we may induce in the recorded behavior are not simply an indirect reflection of changes in the behavior associated with eating.

Another type of extraneous process normally to be avoided in a baseline is one that actually opposes the effect of the manipulated variable. For example, Ferster carried out an experiment to investigate the effects of punishing rapid responses by means of a time-out. His first problem was the selection of a technique for maintaining the baseline behavior upon which the punishment operation was to act. Relevant here is the fact that he rejected a fixed-ratio reinforcement schedule for the baseline because "the schedule factors in the ratio schedule differentially reinforce high rates of responding, which oppose the effects of the punishment" (33, p. 24). This is not to say that the punishment of fixed-ratio behavior is uninteresting. But in the context of Ferster's investigation, the complication of an opposing process was not germane to the problem at hand.

A similar situation often arises in studying the effects of drugs upon behavior. A tranquilizing drug may tend to lower the probability of behavior whose function it is to avoid shock, but such lowered probability will, in turn, increase the frequency with which the subject is shocked. The higher shock frequency may oppose the effect of the drug, and the experimenter may draw the conclusion that the drug has little or no influence on avoidance behavior. The selection of a baseline of avoidance extinction, or of avoidance with intermittent shock, will tend to minimize the effect of shocks in opposing the drug action.

Multi-element baselines. Stimulus control. When the effects of an experimental operation are to be checked against more than one baseline, the traditional procedure has been to employ different groups of subjects for each baseline and then to make intergroup comparisons. To cite a much-performed experiment as an example, suppose we wish to compare the effects of experimental extinction upon two baselines, one of them maintained by continuous reinforcement and the other by some schedule of intermittent reinforcement. The most common procedure in such experiments has been to employ two groups of subjects, the behavior of each being maintained by its own reinforcement schedule. Then, when the extinction operation has been performed, a comparison is made between, say, the average resistance to extinction displayed by each of the two baseline groups.

Such a comparison suffers from the loss of resolving power that is an inevitable consequence of intergroup comparisons. All the unanalyzed factors that produce intersubject variability are confounded both with the baseline conditions and with the effects of the extinction operation on the baselines.

A forward technical step would be to employ the same subjects for each of the baseline conditions. The subjects could, for example, be exposed first to the continuous reinforcement schedule followed by experimental extinction, and then to the intermittent schedule, followed by a second extinction operation. Some of the difficulties involved in such a procedure have already been discussed (Chapter 3). For the present purpose, however, we may note the advantage of eliminating intersubject variability both from the baselines themselves and from their interaction with the experimental operation. But we still do not have as clean a picture as we would like. Although *inter*subject variability has been eliminated, our data are still confounded with all the uncontrolled factors that act through time to produce *intra*subject variability from one experimental period to the next. Unless explicit controls are instituted, our data will be open to the suspicion that any difference in the effects of the extinction operation might have occurred even on two successive applications to the same baseline.

The most elegant solution to this problem would be the use of a multi-element baseline with the individual subject. Within any single experimental period, the subject can be exposed to both baselines. The experimental operation can then be applied to each element of the baseline in rapid succession or, in some cases, even simultaneously.

To follow our example through, we might place our two baselines, one maintained by continuous and the other by intermittent reinforcement, under stimulus control, and present the two schedules to the subject alternately within the experimental session. Let us suppose our subject is a monkey, and his recorded response is that of pressing a lever. When a light located over the lever is white, every lever press will produce a food reinforcement. When the light is red, the response produces food reinforcements only intermittently, according to whatever reinforcement schedule we have decided to employ as the second element in the multiple baseline. The two stimuli themselves, along with their associated reinforcement schedules, can now be programed in any temporal sequence we wish. For simplicity, let us present them alternately for five-minute periods. When the behavior appropriate to each schedule has stabilized in the presence of its correlated stimulus, we can then institute the operation of experimental extinction. By comparing the performance during the two stimuli, we can evaluate the interaction between the extinction operation and each of the baseline elements individually.

We shall have accomplished considerably more here than the elimination of intersubject variability. In the ideal case, stimulus control of each baseline element acts, so to speak, to split the single subject into two (or more) identical organisms, each performing appropriately to its controlling variables, and each strictly comparable with respect to the factors which normally would have produced intrasubject variation. Whether the ideal case is ever actually met in practice is an open question, for there may well be interactions among the elements of the multiple baseline. The advantages of the technique are so great, however, that the attempt is always worth making. The problems arising from potential interactions among the elements can often be overcome, and a more complete discussion of this topic will be undertaken at a later point.

The student should recognize that I do not suggest multi-element baselines as a time-saver. They may demand considerable labor and time both to gain the required behavioral control and to carry out experimental checks of the possibility of interactions. The value of the multi-element baseline consists not so much in convenience but rather in the degree of experimental control it provides over sources of variability that are normally difficult to manage. Furthermore, the multiple element baseline provides frequent and repeated time samples of each element, and any loss of experimental control that may occur becomes immediately evident and can be taken into account in evaluating the data. This virtue of a repeating multi-element baseline is sufficiently outstanding to warrant an evaluative bias in favor of any experiment that utilizes the technique over one that attacks the same problem in a more traditional fashion. The repeated replication of each element of the baseline permits an otherwise impossible degree of confidence in the adequacy of the experimental control.

Many varieties of multi-element baselines have been described in Ferster and Skinner's treatment of multiple reinforcement schedules (34, pp. 503-579). The example I have used here is also that of a multiple reinforcement schedule (continuous and intermittent reinforcement). Another example is depicted in Figure 29 (Chapter 8), which shows five values of a fixed-ratio schedule, each under stimulus control. With this latter procedure, it is possible not only to observe the differential response rates correlated with each value of fixed ratio but also to evaluate the effects, upon each ratio performance individually, of such independent operations as satiation, drug administration, etc.

The concept of multi-element baselines under stimulus control is generalizable to other methods of behavioral manipulation than reinforcement schedules. The two or more stimuli in a multi-element baseline may, to cite some classical variables, be correlated with different shock intensities, with differing amounts or types of reinforcement, with different reinforcement delays, with different intertrial intervals, with topographically different forms of behavior, with discrimination reversals. The number of possible variables to which the technique can be applied is without limit. If the experiment is concerned with avoidance behavior, each avoidance response may, in the presence of stimulus A, postpone a shock one milliampere in intensity; in the presence of stimulus B, the shock to be avoided may be three milliamperes. Or, if it is desired to investigate the effects of a drug upon behavior in both appetitive and aversive situations, we might permit a response to produce food in the presence of stimulus A, and require it to avoid shock in the presence of stimulus B. We might even use the same type of reinforcement schedule in both stimuli. We could require ten responses to produce each food reinforcement in the presence of stimulus A, and, when stimulus B was on every tenth response could postpone a shock. We might then evaluate the effects of a given drug upon each of the individual baseline elements. The full potentialities of the method have yet to be realized, but there are fascinating possibilities of both a methodological and a systematic nature.

MULTI-ELEMENT MANIPULATIONS. Our discussion thus far has been confined to those cases in which we wish to investigate relations between some single experimental operation and more than one behavioral baseline. The multi-element baseline under stimulus control was one suggested procedure. Before going on to other techniques for attacking this type of problem, we can consider the case in which we wish to investigate the interaction between a single behavioral baseline and several qualitatively or quantitatively different experimental operations.

Suppose, for example, the baseline behavior is being maintained by a variable-interval reinforcement schedule. Our general interest may be in the disruption that occurs in this baseline when we present a stimulus whose termination is accompanied by an unavoidable shock. It has been shown that such a stimulus, after a number of presentations with shock, produces a complete cessation (suppression) of the ongoing baseline behavior (see Figures 5 and 6, Chapter 3). Our immediate interest may be in the way this behavioral suppression develops as a function of the probability that shock will occur at the termination of the stimulus. That is to say, will the suppression develop more rapidly, and will it be more complete when every stimulus is paired with a shock than when only, say, 30 per cent of the stimuli are paired with shock?

Instead of employing two groups of subjects, one exposed to each shock percentage, we may correlate the two operations with different stimuli and expose a single organism to both. For example, while the steady-state baseline behavior is in progress, maintained by a variable-interval reinforcement schedule, we may sometimes present the subject with a pure tone and at other times with a clicking noise. Each stimulus presentation lasts, let us say, for three minutes. At the termination of every tone we administer an unavoidable shock to the subject. Only three out of ten times on the average, however, do we administer the shock after the clicking noise. The other clicker stimuli terminate without any shock. We may then observe the separate development of baseline suppression in the presence of each stimulus. Some preliminary data, obtained by Stein, suggest that the behavioral suppression develops more rapidly in the presence of the stimulus that is always paired with shock (89).

Here is a case, then, in which two quantitatively different operations, each under stimulus control, are applied to a single baseline performance. Both operations can thus be evaluated in a single organism. If it is of interest, one could then go on to investigate the interaction of shock probability with a number of other variables, such as shock intensity, reinforcement conditions, etc. Finally, the effects of shock probability upon resistance of extinction could be studied by removing the shock from both stimuli and examining the subsequent baseline recovery in the presence of the two stimuli.

There is no reason why such a multi-element operation need be confined only to two manipulations. By suitable selection of the experimental subject, it will be possible to obtain a series of points which describe a functional relation between the baseline behavior and several quantitative variations of some experimental operation. Such a function will be free of intersubject variability. Intrasubject variability will usually be minimal or, in the event that it is present to any disturbing extent, will often be detectable through unusual variations in the baseline performance.

An excellent example of the multi-element operation has been provided by Guttman and his co-workers, who have used it to investigate the generalization gradient in the pigeon (38). Their baseline procedure was extinction after variable-interval food reinforcement. Extinction was selected as a baseline because food reinforcement would have introduced irrelevant complicating factors into the evaluation of the generalization data. Extinction following a variable-interval schedule was selected because a stable rate is maintained for a long enough period of time to permit a large number of quantitative variations of the experimental operation. The latter operation consisted simply of periodic changes in the wave length of a stimulus which had previously been kept constant throughout the period of variable-interval reinforcement. The subject was exposed to a large number of wave length variations, and the total number of responses in the presence of each wave length was recorded. It was found that the number of responses steadily diminished as the test wave length differed more and more from the one originally present during reinforcement. The result of this multi-element manipulation was a relatively detailed functional relation between wave length and response rate for the individual organism (see Figure 20, Chapter 6).

I have employed a similar technique to obtain a generalization gradient for avoidance behavior. The baseline, instead of being extinction following food reinforcement, was extinction following avoidance conditioning. The subject was monkey in this case, and the stimulus dimension was auditory click frequency rather than wave length. During avoidance conditioning, clicks were presented at a rate of two per second; during extinction, clicks were presented at frequencies ranging from two to six per second. Again, the number of responses decreased as the click frequency differed more greatly from two per second. The subjects, the stimuli, the baseline behavior, and a number of other conditions differed from Guttman's original demonstration, but the remarkable similarity in the results gives evidence that this multi-element operation has great generality.

Other problems, both new and of classical interest, may be attacked by means of similar techniques. An almost untapped wealth of data awaits the combination of multi-element baselines with multi-element operations. For example, we might wish to investigate possible variations in the generalization gradient as a function of shock intensity. To accomplish such an investigation, we can first establish a multiple avoidance baseline in which several shock intensities are correlated with, let us say, different visual stimuli. When the response key is illuminated with one wave length, the subject avoids a shock of one particular intensity. When the key illumination changes, the shock intensity also changes, and so on, through a series of wave lengths and correlated shock intensities.

Throughout all the elements of the multiple baseline, we maintain a continuous input of auditory clicks to the subject, the clicks coming, let us say, at a rate of two per second. Then, during avoidance extinction, we can vary the click frequency in combination with the several shock-intensity elements of our multiple baseline. That is to say, we continue presenting the various key illuminations, each of which controls a rate of responding appropriate to the shock intensity with which it had been associated during avoidance conditioning. But the click frequency which accompanies each wave length now varies with each presentation. In the course of a single experimental session, each click frequency can occur in combination with each of the various wave lengths. We can then plot a family of curves relating response rate to click frequency for each wave length. Thus, with wave length controlling the elements of the multiple baseline, and the various click frequencies comprising the multi-element manipulation, we have a series of generalization curves from a single organism. The gradients will reflect the interactions, if any, between stimulus generalization and shock intensity.

MULTI-ELEMENT BASELINES. CONCURRENT CONTROL. Up to this point, I have discussed only the type of multi-element baseline in which the subject's behavior is fractionated by means of stimulus control over each separate element. Such baselines carry exciting potentialities for bringing to the experimental science of psychology a degree of rigor and precision that its subject matter demands. But they are hardly the last word. So long as the components of a baseline are separated by periods of time, however brief, there is still a chance for uncontrolled factors to affect each element differentially. The next bold step forward is to program two or more behavioral baselines at the same time (34, pp. 703-721).

There are many ways of programing two baselines concurrently, and exploitation of the technique can only be said to have just begun. As always happens in the initial development of a new technique, unexpected problems, both technical and systematic, have arisen. At present, I shall gloss over the problems and simply review two of the major types of concurrent baselines.

Perhaps the most obvious procedure for generating two baselines simultaneously is to employ two responses, each under the control of a separate set of maintaining contingencies. I have already discussed, in Chapter 7, pp. 228-233, two concurrent baselines of this sort. One response was reinforced with food according to a fixed-ratio (or variable-interval) schedule, while the other, simultaneous response had the function of avoiding electric shock. These two baselines were employed to study one aspect of the conditioned suppression phenomenon to which I have referred several times previously.

In Figure 25, Chapter 7, we saw what happened when we presented a stimulus for five minutes once every ten minutes, and delivered an unavoidable shock coincidentally with each stimulus termination. The response of each baseline to the preshock stimulus was typical of that which is observed when the two baseline performances are generated at separate times. The food-reinforced response was suppressed, and the avoidance response was facilitated.

The demonstration is an elegant one. There are no problems arising from individual differences among subjects, and the simultaneous application of the stimulus to both baselines eliminates temporal variations of the sort that contribute to intrasubject instability. As with the multiple baseline under stimulus control, our subject's behavior is fractionated into two samples. In the present case, however, there is no time interval intervening between the application of the experimental operation to each sample. Here, then, we have another way of obtaining two baseline performances from a single subject, with the additional advantage that both performances occur at the same time. There is thus no opportunity for either sample somehow to change its composition while it is sitting on the shelf awaiting assay. Such changes may, of course, still occur between and even during stimulus presentations, but the factors that produce such variations will at least be acting upon both baselines at the same time.

Figure 41 illustrates the behavior generated by another concurrent two-response baseline. Here again, each lever-pressing response

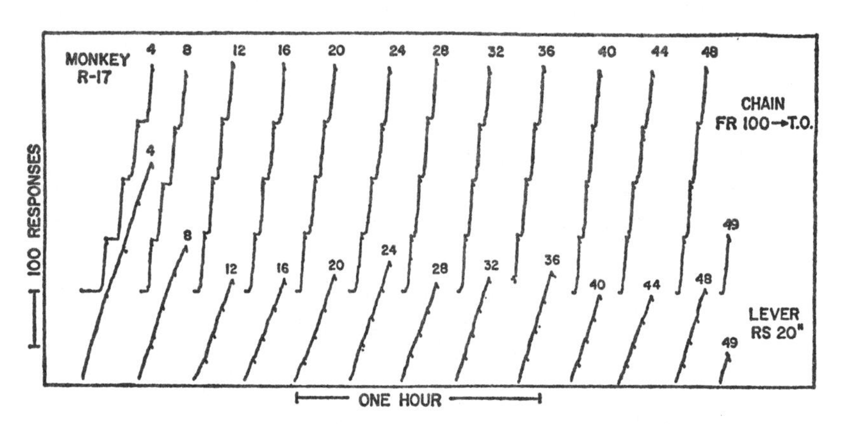

FIGURE 41. Cumulative record of performance on a concurrent two-response procedure. The lower curves show the lever-pressing behavior, where each lever press postponed shock for 20 seconds. The upper curves, on a common time axis, show the chain-pulling behavior, where every hundredth chain pull gave the monkey a five-minute respite (time-out) from the avoidance procedure. The oblique "pips" in both sets of curves denote the time-out periods during which the recorders were stopped. The numbers identify every fourth time-out, to facilitate comparison of the two records.

by the monkey postponed a shock for 20 seconds. The lower set of curves depicts the lever-pressing avoidance behavior. The second response, chain pulling, is reinforced by producing a five-minute period of time-out from the experiment. During the time-out periods, all illumination in the experimental space was extinguished and the shock was disconnected. Each time-out period, therefore, gave the animal five minutes of respite from the avoidance procedure, and, typically, no lever-pressing or chain-pulling responses were emitted at these times.

Not all chain-pulling responses, however, produced the time-out. The reinforcement schedule here was a fixed ratio of 100. That is to say, 100 chain-pulling responses were required to produce each time-out. Furthermore, even the hundredth chain-pulling response could not produce the time out if there had been a lever press within the preceding two seconds. In order for the time-out to occur, in such a case, additional chain pulls had to be made until one occurred at least two seconds following the last lever press. This two-second delay requirement was included in the procedure in order to prevent the lever-pressing response from being adventitiously reinforced by the time-out (see Chapter 12).

The upper set of curves in Figure 41 provides a record of the chain-pulling behavior. Figure 41, therefore, is a concurrent recording of the two responses, and illustrates the eventual development of the fixed-ratio and avoidance baselines. The small vertical markers on the record indicate the time-out periods, during which the recorder was stopped. The two sets of curves are synchronized on the time axis, and every fourth time-out is numbered for convenient identification of corresponding temporal points on the two concurrent records.

Each of the baselines, it may be seen, gives us a picture very similar to that seen when the avoidance and fixed-ratio contingencies are programed separately rather than concurrently. Such differences as do exist from their performance in isolation have turned out not only to be interesting in their own right but also to illuminate the processes involved in isolated avoidance and fixed-ratio behavior. Furthermore, in addition to their intrinsic interest as complex behavioral processes, the concurrent baselines also serve as a useful tool for investigating other phenomena such as the effects of stimuli that precede unavoidable shocks, the factors governing conditioned reinforcement, and the behavioral effects of drugs. Upon each application of a new variable, we are able to take simultaneous recordings of any changes that occur in the two concurrent baselines.

A second major class of concurrent baselines is one in which only a single response is employed. A basic requirement must be met if a single response is to yield two useful concurrent baseline performances: there must be some way of distinguishing the two performances within a single record.

The most effective way of accomplishing such a distinction is to employ baselines that are characterized by different temporal patterns. This imaginative technique, like so many of the others I have discussed, was introduced by Ferster and Skinner (34, pp. 709 ff.). Using only a single response, they programed a fixed-interval food reinforcement schedule concurrently with an avoidance contingency. The characteristic fixed-interval pattern of behavior makes it relatively easy to identify the two components of the baseline. Following each reinforcement, the subject responds at a low stable rate appropriate to the avoidance contingency, as is illustrated in Figure 42. (Normally, as we have seen before, when the fixed-interval schedule is programed alone, the period following reinforcement is devoid of responses.) Eventually, the typical fixed-interval scallop

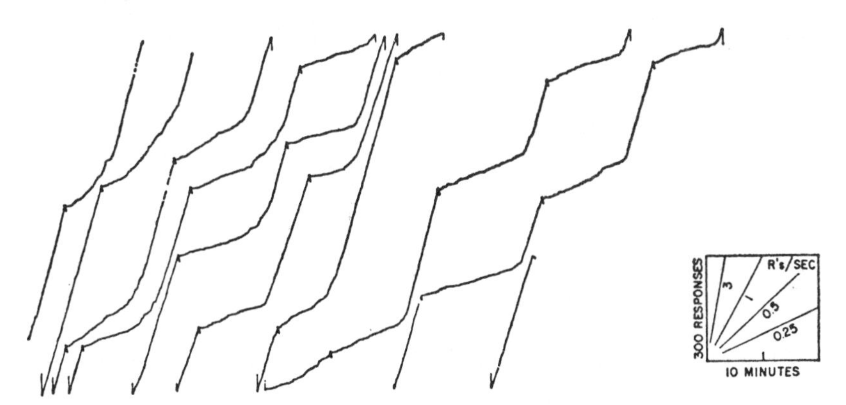

FIGURE 42. A well-developed concurrent performance when shock avoidance and a fixed-interval food-reinforcement schedule are in effect at the same time. The "pips" in the record indicate food reinforcements. (*Adapted from Ferster and Skinner,* 34, p. 714.)

emerges from the initial steady avoidance rate. The performance thus separates out into two components, one controlled by the avoidance contingency and the other by the fixed interval. It is possible now to apply some experimental operation, such as drug administration, and observe its effects upon each component of the concurrent baseline.

SIMULTANEOUS CONTROL OF BEHAVIOR BY A MULTIPLICITY OF VARIABLES

In the preceding discussion, I have several times dodged the chief problem that may be encountered in the use of complex baselines. Whenever we program a multi-element baseline, we are deliberately placing the behavior under the control of a multiplicity of variables. If we are interested in studying the effects of some operation upon each baseline element separately, we must be certain that there are no important interactions among the controlling variables. For example, we may place shock avoidance and food reinforced behavior under separate stimulus control and program each as an element in a multiple baseline. But how adequate is the stimulus control? Are the two baseline elements actually independent of each other, or does the performance on one depend to some extent on variables that are supposedly relevant only to the other? The problem becomes even more acute when the elements of the baseline are programed concurrently. In that case, the variables controlling each baseline element are actually present at the same time. Can their control really be channeled independently to different aspects of the organism's performance?

In the present state of our knowledge, the answers to such questions must be strictly empirical. The important point is that there are techniques available for determining the answers in any specific case (43). Current data indicate that interactions will be encountered in some instances, but that they are not inevitable. The conditions that make either for independence or for interaction among the components of a multi-element baseline remain to be worked out.

But our interest in such interactions should not be confined merely to the problem of eliminating them. The simultaneous control of behavior by a multiplicity of variables may be a nuisance when we want to employ a multi-element baseline as a tool to study the effects of some operation upon each baseline element independently. On the other hand, the deliberate study of such multiple control is, in itself, a fascinating research problem. Even more strongly, it is a research problem that *must* be attacked. Behavior is characteristically under the multiple control of interacting variables, and any adequate systematic account, either descriptive or theoretical, must include such interactions. Furthermore, as a by-product of this independent study, information will emerge which will allow us to evaluate the precision of control in a given multi-element baseline. The techniques for checking such precision are the same as those to be used for the deliberate study of interaction effects.

How does one design experiments to study the simultaneous control of behavior by a multiplicity of variables? The experimenter's first task is to determine whether the procedure he has adopted really does establish such multiple control.

Suppose the procedure in question is a multi-element baseline, with each element under separate stimulus control. One way of checking for interactions among the elements is to run control experiments in which each component appears separately. A comparison can then be made between a given element when programed by itself and when programed as a component of a multiple procedure. If, for example, the procedure in question is a multiple fixed-interval and fixed-ratio schedule, we might run control procedures of fixed interval alone and fixed ratio alone, and observe whether they differ alone and in combination with each other.

Such a control might seem to be the most direct and the most satisfactory one. Actually, it constitutes only a first step and, by itself, is far from adequate. It will help us to determine whether the component behaviors maintain their general characteristics when the schedules are programed in temporal juxtaposition under separate stimulus control. But there may still be quantitative interactions which can be observed only through deliberate experimental manipulation.

Suppose, for example, we make a quantitative alteration in a parameter of one of the components of a multiple schedule. Let us change the value of the fixed ratio from 50 to 200 responses per reinforcement. A change in the ratio performance is to be expected, but the important question here is whether there will also be a change in the fixed-interval behavior. If there is, we must conclude that our two components are not independent of each other and that the interval behavior is governed by both the interval and the ratio contingencies. Programing the two components independently of each other might not have shown this.

Here then, is our second method of checking for simultaneous control by more than one variable. The first method was independent verification; the second consists of functional manipulation. The method of functional manipulation is not only a technique for identifying interaction effects; it is also the primary means for their further investigation. By varying the parameters of control, we can generate a quantitative description of the interaction spectrum. In addition to such basic information, of value in its own right, we may also receive a bonus in the form of a range of parameter values over which there is little or no interaction. If, for other purposes, we wish to establish a multi-element baseline free from interaction effects, we could then select from such parameter values.

Functional manipulation will also give us an inductive basis for identifying processes responsible for interaction effects. Let us go into some finer details of our multiple fixed-interval and fixed-ratio program. The elements of such a program might be scheduled in a number of possible sequences. Suppose we have selected a pattern in which the two schedules, along with their correlated stimuli, alternate after each reinforcement. Applying the technique of functional manipulation, we systematically increase the fixed-ratio requirement. Let us assume that, as we increase the ratio size, not only do we disrupt the ratio performance but we also observe a systematically decreasing output during the fixed-interval component.

There are several conclusions we might draw from such an observation, but I shall arbitrarily select one. We ask ourselves the question: "What processes can be responsible for the interaction between the size of the ratio and the performance on the interval schedule?" Upon re-examining our procedure, we see a possible answer to this question. Behavior in conjunction with the interval stimulus not only produces food according to the fixed-interval requirement; it also produces the stimulus appropriate to the ratio schedule. We may then wonder whether the interval behavior is being controlled by both of its consequences, the food reinforcement and the ratio schedule, in combination. Increasing the ratio size might, in such an event, decrease the reinforcing value of the combination, and this could perhaps account for the lowered fixed-interval output.

We are then off on a new series of experiments. One variation of the original procedure might be to interpose a period of time-out between each component. This would provide a temporal separation between the interval and ratio schedules, and would keep the immediate consequences of the interval behavior constant even while we varied the ratio size. Increasing the ratio size might then have no effect upon the interval performance.

Another course of action might be to alternate the schedules only after every second reinforcement. We would then have alternating sequences of two ratio runs, two intervals, etc. This would maintain a constant set of consequences for the first interval performance of each pair, while the second interval of the pair would be expected to show the deleterious effects of an increasing ratio size. If we wish then to reduce still further the interaction between ratio and interval, we might change the alternation pattern even more drastically by switching the schedule, say, after every tenth reinforcement.

If such manipulations do indeed work out as expected not only will we have identified a source of multiple determination of behavior but we will have provided ourselves with the means for eliminating the interactions. This is perhaps the chief advantage of functional manipulation over a statistical analysis of interaction effects. Statistical techniques—for example, analysis of variance—can at best indicate that interactions are present in a given set of data. Functional manipulation not only provides this information in greater detail but also accomplishes the more advanced objectives of experimental control over and systematic understanding of the interaction in question.

If, as may often be the case, it is impossible to eliminate the interactions among several controlling variables, the method of functional manipulation will tell us this. In such a case we must learn to live with behavior as we find it. If two or more variables are found to be inextricably interlocked in their control of an individual's behavior, then we have discovered a fact of nature. Our only course is to investigate the interaction by means of functional manipulations, so that its magnitude and intricacies are made known over a wide variety of conditions. If behavior under experimental observation is controlled simultaneously by two or more variables, no amount of statistical manipulation can immobilize any of the confounded factors. Statistical control of multiple causation is a device for manipulating the verbal behavior of the experimenter; it has no effect upon the behavior of the experimental subject.

Two or more variables may be confounded in nature, or they may deliberately be combined by the experimenter whose interest is in multiple causation. In the latter case, it may be desirable to use an experimental design that permits a continuous evaluation of the interaction against a baseline in which each of the component variables acts independently. Suppose we want to investigate behavior that is under the simultaneous control of a shock-avoidance contingency and a variable-interval food reinforcement schedule. One way to accomplish this would be to program each of these procedures concurrently, so that a given response performs the simultaneous functions of avoiding shock and procuring food. Our plan now is to manipulate some of the variables that are known to be relevant when each of these types of control is acting independently of the other. Let us start with shock intensity. Suppose we find, in general, that as we increase the shock intensity the response rate also increases. We shall then want to know whether the amount of increase is in any way conditioned by the presence of the concurrent variable-interval schedule. Is the behavioral response to changes in shock intensity governed by an interaction with the variable-interval food-reinforcement schedule, or is this response simply the same as would be seen if the avoidance contingency were programed separately?

It may be possible to answer this question by including our concurrent procedure as one of the elements of a multiple baseline under stimulus control. The multiple baseline would consist of three components: the variable-interval schedule alone, the avoidance contingency alone, and both of these programed concurrently. Each of the three elements would be correlated with its own stimulus. We could then vary shock intensity and observe its effects upon each baseline component.

Since this experiment has not, to my knowledge, been performed, I am free to speculate on its possibilities. We might find, with rising shock intensity, that the response rate increases during the concurrent element of the multiple baseline. Let us suppose that the change is several times greater than the increase that also occurs in the separate avoidance component. This would certainly indicate that the effect of shock intensity in the concurrent element is conditioned by an interaction with the accompanying variable-interval schedule.

We will also want to examine the variable-interval component of the multiple baseline. Whatever we observe here will be of interest. If the variable-interval response rate by itself shows no change as a function of shock intensity, then we are faced with a challenge. How, in such a case, could the concurrent variable-interval schedule increase the sensitivity of the avoidance behavior to changes in shock intensity?

If, on the other hand, the variable-interval response rate should decline as we increase shock intensity, then we have a possible clue as to the nature of the interaction in the concurrent element. Such a result would suggest that the variable-interval schedule acts as a brake upon the rate of concurrent avoidance responding at low shock intensities, but that the braking action is eliminated when higher shock intensities depress the variable-interval rate. We could then go on to check this notion in other ways.

The third possible result would be an increase in response rate during the variable-interval component. In such an event, we would then attribute the rate increase during the concurrent element to a summation, or perhaps a more complex function, of the changes observed during the two independent components of the baseline.

I could go on to suggest other possibilities in this situation, but these should be evident by now to the alert reader. In any case, my purpose here is not to provide the student with a thesis problem. I am simply suggesting an experimental methodology for attacking the problem of simultaneous interaction among several variables.

The method depends upon the availability and utilization of a behavioral technology that allows the precise control of individual behavior. Furthermore, it is not an experimental design intended to provide any final answers. As our example demonstrated, almost any result will demand further investigation. It is a procedure which will be found congenial by those experimenters who wish to enlarge their universe of discourse rather than to seek closure.

Chapter 12

Control Techniques

THE TOPIC OF EXPERIMENTAL CONTROL is by no means independent of the material in the preceding chapters, and I have already referred to it in many places. Control techniques are relevant to any general discussion of data evaluation, as well as to problems of replication, variability, and experimental design. The student may have noticed, however, both in the present context and in his other reading, that the term "control" does not always have the same intended meaning. For example, I have often referred to the investigator's obligation to secure as tight a degree of experimental control as possible over the behaving individual who serves as his subject.

In this sense, experimental control refers to the investigator's ability to manipulate an individual subject's behavior in a precise and reliable fashion. To be able to turn some quantitatively consistent aspect of behavior on and off by the manipulation of specifiable variables demonstrates a high order of control. To be able to run some aspect of behavior reliably through a graded series of different states represents an even higher level of control.

The well-developed behavioral technology implicit in this use of the term is also required when the term is employed in a second prevalent meaning. We often talk about "control experiments," or "control observations." In this sense, we are referring to techniques for determining whether our experimental results are actually a product of our explicit manipulations, or whether they stem from the operation of some other known or even unsuspected factors. If, for example, we introduce a new variable and observe a change in some ongoing baseline, we might wonder whether the change would have occurred at that point anyway, even if we had not altered the experimental conditions. We might then perform a control experiment to check upon this possibility. Or we might wonder whether a particular observation resulted solely from our current experimental manipulations or whether the organism's behavioral history also played a role. In such a case we would run control experiments with subjects possessing different histories.

Experimental control, then, refers to our ability to manipulate behavior. *Control experiment*, on the other hand, denotes a technique for checking our understanding of the manipulations we have performed. Can we be sure that our data result from our explicit experimental manipulations, or are there other factors at work? What kinds of variables are likely to deceive us into unwarranted conclusions?

The student should bear in mind that experimental control is as basic to our understanding of behavior as it is to our manipulation of behavior. Skillful manipulation is the most productive method for gaining understanding. It is because of this relation that I have already discussed much of the material on control techniques in the preceding chapters. I shall, therefore, include here only such problems of control technique as were not more appropriately discussed in other contexts.

Control Techniques

STANDARDIZATION OF TECHNIQUE

VERY OFTEN the necessity for control experiments does not arise, or is not recognized, until another investigator discovers that he cannot replicate the original findings. On the assumption that both the original experiment and the replicative attempt were competently performed, the reason for the discrepancy is often sought in differences of technique. Perhaps one investigator uses a food magazine in which the empty cup remains accessible to the subject between reinforcements, whereas the other investigator removes the cup from the subject's reach immediately after each reinforcement. Or one laboratory may customarily employ a constant-current shocking device while another prefers a constant-voltage shock. There may be differences in the type and size of the reinforcements, in the type of switching action built into the response key, in the duration of the experimental sessions, in the method of terminating each session (e.g., on the basis of a fixed period of time or a fixed number of reinforcements), in the size of the experimental space, and in many other details of experimental technique.

One point of view holds that such technical details, while admittedly important, are not germane to the major goals of behavioral research. It is felt that they are specific to certain laboratory procedures and are of no value in terms of generalizable behavioral principles. Control experiments necessitated by variations in the finer details of experimental technique are considered wasteful of time and effort. One suggestion for eliminating such wasteful confusion is that experimental technique in a given area of research be standardized. A set of conventions should be agreed upon and employed by all workers in the area.

A suggested basis for standardizing any aspect of technique is that the technique provide the highest possible level of behavioral control. The response key, for example, should be characterized by a level of sensitivity, a physical conformation, and a location in the experimental space that will effectively minimize competing behavior which would otherwise interfere with the recorded response. A standard food reinforcement should be adopted, of such a composition that animals of a given species can be maintained in good health solely by the reinforcements they obtain in each experimental session. Such standardization would permit a rigorous control of body weight, consistent from one laboratory to another. It would also minimize any variability which might arise from the reinforcement of unspecified behavior in the home environment between experimental sessions.

There is much to be said in favor of the standardization of experimental technique. The student should carefully consider the possibility of standardization before he goes off and devises idiosyncratic apparatus and procedures. He is likely thereby to save himself and others a considerable amount of labor which would otherwise be expended upon control experiments designed to reconcile differences between his data and those gathered by others in related investigations. He should pay particular attention to aspects of technique which are common to many experimental problems. If necessary, he should visit or correspond with investigators whose work has demonstrated their technical proficiency and obtain from them the specifications necessary for standardization.

Nonstandardized experimental techniques will, in the long run, retard the progress of any experimental science. There can be little developmental continuity if each experimenter works in a vacuum, governed solely by his own ingenuity and limited by the available supply of rubber bands, paper clips, and other assorted bits of apparatus left in the laboratory stockroom from bygone days. Psychology is presently suffering from just such a form of chaos, attested to by the considerable amount of journal space devoted to controversies, control experiments, and procedural minutiae which are a direct consequence of nonstandardized techniques.

Nonetheless, there are some cogent arguments against standardization. Do we have enough information about the relative effectiveness of the many possible variations on any experimental technique? There has been little systematic exploration of such variations. In many cases, important variations in technique have been adopted for reasons difficult to specify. They are simply part of the laboratory lore, a compound of incomplete observations, hunches, and historical accidents. Thus, one laboratory employs a response key which is so sensitive that it can almost be operated by blowing upon it, while in another laboratory, all keys are constructed so as to require at least a half-inch excursion before they will close. In establishing a fixed-interval baseline, one group of investigators times each successive interval from a reinforced response, while another group times the intervals solely by means of a clock, with no reference to the subject's behavior. Those who argue against standardization of technique point out that we do not know which of these and other similar variations produce the most effective behavioral control. They argue that standardization would therefore be premature.

Where does this leave the student? Eager to start off on an investigation whereby he hopes to learn something about behavior, he may be unwilling to sidetrack his efforts into technical problems. The answer must be in the form of a compromise. Unless he is working in an area in which there is no precedent, he would be foolish not to pattern his techniques after those which have already proved most successful. On the other hand, personal experience with a variety of technical variations is a time-tested method for giving the investigator the maturity of judgment required for proper evaluation of his own and others' data. Every student should, therefore, spend some time as a technical apprentice before he launches his investigative career. If his teachers do not make explicit provision for such an apprenticeship, he should undertake it on his own. The period of apprenticeship should not only help to provide the student with some notion as to how far he can carry technical standardization but also leave him with a permanent attitude of skepticism in matters of technique. That is to say, he should explicitly recognize that some aspects of his own techniques and of those employed by others are firmly based upon evidence or upon relatively solid general principles, but that others are simply derived from laboratory lore. The former will remain standardized; the latter are likely to undergo further development. The compromise, then, is to standardize technique as much as possible in order to maintain experimental continuity within the field, but to be prepared for technical advance when new evidence prompts it.

A second objection to technical standardization may also be resolved by the application of prudence and an attitude of skepticism. Variations in technique often yield data that are important in a systematic context. Technical standardization might effectively prevent, or at least delay, the acquisition of such data.

For example, through an application of what I now recognize to be poor reinforcement technique, I was able to observe, for the first time, the adventitious involvement of a food-reinforced response in an avoidance contingency. This observation occurred in the context of a concurrent two-response procedure, with monkeys as subjects. One response was maintained by a reinforcement of sweetened orange juice, available to the subjects on a four-minute variable-interval schedule. A second response, simultaneously available, had the function of avoiding shock.

The conditions maintaining the food-reinforced response generated very poor control. This was demonstrated by a low, irregular rate of food-reinforced responding whenever the avoidance behavior was extinguished. But each time the shock-avoidance contingency was reintroduced, exerting a relatively strong form of control over the second response, the food-reinforced behavior also increased in rate and regularity.

Further investigation revealed that the food response had adventitiously entered into the avoidance contingency and had become, unrealistically from the observer's point of view, a component of the avoidance behavior (see pp. 228-233). Additional work indicated that if I had originally employed a more effective reinforcer than orange juice, and had used a schedule which made reinforcements available more frequently than once every four minutes, this phenomenon would never have been observed. Instead, the avoidance response would have become a component of the food-reinforced behavior, a phenomenon of great interest but nonetheless a different one, and one which had already been observed in several laboratories.

To standardize a technique solely upon the basis of a high degree of experimental control may, then, automatically prevent the observation of important behavioral phenomena. Variables that are immobilized by technical specification may turn out to be significant parameters of a behavioral process. Low motivation, for example, is known to allow only weak experimental control and is thereby shunned by most experimenters. But the behavior of subjects under low motivation may reveal new phenomena and may require radical changes in our systematic account of behavior.

The solution to this problem, insofar as there is one, does not lie in the abandonment of technical standardization. It will involve, rather, the adoption of a more flexible basis for standardizing technique. Rigorousness of experimental control will still form the major criterion, but the level of control must be evaluated in terms of the purpose of a given experiment. If one wishes to investigate phenomena associated with weak behavioral control, there is no choice but to depart from standard practice. If a new area of research problems is then uncovered, technique within that area will gradually develop its own standardization. Even if a departure from standard practice does not yield new findings, the attempt will provide direct evidence for or against the desirability of standardizing that particular aspect of technique. We will then know whether a particular variable is of general or only of technical interest. But one should always be prepared to discover that a previously taken-for-granted and frozen aspect of technique actually controls a number of highly informative and exciting behavioral phenomena.

Such factors as deprivation or satiation, size and type of reinforcement, key sensitivity, size of the experimental space, etc., are commonly subject to explicit control techniques. There are a number of variables, however which have received relatively little experimental attention and which, therefore, are not generally recognized as requiring deliberate control. These variables are the borderline provinces of our empirical knowledge. There is enough evidence, published and unpublished, to suggest not only that they require the application of control techniques but also that they will repay intensive investigation in their own right. It is such investigation, of course, that will reveal the most effective control techniques and will delineate the specific situations in which control techniques are necessary. Meanwhile, it will be of some value simply to point out some of these borderline variables and to indicate their potential control requirements.

ADVENTITIOUS REINFORCEMENT

IN SPITE OF MANY ATTEMPTS to derive it rationally, the principle of reinforcement remains an empirical statement. The basic experimental observation is that there are events which, when contingent upon a response, will increase the probability of occurrence of that response. Identification of the precise conditions under which such events will function as reinforcers has been one of the main preoccupations of experimental psychologists during the past twenty-five years or more.

For our present purpose we can concentrate on a generally neglected aspect of the empirical statement. Note that there is no reference either to the intent of the subject or, even more important, to the intent of the experimenter. The operation of a reinforcing event is automatic. Whenever such an event occurs in proper relation to behavior it will exert its reinforcing effect, regardless of whether or not the investigator has included such an effect in his experimental design and regardless of whether or not he records the behavior so affected.

An early demonstration of the automatic action of reinforcing events was provided by B. F. Skinner (82). Perhaps because of its intriguing title, " 'Superstition' in the Pigeon," the mundane implications of Skinner's paper for experimental control techniques were not immediately appreciated by most investigators. The demonstration was a simple one. Hungry pigeons were placed in an experimental space and were periodically given access to grain for a few seconds. No particular behavior was required of the pigeons in order for the grain to be delivered. After leaving the pigeons in this situation overnight, Skinner returned in the morning to find them performing well-definable stereotyped patterns of behavior.

One bird was conditioned to turn counter-clockwise about the cage, making two or three turns between reinforcements. Another repeatedly thrust its head into one of the upper corners of the cage. A third developed a "tossing" response, as if placing its head beneath an invisible bar and lifting it repeatedly. Two birds developed a pendulum motion of the head and body, in which the head was extended forward and swung from right to left with a sharp movement followed by a somewhat slower return. The body generally followed the movement and a few steps might be taken when it was extensive. Another bird was conditioned to make incomplete pecking or brushing movements directed toward but not touching the floor. . . .

The conditioning process is usually obvious. The bird happens to be executing some response as the hopper appears; as a result it tends to repeat this response. If the interval before the next presentation is not so great that extinction takes place, a second "contingency" is probable.

This strengthens the response still further and subsequent reinforcement becomes more probable (82, p. 168).

In recent years, observations closely related to those described by Skinner have become increasingly frequent. Reinforcement which strengthens behavior without there being any causal relation between the two in fact has been termed "adventitious reinforcement." The phenomenon has been found useful in helping to explain such seemingly diverse forms of behavior as neurotic or psychotic disturbances and scientific theory construction. Both of these forms of activity are often characterized by adventitious correlations between behavior and subsequent reinforcing events. Fascinating though this line of inquiry may seem, however, our present concern is with the implications of adventitious reinforcement for control techniques. There are a number of specific experimental situations in which adventitious reinforcement has been shown to play a role which, if not controlled, can greatly distort our evaluation of the resulting data.

DISCRIMINATION EXPERIMENTS. To place a sample of behavior under stimulus control is often desirable either for technical reasons, as in a multi-element baseline, or in order to investigate the processes involved in such stimulus control. We may be concerned with the specificity of the stimulus control, as in generalization experiments; with the course of development of the stimulus control, as in discrimination-learning experiments; with relations between specific stimulus dimensions and sensory capacity, as in psychophysical experiments; with physiological concomitants of stimulus control as revealed, for example, by concurrent electrophysiological recording. All of these types of experiment require the assumption that the stimuli in question do, indeed, exercise some degree of control over behavior. But it is not enough simply to make the assumption; the fact of control and the degree of control must be demonstrated. Such a demonstration may prove impossible if it is not recognized that discriminative stimuli also exercise conditioned aversive or reinforcing functions and that these functions may act, adventitiously, to obscure the discriminative control which is of major interest.

A simple illustration should make this point clear. What is the most unequivocal demonstration that a given stimulus controls the emission of a specified sample of behavior? It is the establishment of a baseline in which the desired behavior always appears whenever the stimulus is present, and rarely occurs in the absence of the stimulus in question. Every student who has had the elementary experimental psychology course has either performed this demonstration or has been told how to go about it. Those who performed the experiment as part of their laboratory assignment can, however, if they think back, undoubtedly remember a number of cases in which the results were not quite as anticipated. Some of their subjects, although reinforced only in the presence of a certain stimulus, never did cease responding in the absence of this stimulus. The discrimination never "came in."

If the graduate assistant who conducted the laboratory section was on the ball, he probably seized upon the negative results as an opportunity to demonstrate the action of adventitious conditioned reinforcement. The discriminative stimulus in such experiments is usually presented at arbitrary times, without reference to the ongoing behavior of the subject. Such an arbitrary schedule of stimulus presentation permits an occasional chance correlation between the recorded response and the onset of the stimulus.

Look at it from the subject's point of view. Let us suppose he is just beginning to learn that a particular response is reinforced only in the presence of a certain stimulus when, lo and behold, the stimulus itself appears just after he has emitted one of these responses. He is in essentially the same position as Skinner's superstitious pigeons. His behavior has produced a stimulus in whose presence reinforcement was forthcoming. The fact that the stimulus would have appeared anyway, even without the response, is of no consequence. The conditioned reinforcing function of the stimulus is independent of the experimenter's intentions.

The end result is an increase in the likelihood that the response will occur again during the next stimulus-off period, and a corresponding increase in the likelihood that the response will again "produce" the stimulus. The process spirals, and if the original purpose was to demonstrate behavior under stimulus control, the experiment turns out to be a failure. The behavior may occur just as often in the absence as in the presence of the stimulus. If the experimenter is not alert to the possibility of adventitious reinforcement, he may conclude that the subject is deaf, or blind, or otherwise lacking in discriminative capacity, and he may discard his data.

Adventitious reinforcement by a discriminative stimulus is neither a transient nor a weak form of behavioral control (57). Behavior may be maintained adventitiously for an indefinite period of time, even by a conditioned reinforcer. Furthermore, the behavior so maintained may exhibit all of the characteristics normally observed when the contingency is a real one. If, in our demonstration experiment, for example, the stimulus-off period has a fixed duration, the adventitiously reinforced behavior will conform to a fixed-interval pattern. Figure 43 illustrates an instance. The procedure here was a

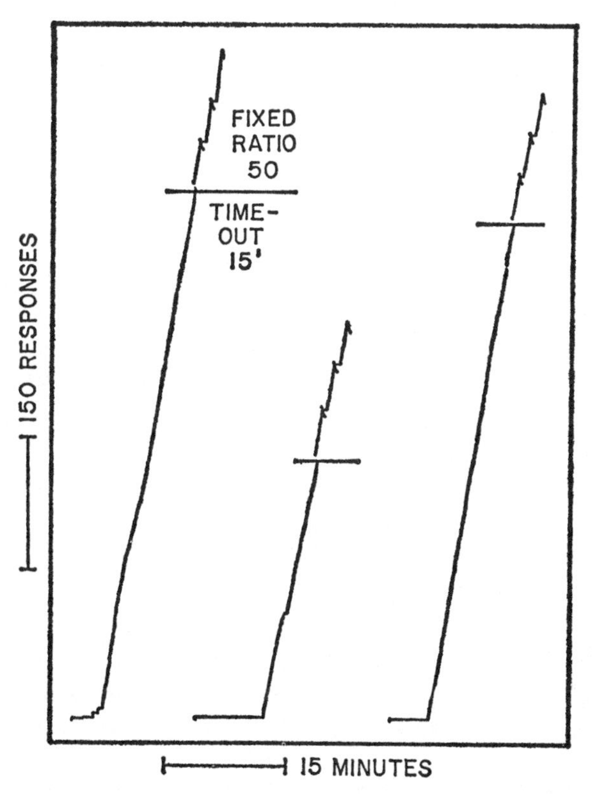

FIGURE 43. Segments of a rat's performance on a multiple schedule in which 15-minute periods of time-out alternated with a fixed-ratio reinforcement schedule. The horizontal lines separate the records of time-out behavior from the records of fixed-ratio behavior. (*Data generously supplied by R. Hill.*)

multiple schedule, with alternating periods of extinction (time-out) and fixed-ratio reinforcement. After each 15-minute extinction period a new stimulus appeared. In the presence of this stimulus, three reinforcements were delivered, each of them after a run of 50 responses.

Note the fixed-interval scallops during the 15-minute extinction periods. Not only is the behavior during extinction periods being reinforced adventitiously by the stimulus correlated with fixed-ratio reinforcement, but it is being maintained in a manner consistent with the periodicity of the stimulus. All this in spite of the fact that responses during the extinction period have, in reality, no influence at all upon the presentation of the fixed-ratio stimulus.

This example of the power of adventitious reinforcement gives us a clue to one control technique that is applicable in discrimination experiments. In demonstrating the discriminative control exercised by a stimulus, it is not necessary to have zero responding in the absence of that stimulus. If the two functions of the stimulus, discriminative and reinforcing, generate two distinct temporal patterns of behavior, we will have accomplished our purpose, and Figure 43 is certainly an adequate demonstration of stimulus control.

In designing a discrimination experiment, then, it would be foresighted to arrange both the primary reinforcement schedule and the stimulus presentation schedule in such a way that, even should an adventitious contingency occur, the behavior patterns would differ in the presence and absence of the stimulus. If, for example, we were to use a variable-interval schedule in the presence of the stimulus, and also randomly vary the duration of the extinction periods, we might end up with indistinguishable behavior patterns in the two stimulus conditions.

A related method of dealing with this problem is to program an explicit contingency between the behavior and the presentation of the stimulus correlated with positive reinforcement. Instead of banking upon adventitious reinforcement to generate a distinctive behavior pattern in the absence of the stimulus, one can utilize the chaining technique developed by Ferster and Skinner. This technique is our most powerful tool for demonstrating and investigating conditioned reinforcement. It is also an excellent method for demonstrating stimulus control. Primary reinforcement is available only in the presence of a given stimulus, but the presentation of this discriminative stimulus is also dependent on the subject's behavior (conditioned reinforcement). The schedules of primary and conditioned reinforcement may differ enough to produce different behavior patterns, thus demonstrating stimulus control. The data of Figure 43 might well have been obtained in this direct manner instead of relying upon an adventitious contingency.

A third technique of control for adventitious reinforcement in discrimination experiments is appropriate when, for one reason or another, we require zero responding in the absence of the discriminative stimulus. This technique, attributed in its original form to Page, makes the appearance of the stimulus contingent on the absence of responding (94). We can schedule the stimulus to come on, let us say, after 15 minutes of extinction, but only if there has been no response during the minute preceding the scheduled presentation. Each response during this critical 60-second period serves only to postpone the onset of the stimulus until the required criterion of no response has been met.

With this technique, the stimulus can never appear earlier than 60 seconds after a response, and the possibility of adventitious reinforcement is eliminated. The method, however, is in principle no different from the chaining procedure. Both cases take advantage of the conditioned reinforcing function of the discriminative stimulus. One procedure uses the stimulus to reinforce the recorded response; the other uses the stimulus to reinforce any behavior except the recorded response. Neither procedure would work if the stimulus were not a conditioned reinforcer. On the other hand, neither would be necessary if that were the case.

All of the above control techniques, then, have in common the feature that behavior in the absence of the discriminative stimulus is still under the control of a reinforcement contingency, deliberate or adventitious. For some purposes, such control may be undesirable. With a behavioral baseline such as that in Figure 43, for example, we might be interested in the effect of a shock upon the discriminative control exercised by the stimulus. Or we might wish to check the effect of a drug upon such control. Administration of a shock or a drug might be found to alter the scallop and make the pre-stimulus behavior resemble the fixed-ratio component of the baseline. Can we now say that our experimental operations wiped out the discriminative control of the stimulus? Stated more loosely, does the shock, or the drug, prevent the subject from telling the difference between stimulus-off and stimulus-on? This would be a too-hasty conclusion. The effect of the shock or the drug might simply have been specific to fixed-interval scallops. Perhaps the same result would have been observed if a fixed-interval schedule had been programed independently, without the discriminative stimulus control. We would then have to carry out an experimental check on this possibility, even though the original scallop may have been generated and maintained by adventitious reinforcement.

It may, however, prove impossible to carry out such an experimental check. There is an important difference between any explicitly programed reinforcement contingency and its adventitious counterpart. This difference raises what may be an insoluble control problem and provides enough reason, perhaps, to design experiments so as to minimize adventitious control. It concerns the potential reversibility of an experimentally produced change in the baseline behavior.

If the baseline behavior is maintained by an explicitly programed reinforcement contingency, an experimental operation such as drug administration may alter the degree of control exercised by the contingency. But when the effect of the drug has worn off, the reinforcement contingency, since it is still being programed, can be expected to take control again. Suppose, for example, we generate a baseline similar in appearance to that of Figure 43 but with the fixed-interval component deliberately built in. That is to say, the fixed-ratio stimulus actually appears only after the first response which follows the lapse of a 15-minute fixed interval. A drug may now cause the fixed-interval behavior nearly to disappear, thereby increasing the duration of the fixed intervals. But the contingency is still present. A response is still required to produce the fixed-ratio stimulus. As the drug wears off and the contingency again takes hold, we may expect a return of the normal fixed-interval pattern.

Such a return may never take place if the fixed-interval contingency was an adventitious one, not deliberately programed. Even if the drug delays responding beyond the 15-minute stimulus-off period, the fixed-ratio stimulus will come on anyway since it never did *require* a response to produce it. The appearance of the stimulus, uncorrelated with a recorded response, may reinforce other behavior, and the new pattern may persist. The original adventitiously reinforced interval behavior may never return during the stimulus-off periods. This is a case in which a transitory change in behavior permits the entrance of new variables into the picture, thus preventing a return to the original baseline performance.

The chances of such an irreversible effect are great when the baseline behavior is governed by factors not under deliberate experimental control. Adventitious contingencies fall into this class of controlling factors. If such contingencies are playing a role in any given experiment, the investigator is likely to feel that the behavior of his subjects is wraith-like, coming and going at the will of unseen forces, eluding all attempts to fence it in with the solid stuff of science.

MULTIPLE-RESPONSE EXPERIMENTS. Laboratory workers have long contended, in friendly (sometimes!) discussion with the clinical investigator, that the study of complex behavior will be more profitable in the long run if we first gain systematic understanding of, and technical competence in dealing with, simpler phenomena. And it turns out, indeed, that as our systematic and technical sophistication increases, more and more complex behavioral processes come within our experimental grasp. But one should not conclude that the study of complex processes then becomes a simple matter of additive combination. While simple principles will be found to be operating, and the extension of simple techniques will facilitate investigation, the study of complex phenomena inevitably raises new problems, both systematic and technical.

An area of complexity now receiving considerable experimental attention is the situation in which we investigate two or more forms of behavior simultaneously. This is the concurrent multi-element baseline I discussed in the preceding chapter. We arrange a separate reinforcement contingency for each response, and program these contingencies concurrently. Concurrent baselines provide unique opportunities for the adventitious occurrence of unplanned and often undesirable contingencies. The simple addition of one response to an otherwise relatively well-explored experimental arrangement may introduce an entirely new order of complexity. As soon as we place more than one response under simultaneous experimental control we introduce the possibility of uncontrolled interactions, mediated by adventitious reinforcement contingencies.

Let us consider one of the simplest cases first. Much is known about the parameters involved in behavioral control via the variable-interval reinforcement schedule. It is usually considered safe to employ this schedule to generate stable baseline behavior for the study of other variables. What happens when we apply this well-known schedule to two responses concurrently? The consequences of this arrangement have been most concisely described by Skinner, referring to an experiment in which pigeons were occasionally reinforced by pecking on either of two available keys. The reinforcement on each key was programed by equal and independent variable-interval schedules; that is to say, a reinforcement on one key did not alter the probability of reinforcement on the other key. The following is taken from Skinner's discussion of this experiment.

> By occasionally reinforcing a response on one key or the other without favoring either key, we obtain equal rates of responding on the two keys. The behavior approaches a simple alternation from one key to the other. This follows the rule that tendencies to respond eventually correspond to the probabilities of reinforcement. Given a system in which one key or the other is occasionally connected with the magazine by an external clock, then if the right key has just been struck, the probability of reinforcement *via* the left key is higher than that *via* the right since a greater interval of time has elapsed during which the clock may have closed the circuit to the left key. *But the bird's behavior does not correspond to this probability merely out of respect for mathematics.* [ITALICS MINE.] The specific result of such a contingency of reinforcement is that changing-to-the-other-key-and-striking is more often reinforced than striking-the-same-key-a-second-time (83, p. 211).

Skinner goes on to demonstrate that when the two responses are topographically the same, we must take into account additional behavior; that which is involved in the changeover from one key to the other. Although we deliberately reinforce only key pecking, the contingency actually generates a chain of responses: key pecking, followed by changeover, followed by key pecking. The middle member of this chain, the changeover, is an adventitious and unrecorded, but powerful, partner in the reinforcement contingency.

Changeover, or switching, behavior is an inherent component of any multiple response situation in which the subject does not simply confine himself to one of the available responses. As long as more than one of the programed responses are emitted, switching behavior is a necessary accompaniment. Following Skinner's analysis, we should be able to eliminate switching by programing the two variable-interval schedules nonindependently. Suppose we use a single programing tape for the two keys. In that case, a changeover from one key to the other is no more likely to be reinforced than is a repetition on the same key. Such an arrangement does indeed eliminate switching. Unfortunately, it also destroys the concurrent baseline, for the subject comes to use only one key predominantly.

It is impossible to eliminate the switching behavior without disrupting the concurrent baseline. The only alternative, if you are trying to minimize the control exercised by unprogramed switching behavior, is somehow to prevent it from participating in the reinforcement contingency. One method of accomplishing this is to interpose a delay contingency such that a response on one key cannot be reinforced if there has been a response on the other key within the preceding, say, five seconds. At least five seconds must elapse between a response on one key and a reinforcement on the other key. This procedure sometimes works, but the conditions under which it is successful are not thoroughly understood. It often does not accomplish its purpose, for the delay, too, can become an integral component of the adventitious reinforcement contingency.

There are two major kinds of behavioral adjustment through which the delay can work itself into an adventitiously reinforced chain of behavior. Let us consider the possible effects of a delay upon the sequence "key A response, followed by switching response, followed by key B response."

If the switching response immediately follows a response on key A, the delay requirement will necessitate the lapse of at least five seconds before key B can produce reinforcement. The subject can fill this time by continuing to respond on key B for five seconds. Then, if the schedule does not provide a reinforcement, he can switch back to key A for five seconds. Findley was able to observe

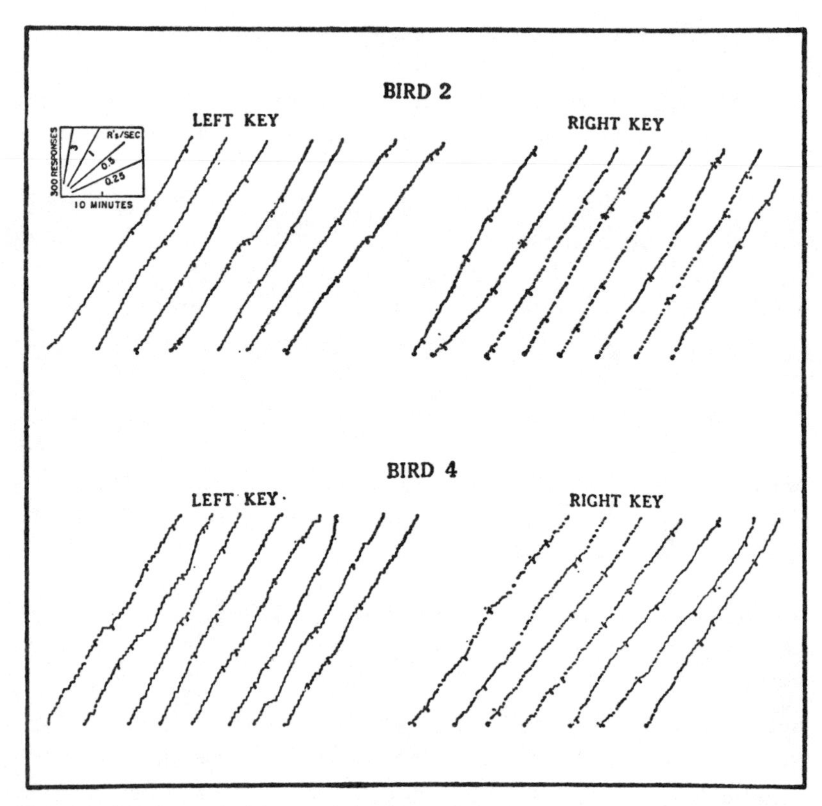

FIGURE 44. Cumulative records from two pigeons on a two-response concurrent variable-interval reinforcement schedule. The birds could not produce a reinforcement on one key unless at least five seconds had elapsed since a response on the other key. Responses therefore tended to occur in bursts, with pauses indicating a switch to the other key. (*From Findley*, 36.)

this type of adjustment very nicely by recording the two keys on separate cumulative recorders, as in Figure 44.

Since the time axis of both recorders ran continuously, the record from one key also included the time devoted to responding on the other. Figure 44 shows the resulting step-wise recordings for two birds. In this type of record, switches from one key to another were not difficult to infer, since the birds worked a fairly definite period of time at each key as a consequence of the delay contingency. But when the delay contingency was subsequently removed, the switching rates approximately doubled and consequently removed much of the stepwise character from each record (36, p. 124).

The second type of adjustment involves pausing rather than responding during the delay period. The subject may respond on key A, and then, instead of switching immediately to key B, he may delay the switching response for five seconds. In this case, we will not observe alternating periods of sustained behavior on each key. The pattern will consist rather of a single response on one key, followed by a period of no responding on either key and then a single response on the alternate key. The delay contingency will show up as a period of no response instead of a period of sustained response.

Other patterns may also develop, but they will be essentially combinations of the two I have described. The major point is that the type of adjustment is not under the experimenter's control. It will depend upon fortuitous temporal correlations between the switching behavior and subsequent reinforcement.

Switching, or changeover, behavior is an essential component of any multiple response experiment. Eliminating the reinforcement for switching will be tantamount to reducing our complex situation to the single-response case. Instead of eliminating the switching behavior, our solution must be to gain experimental control over its sources of reinforcement. We will then be able to account for it in our systematizations, and to let it play as major or as minor a role as we please in any particular experiment. I recommend to the student Findley's researches on switching behavior. These are among the finest examples of research yielding both new control techniques and exciting new behavioral phenomena that are of interest in their own right (36).

Up to now I have been discussing problems of adventitious reinforcement in multi-response situations in which the recorded responses are topographically similar. Skinner has shown that it is sufficient to consider the recorded behavior in such experiments as a single operant. Most of the explanatory burden is carried by the notion of adventitious reinforcement of switching behavior. As Skinner noted, the situation is more complex when the recorded responses differ in topography (83). Any differences among the responses which prevent us from treating them as a single operant will force us to consider other processes in addition to the adventitious reinforcement of switching behavior. The recorded responses themselves may become linked together in an adventitiously reinforced chain. An example has already been described in Chapter 3, pages 104-107, where one response produced food reinforcement, and another served the function of avoiding a time-out. The avoidance response, since it was sometimes followed by food-reinforced behavior, also came under the control of the food reinforcement. An adventitiously reinforced chain was thus set up, consisting of avoidance response, followed by switching behavior, followed by food response.

Whenever one response in a multiple response baseline becomes involved in the reinforcement contingency which maintains a different response component, a degree of experimental control is lost. The elements of the baseline can no longer be manipulated independently of each other. A simple illustration of this point comes from an experiment involving two concurrently maintained responses, with monkey as subject. One response, chain pulling, produced food according to a variable-interval schedule. An avoidance contingency was programed concurrently for the lever-pressing response. Each lever press postponed an electric shock for twenty seconds. Because of an adventitious contingency, however, the two responses were not independent of each other. The parameters of the situation were such that the chain-pulling response was most frequently followed by a repeated sequence of lever presses. Because of this, the food response became adventitiously involved in the avoidance contingency. The sequence, chain pull, followed by switching behavior, followed by lever presses, became established as an adventitiously reinforced avoidance response (74).

Figure 45 illustrates how the adventitious contingency prevented independent experimental manipulation of the chain-pulling response by means of the food reinforcement. The first section of Figure 45 depicts the frequency of each response when the shock was removed, *i.e.*, during avoidance extinction. When the avoidance contingency was reinstated, with no change in the food reinforcement schedule, we see in the second section of Figure 45 a sub-

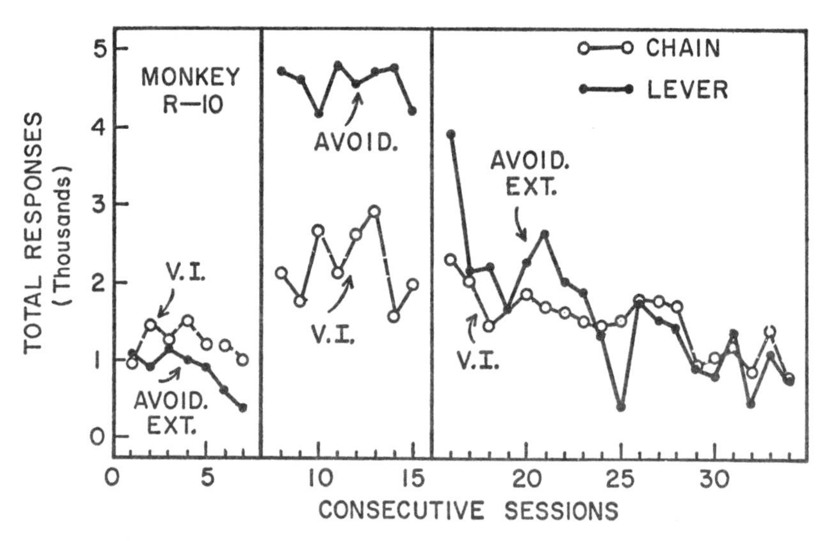

FIGURE 45. An illustration of nonindependence of the two responses in a concurrent avoidance and variable-interval procedure. (*Unpublished data from Sidman,* 74.)

stantial increase in the output of *both* responses. In the third section of the figure there is a decline in both responses when the avoidance contingency if removed, even though the food schedule is still in force.

We see, then, that the avoidance contingency has gained a degree of control over the food-reinforced response. This unprogramed control is likely to cloud the interpretation of any experimental operation designed to manipulate only the lever-pressing response. Any change in the avoidance behavior is likely to produce, as a by-product, a change in the food behavior also.

Let us consider means by which such adventitious contingencies might be eliminated. One method might be to program a delay requirement. We could make the avoidance response effective in postponing the shock only if at least five seconds have elapsed since the last food response. As in the other cases I have discussed, however, the delay might simply work itself into the adventitious contingency, forming a more complex but equally powerful linkage between the two responses. Or it might even negate the purpose of our multiple-response baseline by preventing the occurrence of switching behavior. This is especially likely to happen if the delay increases the probability that switching behavior will itself be shocked.

A second method is to alter the programed contingencies so as to minimize response sequences of a type conducive to the establishment of adventitious chains. For example, instead of a variable-interval schedule, in the experiment of Figure 45, we might program the food reinforcement on a fixed-ratio schedule. The characteristics of the ratio schedule are such as to maximize the frequency of successively emitted food responses, and to minimize the frequency with which food responses are followed by an avoidance response. In this way the sequence—food response followed by switching behavior followed by avoidance response—may be made to occur so infrequently as to prevent its establishment as an adventitious chain.

This device of preventing adventitious contingencies by means of the judicious selection of reinforcement schedules seems a promising one. In our present state of knowledge, however, it is still not the final answer. For little is known of the factors that determine the direction in which an adventitious chain of behavior will develop. In the preceding example, we saw the food response chained to the avoidance behavior. Changing the food schedule from variable interval to fixed ratio broke up this adventitious chain, but there was evidence to suggest that the chain simply reversed its direction. That is to say, the avoidance response then became tied in with the food reinforcement. There are also more subtle factors which no one has yet even begun to work out. It is probably not necessary for a response to be linked immediately with a terminal primary reinforcement in order for an adventitious chain to develop. There are some reinforcement contingencies which generate powerful internal control by making the responses themselves act as conditioned reinforcers, as in fixed-ratio behavior and the terminal portion of a fixed-interval scallop. Other behavior which takes place during a ratio run or an interval scallop may become adventitiously involved in the reinforcement contingencies even though the irrelevant responses do not occur in close temporal proximity to the terminal reinforcement. The conditioned reinforcement provided by the early responses in a fixed-ratio run, for example, may be sufficient to trap other behavior into a spurious chaining relationship.

We see, then, that adventitious reinforcement in a multiple-response situation is a factor still in need of adequate control techniques. The best I can do at this stage is to provide the student with an appreciation of the problem. The only general point that has some validity is that adventitious contingencies are an inevitable and integral feature of multiple-response situations, and that control techniques must permit us to evaluate, rather than eliminate, such contingencies.

Chapter 13

Control Techniques (Continued)

In any experiment, there is much behavior that goes unrecorded and even unobserved. Because such behavior has not been selected for observation, we sometimes make the mistake of ignoring its possible systematic or technical importance; yet it may play an important mediating role in the processes we are investigating. To ignore such behavior in our explanatory scheme is a misapplication of the operational principle. If the behavior is potentially observable, then it cannot be excluded from consideration because of an arbitrary decision, in a particular instance, to leave it unrecorded.

The switching, or changeover, behavior to which I referred in the preceding sections is a case in point. The understanding and control of such normally unrecorded behavior, and of its participation in unprogramed contingencies, is vital to the study of complex multiple-response situations.

THE INVOLVEMENT OF UNRECORDED BEHAVIOR IN ADVENTITIOUS CONTINGENCIES

MAGAZINE BEHAVIOR. Another example of generally unrecorded behavior (to which I have alluded briefly in previous sections) is that involved in procuring the reinforcement after it has been delivered from the magazine. Magazine behavior is especially prepotent because it is reinforced immediately. Animals reinforced with food are often observed to spend a considerable portion of their experimental time in such activities as licking, grasping, or nosing whatever portion of the food delivery mechanism is accessible to them. Such behavior can easily occur with a sufficiently high frequency to interfere with both the temporal pattern and the rate of occurrence of the recorded behavior. It may even set an effective upper limit upon the rate of the recorded behavior, thus diminishing the sensitivity of the baseline when experimental operations are introduced. Furthermore, since excessive magazine behavior is not under direct experimental control, the extent of its influence is likely to be highly variable from one experiment to another, and from one experimenter to another. In fact, the degree to which the occurrence of magazine behavior is restricted to those occasions on which it is appropriate, *i.e.*, the delivery of a reinforcement, is a criterion the experienced investigator often uses to assess the technical competence of a newcomer to the field.

Excessive magazine behavior is originally generated because of poor stimulus control. Once having been generated, however, it may be perpetuated through its participation in an adventitious contingency. Let us consider first the way in which it is generated. The careful experimenter, before establishing his recorded baseline behavior, first puts his subjects through a course of magazine training. This consists simply of the repeated free delivery of reinforcements, without making them contingent upon any particular behavior. In fact, care must be taken, as we shall see in a moment, to ensure that no response is consistently correlated with reinforcement delivery.

Magazine training serves two functions. First, it teaches the subject where to find the reinforcement and how to deal with it. Second, it establishes the discriminative function of the stimuli which are correlated with reinforcement delivery (31). That is to say, the correlated stimuli come to mark those occasions upon which magazine behavior will be reinforced. When the stimuli occur, magazine approach is followed immediately by reinforcement.

Establishment of a discriminative function for the stimuli correlated with reinforcement delivery also serves a twofold purpose. First, it ensures rapid subsequent conditioning of the response that has been selected for observation and manipulation. When this response is made available to the subject, its first occurrence will produce the magazine stimuli; these in turn will bring the subject immediately into contact with the reinforcement. The magazine stimuli serve both as a conditioned reinforcer for the response that produced them and as a discriminative event which ensures minimal delay in the receipt of the primary reinforcement. As a result, rapid conditioning takes place.

Secondly, and more important for the present discussion, good discriminative control on the part of the magazine stimuli will ensure that the magazine behavior never occurs in the absence of these stimuli. In the early stages of magazine training, subjects engage in a considerable amount of magazine-oriented behavior, for that is the behavior most closely correlated with reinforcement. Care must be taken to ensure that prior magazine activity does not consistently precede reinforcement delivery. Otherwise, inappropriate magazine behavior will become adventitiously conditioned and will interfere with the behavior which is to be of experimental concern. Providing discriminative training for the magazine behavior with respect to the stimuli correlated with reinforcement delivery, and ensuring that no specific behavior becomes adventitiously correlated with the production of magazine stimuli, are appropriate precautions.

That the magazine stimuli be distinctive and easily discriminable from other aspects of the environment is a basic requirement. The experienced investigator generally adds distinctive visual, auditory, or tactile components to the naturally occurring magazine stimuli. For example, a light may flash or a tone sound while the reinforcement is being delivered. Since reinforcement is never delivered except in the presence of these stimuli, the necessary ingredients for discriminative training are automatically present in the situation. The remaining, and more difficult, task is to ensure that the reinforcement is not consistently delivered while the subject is engaging in extra magazine behavior—or in any other consistent form of behavior. Contact relays, photoelectric cells, and various position-signaling devices can help automatize this task. Certain aspects of magazine and other behavior can be controlled automatically with respect to their correlation with reinforcement delivery during magazine training. Without such devices, and perhaps even with them, direct observation of the subjects and manual control of reinforcement delivery will be required. Any behavior that becomes prepotent by virtue of accidental correlations with reinforcement delivery must then be made to undergo an extinction process.

Such a procedure is laborious and time-consuming. Until recently, it has been possible to compromise and to achieve only such rigor of control over magazine behavior as was necessary for the purpose at hand. But with the growing interest in complex processes, and with the increasing quantitative precision that has been made possible by other developments in behavioral technology, we can no longer sidestep the problem. If the response to be recorded is made available to the subject before we have confined magazine behavior to its appropriate discriminative occasion, a more complex adventitious chain is likely to develop. If it occurs frequently in the absence of its appropriate stimuli, magazine behavior will inevitably be followed by some reinforced instances of the recorded response, and we are likely to observe frequent and rapid alternation of the two. Magazine behavior will become, adventitiously, part of the discriminative occasion on which the recorded responses are reinforced. To the extent that this discriminative occasion has not been deliberately programed by the experimenter, he will have lost some degree of experimental control over the behavior he has selected for observation.

Aversive behavior. Experimental studies of punishment and avoidance behavior make deliberate use of adventitious contingencies. In most avoidance experiments, in which shocks follow some temporal schedule, we renounce precision of control over the relation between shock onset and any particular response—with the exception, of course, of the avoidance response. As Dinsmoor has pointed out, we control and record the avoidance response within relatively narrow limits, but we permit the class of punished responses to include all the rest of the subject's behavior (25). In punishment experiments, the procedure is typically the opposite. We specify and record the punished behavior within relatively narrow limits, but we permit the class of avoidance responses to include all the rest of the subject's behavior.

These distinctions carry some interesting theoretical implications, but a discussion of them will be more appropriate elsewhere. My purpose here is simply to point out that the abandonment of direct control, in punishment and avoidance experiments, over some very powerful contingencies does not exempt these contingencies from systematic and technical consideration. They still play important roles in controlling the behavior we do observe, and these roles are determined by unevaluated factors. The situation is maximally conducive to adventitious contingencies.

The behavior most closely and most frequently paired with shock in an avoidance situation will have been determined, in part, by the history which the subject brings to the experiment. It will also include responses which are necessary components of the avoidance behavior but which cannot, by themselves, succeed in postponing the shock. Such behavior has special status because it draws extra strength from the success of the avoidance response and also because it detracts from the strength of the avoidance response. To take an example, let us say we have specified lever pressing as the avoidance response. The shock is postponed when the subject, by pressing the lever, closes a switch and sends out a momentary electrical pulse to the circuit which delays the appearance of the shock. We have thus arranged that only a very restricted segment of the movements involved in lever pressing will succeed in avoiding the shock. This is the segment that encompasses the initial closure of the switch.

But there are other movements, both antecedent to and following the switch closure, which do not themselves succeed in preventing the shock but which are necessary accompaniments of the switch-closing behavior. The subject must orient toward the lever, reach for it, touch it, and begin to press it, all before switch closure can be accomplished. Once the switch has initially been operated, the subject must, if only through inertia, maintain the lever depression for some finite period of time. These components of the lever-pressing behavior all share in the reinforcing effects of shock avoidance. They may, however, often be shocked. Shock may occur, for example, just as the subject touches the lever preparatory to depressing it. Or the subject may depress the lever, postpone the shock, and then hold the lever down until the next shock occurs. In this respect, the preparatory behavior and the lever-holding behavior are simply part of the large class of unspecified punishable responses. They differ from other members of the class, however, in that they are also reinforced by shock avoidance on those occasions when the lever press is carried through to completion. Therefore they are likely to become prepotent over other punishable responses. On the other hand, their occasional adventitious correlation with shock onset will reduce their probability of occurrence at least temporarily. Such a reduction will necessarily lower the frequency of the specified avoidance behavior also. The net result will be some degree of uncontrolled variability in the avoidance behavior.

There is no way of eliminating variability that arises from the adventitious contingencies actually built into our techniques. The only solution lies in the introduction of new techniques which will not leave the development of punishment and avoidance contingencies to circumstance. It may be possible here to use a rational approach in developing such a new technique. We want to be able to specify and control, with some precision, *both* the punished behavior and the avoidance behavior. This means, first of all, that the shock, or whatever aversive stimulus we use, cannot be delivered on a purely temporal schedule. We must correlate the shock with some specific identifiable response. To establish such a correlation in relatively stable form, it will be necessary to give the punished behavior a source of strength sufficient to maintain it in the face of occasional punishment.

These requirements can be met, in part, by placing a response on some schedule of intermittent positive reinforcement, and by making the same response produce a shock according to some independent but concurrent schedule. For example, we can maintain lever pressing in a hungry rat by means of a variable-interval schedule of food reinforcement. Concurrently, the lever-pressing response can also produce a brief shock on a fixed-ratio schedule. Let us say that every fiftieth occurrence of the response will produce the shock.

Up to this point we have a method for studying punishment, but avoidance behavior is uncontrolled. The shocks will lower the rate of food-reinforced lever pressing, but the behavior that replaces lever pressing is unspecified. It can be any other behavior in the subject's repertoire.

To bring a specified avoidance response into the picture, we need only add one more condition to govern the occurrence of shock: lever pressing can produce the shock only if some other specified response fails to occur. Let us select panel pushing as the avoidance response. Each time the animal pushes the panel, the ratio counter resets back to zero and starts anew. If the subject were perfectly efficient, he could emit 49 lever-pressing responses, some of which would produce food, and then emit one panel-pushing response. Pushing the panel would reset the ratio counter, preventing the fiftieth lever press from producing a shock.

Such a technique permits us to specify both the punished behavior (lever pressing) and the avoidance behavior (panel pushing). Neither contingency is left to chance or to uncontrolled variables.

Furthermore, no component of the avoidance response can be shocked, for it takes a lever press to produce the shock. Shocks can never occur while the animal is approaching the panel or nosing it, or during any of the preliminary stages of the panel-pushing response. There can be no adventitious correlation between any unrecorded aspect of the avoidance response and the occurrence of shock.

Such a technique would permit us to examine the effects of punishment on the lever-pressing response, the effects of the avoidance contingency upon the panel-pushing response, or both sides of the picture along with their interactions. No instability will be caused by adventitious correlations between unrecorded behavior and shocks. There are infinite variations to be played upon this theme, and I leave it to the interested student to work them out.

DELAYED REINFORCEMENT. Whenever a delay occurs between the recorded behavior and its programed consequence, we can be sure that the period of delay is not empty. Some behavior is taking place all the time, and even though such behavior is unrecorded it may still play a vital role in mediating the effects of the delay.

A classic example is delayed reinforcement. Many experiments have been performed to investigate the effects of interposing a period of time between the occurrence of a response and the delivery of its primary reinforcement. The conclusion usually drawn from these experiments is that the effectiveness of the reinforcer decreases with longer delays. Immediate reinforcement is found to be most effective in conditioning and maintaining a given response.

In view of the inevitable adventitious contingencies in a delayed reinforcement study, this conclusion is not surprising. If the reinforcement does not immediately follow the response that was required for its production, then it will follow some other behavior. Its major effect will then be upon the behavior that bears, adventitiously to be sure, the closest prior temporal relationship to the reinforcement. The effect of a delay, it might be said, is to dissipate the reinforcement over a number of unrecorded responses instead of concentrating it on the recorded behavior.

Because of the mediating effects of adventitious contingencies, then, delayed reinforcement appears to be less effective than immediate reinforcement. It is possible, however, by appropriate experimental manipulation, to turn this mediating effect in the opposite direction. We can actually make use of adventitious contingencies to support behavior whose primary reinforcement is extremely long-delayed. One method of accomplishing this is to start with a short delay, and then to increase it gradually. Such a procedure, building up to a 60-second delay, was demonstrated by Ferster, using pigeons as subjects. The following is a portion of Ferster's analysis:

Because of the extinction taking place during the 60-second delay the opening of the magazine is preceded by a wide variety of behaviors and no single response is likely to be reinforced frequently enough to acquire any strength. If the delays are the order of one to five seconds, however, the likelihood of the same response occurring prior to the opening of the magazine is high, and members of a single response class will be reinforced frequently enough to be conditioned. When the delay interval is lengthened after a number of reinforcements of the same response, the delay defines a fixed-interval schedule of reinforcement of the "superstitious" response. The schedule is different from those ordinarily employed only in that the magazine will open whether or not the response is made. To maintain the "superstitious" behavior . . . it is necessary to adjust the interval of the delay so that the magazine will open when the frequency of the "superstitious" response is highest (30, p. 223).

Ferster's demonstration shows how to put adventitious contingencies to good use in studying behavior whose reinforcement is long delayed. The technique of gradually increasing the delay, however, has one serious drawback from the point of view of experimental control. The response that becomes involved in the adventitious contingency cannot be specified in advance and is likely to vary from one subject to another. The effect of an experimental operation may well be a function of the particular behavior which becomes involved in the adventitious contingency. As a result, we may be plagued with excessive intersubject variability in our data.

Ferster has also shown us the way out of this difficulty. His technique involves, first of all, the deliberate conditioning, by immediate reinforcement, of the response that is eventually to comprise the mediating behavior in a delayed reinforcement contingency. This behavior is also placed under stimulus control. He then makes the onset of the stimulus that controls the mediating behavior depend upon the emission of another response. In the third stage, the reinforcement for the mediating behavior is programed solely by a clock, and is actually independent of the occurrence of any specific behavior except the remote response which turned on the stimulus and started the clock. However, since a specific response has already been conditioned in some strength, this response is "caught" by the reinforcement and is maintained by the now adventitious contingency.

The reinforcement schedule employed in the initial stage of this procedure is critical, and its selection demands the application of behavioral technology which has been developed in other contexts. Again, I quote directly from Ferster, who used a fixed-interval schedule for the original conditioning of the mediating behavior:

The properties of a fixed-interval schedule of reinforcement will have a crucial bearing on whether a rate of occurrence of the "superstitious" response will be high at the time that the magazine opens. A fixed-interval schedule produces different effects after long training, when a stable performance is reached, than it does early in training. In the early stages of fixed-interval reinforcement the frequency of the behavior is high at the beginning of the interval and declines regularly until the next reinforcement occurs. These conditions are adverse for the maintenance of the "superstitious" behavior unless the delay is adjusted so that the magazine opens at a time when the rate of response due to the preceding reinforcement is still high. After sufficient training, however, the rate picture is reversed. The rate is low at the beginning of the interval and gradually increases until a stable rate (characteristic of the fixed interval) is reached. Under these conditions the delay interval can be lengthened more rapidly without producing many instances of the opening of the magazine being preceded by a response other than the one previously conditioned (30, pp. 223-224).

By the establishment of an appropriate reinforcement history for a given response, we can almost guarantee that this response will be the one adventitiously reinforced by a delayed reinforcement. The consistent behavior pattern, along with its associated environmental stimuli, will comprise an immediate conditioned reinforcer strong enough to maintain the behavior whose primary reinforcement is delayed. This technique has the advantage of allowing us to specify, control, and record the adventitiously maintained mediating behavior, and to keep this behavior consistent from subject to subject.

There is still, however, a complication which may introduce undesirable ambiguities into the evaluation of data from delayed-reinforcement studies. This complication is inherent in any experiment in which adventitious contingencies play a role. It derives from the fact that, no matter how such contingencies are initially generated, they remain susceptible to variables that are not under direct experimental control. In the experiment I last described above, for example, Ferster shows us how to restrict an adventitious contingency to specified behavior. This technique marks a considerable advance in the study of behavior whose reinforcement is long delayed. But even an adventitious contingency that we initially mold into some desired configuration, through the deliberate application of behavioral technology, eventually takes on a life of its own. The mediating behavior is in fact not necessary for the occurrence of the consequences which maintain it. If some experimental operation, or even some uncontrolled variable, temporarily breaks the correlation between the behavior and its adventitious consequences, that behavior may disappear, never to return. It will be replaced by behavior not of the experimenter's choosing, thereby raising again the problems of variability and inadequate control over relevant variables.

The solution to this problem in delayed-reinforcement studies actually appears in the intermediate step of Ferster's technique for establishing the adventitiously reinforced mediating behavior. This intermediate step constituted a chain of the sort I described previously in connection with discrimination experiments (pp. 352-353). Instead of producing a terminal reinforcement, a response is made to produce a discriminative stimulus. In the presence of this stimulus, the same response, or even a different one, then produces the primary, or terminal, reinforcement. Both components of this chain, the one whose consequence is a conditioned reinforcer and the one correlated with primary reinforcement, can be controlled by different and independent schedules. Placing the second member on an interval schedule permits a precisely controlled period of delay in the delivery of terminal reinforcement. The delay of course, is measured from the initial element of the chain. Placing the first component on an intermittent schedule of conditioned reinforcement increases the sensitivity of the baseline and permits a wide range of controlled variation as a function of different delays.

Chaining and delayed reinforcement are not traditionally lumped into the same pot. But delayed reinforcement actually generates a chain whose final component is usually not specified or controlled in any direct way. The response whose reinforcement is delayed is always followed by unanalyzed behavior which can act as a stimulus to bridge the delay. A deliberate chaining technique simply makes the sequence explicit and exposes it for examination and manipulation. Delayed reinforcement always involves some terminal behavior immediately prior to the delivery of primary reinforcement. The properties of this behavior are a critical factor in mediating the effects of delayed reinforcement. Why not make the mediating behavior both explicit and permanent? The loss of behavioral control in Ferster's experiment (30), following the change from a real to an adventitious contingency, demonstrates the intrinsic weakness of the latter in the long-term maintenance of behavior.

DELAYED RESPONSE. There are several types of delayed-response experiments, and all of them are ideal spawning grounds for adventitious contingencies. In the classical procedure, the subject is presented with a stimulus but is prevented from immediately executing the response appropriate to that stimulus. After a period of time the restraint is removed and the subject has an opportunity to emit either the appropriate response or any of several alternative ones. For example, a monkey may be permitted to view a grape being placed in one of several different containers. A barrier is then interposed to prevent the monkey from reaching the container. After a period of delay, the experimenter removes the barrier and notes whether or not the subject selects the correct container. This procedure has been viewed as a test of memory, or even of "higher mental processes."

Several investigators, however, whose concern has been more with behavioral processes than with hypothesized intellectual entities, have noted certain regularities in their subjects' behavior during the delay period. These are sometimes described as orienting responses. The subject will often adopt a posture in which his whole body or a part of it maintains a consistent position relative to the correct container. Such mediating behavior may enable the subject to select the correct container even after the lapse of a considerable period of time. The effects of other variables, such as central nervous system lesions or pharmacologic agents, may well depend not only upon the presence or absence of such mediating behavior but also upon its qualitative and quantitative characteristics.

For the purpose of our discussion here, we may simply note that the mediating behavior in delayed-response experiments is controlled by an adventitious contingency. The experimenter does not require specific orienting behavior before he makes the grape available to the monkey. Nonetheless, since the reinforced response must be preceded by some other form of behavior during the delay period, it is actually the whole sequence that feels the strengthening effect of the reinforcement.

This type of adventitious contingency has one feature somewhat different from the others I have discussed. Although the experimenter does not include mediating behavior in the programed contingencies, such behavior does permit a more successful behavioral adaptation. Responses preceded by appropriate orienting behavior will be more frequently reinforced than those which follow either inadequate orientations or some inconsistent form of behavior.

The delayed-response situation, then, contains inherent restrictions upon the type of behavior which can become involved in the adventitious contingency. We have here a case of differential adventitious reinforcement. In one sense, this makes our control task easier. If we continue the experiment for a long enough time, the procedure itself is likely to select out the most efficient form of mediating behavior. Intersubject variability will then be minimized. Also, the problem of irreversibility will not be as serious as it is in other types of adventitious contingencies. For if a given experimental operation should temporarily alter the mediating behavior, differential reinforcement will restore it to its most efficient form.

Though the problems of variability and irreversibility diminish in severity, they are by no means absent from the delayed-response experiment. For one thing, it may take a long time before the mediating behavior shapes up to its most efficient form. Until one has had considerable experience, there will be no way of judging whether a given experiment has reached that stage. Secondly, to the extent that there may be more than one optimal, or nearly optimal, form of mediating behavior, the problems of variability and irreversibility will still be present. But there is another sense in which the automatic shaping of the mediating behavior makes our control problem even more pressing than usual. The fact that a particular form of mediating behavior receives differential reinforcement indicates that the adventitious contingencies are not just bothersome side issues in delayed-response experiments but rather are vital aspects of the behavioral process we are examining. Such mediating behavior therefore requires the highest degree of experimental control and the greatest precision of recording of which we are capable.

Automatization is the first requirement. Without it, the labor involved in extending the delayed-response experiment over a period of time sufficiently long to stabilize the mediating behavior would be prohibitive. Also, without automatization, precise and continuous recording of the mediating behavior would not be feasible. But automatic control will permit us to go even further than this. With it, we can select for differential reinforcement any form of mediating behavior we wish, this completely eliminating the problems of irreversibility and intersubject variability, and cutting down the time required for the achievement of stability. By using a type of mediating behavior whose characteristics are known, we will also be able to apply a valid stability criterion.

To program arbitrary forms of mediating behavior is simple enough. We arrange an environment in which several recordable responses are possible, some of them to be made available to the subject at the end of the delay period and the others to be used as mediating behavior during the delay. We set up the control equipment so as to correlate each mediating response with a corresponding choice response. Then, depending upon the initial pre-delay stimulus, which specifies the correct choice response, we require that the subject emit only the appropriate mediating behavior during the delay. If other mediating behavior occurs, the choice response will go unreinforced, even if it is the correct one.

Let me describe a specific example. If we were to use the pigeon as subject, the experimental situation could be similar to the one shown in Chapter 7, Figure 22. The situation need be modified only by additional keys on both sides of the center bar. The pigeon then will be faced with an array of five components: the center bar, two keys arranged horizontally on the left side of the bar, and two other keys arranged similarly on the right side of the bar. We will call the two keys immediately adjacent to the bar the *inner keys*, left and right respectively, and the two keys located at the extreme end of the lineup, the *outer keys*, left and right respectively. The center bar will provide the stimulus which initiates the delay period; pecking at the inner keys will constitute the mediating behavior; pecking at the outer keys will constitute the choice response.

A trial begins when the center bar is illuminated either by a red or by a green light. (Some time later, the bird is going to be "asked" to peck at the particular outer key which is illuminated with the same color.) To ensure that the pigeon observes the center bar, it remains illuminated until the pigeon pecks it. With the first peck, the light on the center bar goes out and the delay period begins.

At the end of the delay period, both outer keys will be illuminated, one of them red and the other green. A peck at the key that matches the original bar stimulus will bring some food within the reach of the hungry pigeon *if* its behavior during the delay period has been of an appropriate sort, which I shall now describe.

If the delayed choice response is to be reinforced, not only must it be the correct response but also the bird must have pecked one, and only one, of the inner keys during the delay period. If the bar was red, the bird must peck only the left inner key during the delay period; if the bar was green, only the right inner key must be pecked during the delay period; if the bird pecked neither inner key, or if it pecked both of them, the choice response would not produce reinforcement.

Mediating behavior is thus forced by making it part of the reinforcement contingency. Without the correct mediating behavior during the delay period, even the correct choice response will not produce reinforcement. The mediating behavior is specifiable and recordable, two features which would probably be impossible if we had relied upon adventitious contingencies. With a constant delay period, the mediating behavior will probably take on fixed-interval characteristics, and the usual measures of fixed-interval behavior will provide detailed, quantitative information about the state of the mediating behavior during any phase of the experiment.

We could simplify the procedure, from a technical point of view, by eliminating two of the keys and using the same response as both mediating and choice behavior. Such a modification brings out the close resemblance between the delayed response experiment and the chained multi-element baseline under stimulus control (see pages 352-353). The chief difference between the two situations lies in the relative durations of the discriminative stimuli. In the chaining situation, the stimuli controlling each element of the chain are usually present continuously. When the controlling stimuli for the elements of a multiple baseline are brief, then the behavior itself must carry the discriminative load. This is the essence of the mediating function taken on by adventitiously reinforced behavior in the delayed-response experiment.

The classical delayed-response technique, of which our example was a modification, interposes a delay between the presentation of exteroceptive stimuli and the subject's opportunity to respond appropriately. The duration of the delay between stimulus and response is independent of the subject's behavior. At the termination of the delay, the experimenter again presents the stimuli and records the stimulus element to which the subject's response is directed. When the response is appropriate to the reinforcement contingency, the subject is considered to have bridged the temporal gap successfully. By varying the length of the delay, and recording correct and incorrect stimulus choices, we may obtain a functional relation which describes the subject's success in bridging different time intervals.

We can gain similar information by other techniques. The element of delay which is common to all of them requires continuing attention to adventitious contingencies. We may, for example, present the subject with a single stimulus and require that he postpone his response for a fixed period of time after stimulus presentation. If the response occurs too soon, it is simply not reinforced. In this procedure, we restrict the exteroceptive stimulus to a single component. The time between stimulus and response, however, is under the subject's control, and our record consists of a tabulation of these intervals. Again, we may obtain functional relations which describe the subject's success in bridging time periods of different durations. The spaced-responding procedure (see p. 404) is essentially a variation of this technique whereby the stimulus that initiates the delay period arises from the subject's own behavior rather than from the environment.

As with the classical delayed-response technique, data obtained by means of the spaced-responding technique or any of its variants require the evaluation of the mediating behavior which takes place during the delay period. A reinforced response following a successful delay must be preceded by some other behavior, and the reinforcing effect may be expected to extend back to that behavior. Because of such adventitious reinforcement, a chain of behavior may develop. Many investigators have, in fact, confirmed Wilson and Keller's original observation that a stereotyped sequence of behavior may develop during the delay period (94). As in the classical delayed-response experiment, this stereotyped behavior may perform a useful function by helping the subject to span the delay period. Any adventitious chain that develops will be differentially reinforced with respect to its speed of execution. If the chain is too brief, the subsequent recorded response will not be reinforced. The sequence is analogous to a system of counting, with the terminal response being triggered off when a certain number is reached.

The conditions under which mediating behavior will develop in the spaced-responding situation are not yet clearly understood, for it is not always observed. This makes our control problem even more pressing. Furthermore, unlike the traditional delayed-response procedure in which the mediating behavior is automatically restricted to some form of orienting response, the spaced-responding technique in no way restricts the form of the mediating responses. Again, then, we face the twin specters of intersubject variability and irreversibility. Such variability may, for example, help to explain why the ability of white rats to space their responses effectively seems to be only temporarily lost when certain cortical areas of the brain are removed. The operation may serve only to destroy the particular mediating behavior that the subject was using, with recovery taking place when a new sequence is adventitiously reinforced.

The above speculation need not be correct in order to drive home the point that adventitiously conditioned mediating behavior can play a vital role in the behavioral processes generated by a spaced-responding technique. Until this role is clarified, we cannot be certain of the most effective control methods. One possibility is to arrange a situation in which the experimental procedure restricts the form of the mediating behavior. Recent investigations by Mechner are relevant here (54). His technique involves a two-response situation. Reinforcement for one response depends upon a fixed number of prior occurrences of the other response. The subject must, for example, press lever A ten times in succession before a response on lever B can procure a reinforcement. In this way, the mediating behavior is uniquely specified and independently measurable. In view of our ignorance about the role played by mediating behavior in the spaced-responding experiment, the relevance of Mechner's technique may be debatable. But insofar as spaced responding is controlled by unrecorded adventitious chains, the two-response "counting" situation simply makes this control explicit.

MISCELLANEOUS TYPES OF ADVENTITIOUS CONTINGENCIES. An experimental operation applied to an ongoing behavioral baseline may reduce, at least temporarily, the frequency of reinforcement. While the behavior may eventually adjust to the new conditions and recover the original reinforcement frequency, the initial temporary decline can be self-perpetuating. This is particularly likely if the initiation of the change is marked by a recurring stimulus condition such as exists at the start of the experimental session.

Suppose, for example, the baseline behavior is maintained by a variable-interval reinforcement schedule. As the schedule is normally applied, each time the programer sets up a reinforcement it remains available until the next response occurs. An experimental operation might consist of limiting the period of availability of the reinforcement. If a response is not made within, let us say, a half second after the reinforcement has become available, the subject loses that opportunity to secure a reinforcement. Let us suppose we have introduced this "limited-hold" contingency at the start of an experimental period. Its initial effect is likely to be a marked reduction in reinforcement frequency. Later in the session the behavior may adjust appropriately by increasing in rate as the new contingency takes hold. But the stimuli coincident with the beginning of the session have become correlated with a low reinforcement frequency. The low frequency, in turn, generates a low rate, and low response rates may then characterize the start of each succeeding session.

This process is self-perpetuating. The low rate early in the session maintains the frequency of reinforcement at a correspondingly low level, and this circular process ensures a continuing correlation between the start of a session and infrequent reinforcement. But while this warm-up effect may be consistent within a given subject, it may not be observed in all subjects. Its presence will depend upon the original baseline response rate, the length of the limited hold, and probably upon some function of these variables in combination.

Other relevant factors will include the degree of stability normally observed in the original baseline, the subject's state of deprivation, the uniqueness of the stimuli correlated with the beginning of the experimental sessions, and the subject's behavioral history. Any variable which permits even a brief exposure of the subject to the true contingency at the start of the session may break down the spurious correlation.

As with all adventitious contingencies, the lack of direct control magnifies the effects of variables which might be almost completely powerless in the face of a deliberately programed contingency. And, in addition to the hazards of variability, we must also contend with ambiguity in our understanding of the behavioral process under observation. For if we do not recognize the possibility of adventitious extinction, we may devote considerable experimental and speculative effort to a search for other processes to explain the warm-up phenomenon.

The occurrence of adventitious extinction need not be confined to the start of an experimental session. The problem is the more general one of fortuitous relations between reinforcement frequency and particular stimuli. The relation may be a purely chance one, and may generate either a higher or lower response probability. All that is required is some degree of irregularity in the baseline behavior. Morse and Skinner have presented a unique and definitive demonstration (61). With pigeons as subjects, the baseline behavior was a low average rate of responding maintained by a variable-interval reinforcement schedule. The response key was normally illuminated by an orange light, but once an hour a blue light was projected on the key for four minutes. The schedule of presentation of the blue stimulus was independent of the reinforcement schedule.

Although the blue light was not programed as part of any reinforcement contingency, the response rate did come under the control of this stimulus. In some cases, the response rate dropped to a very low level during the blue stimulus, and in other instances the rate was consistently higher than the baseline. Morse and Skinner's discussion gives us a concise analysis of the findings.

A stimulus present when a response is reinforced may acquire discriminative control over the response even though its presence at

> reinforcement is adventitious. Suppose, for example, that an organism is responding at a moderate rate on a variable-interval schedule of reinforcement, and let an incidental stimulus (A) occasionally appear for a brief period. Even though there is no explicit temporal relation between the appearance of A and the program of reinforcement, a response will occasionally be reinforced in the presence of A. For a brief period the frequency of such reinforcement may be appreciably greater than in the absence of A. An organism which is sensitive to slight differences in rate of reinforcement will form a discrimination; its rate of responding in the presence of A will become greater than in the absence of A. This might be called a positive sensory superstition. If, on the other hand, reinforcements happen to occur relatively infrequently in the presence of A, a discrimination will develop in the opposite direction, as the result of which the rate in the presence of A will be relatively low—a sort of negative sensory superstition.
>
> When an accidental contingency has produced a higher or lower rate of responding in the presence of an incidental stimulus, a second effect follows. If the rate has fallen in the presence of A (because reinforcements have been relatively infrequent), responses will be even less likely to be reinforced in the presence of A. In the limiting case no responses will be made in the presence of A, and no response, of course, reinforced. Moreover, reinforcements which are made available during A are not obtained because responses are not made. The first response following the withdrawal of A is then reinforced, and the discrimination is further strengthened. Similarly, when the rate is increased during A because of favorable accidental reinforcement, all reinforcements set up during A are likely to be obtained, and if the preceding condition commands a relatively low rate, some reinforcements set up at that time may actually be obtained after A has appeared, to strengthen the discrimination (61, p. 308).

Morse and Skinner go on to point out that the direction of the adventitious contingency is not necessarily stable, for over a long period of time the chance relations are likely to oscillate. Furthermore, the establishment of an accidental contingency will be a function of such variables as the duration of the incidental stimulus relative to the length of the session, the reinforcement schedule, and the type of performance generated. All of these factors combine to pose a control problem to which few, if any, investigators have given their attention.

The implications of adventitious discriminative control of the sort demonstrated by Morse and Skinner are especially cogent for experiments in which the conditioned suppression technique is used. When a preshock stimulus suppresses an ongoing baseline of positively reinforced behavior, there is a concomitant shift in the distribution of reinforcements. Because of the lowered response rate during the preshock stimulus there will be few, if any, reinforcements delivered in its presence. The subject will receive most of his reinforcements in the absence of the preshock stimulus. The situation is thus optimal for the development of a correlation between the stimulus and a low rate of reinforcement, a correlation whose effect may summate with that of the unavoidable shock in maintaining a low response rate during the preshock stimulus. The confounding of these two factors will be further enhanced if a reinforcement, made available during the preshock stimulus but not received because of the low response rate, is then procured immediately upon termination of the stimulus.

Similar considerations apply when we place a punishment contingency under stimulus control. If a positively reinforced baseline response is made to produce a shock in the presence of a given stimulus, the resulting low response rate during the stimulus will automatically be correlated with a low reinforcement rate. This correlation may itself contribute to the maintenance of the low rate. Whether such correlations can be controlled and eliminated, or even whether it is desirable to do so, is, at present, a matter of speculation.

BEHAVIORAL HISTORY

An organism's behavior is determined by his past experiences as well as by the current situation, and experimental psychologists have spent much effort in the investigation and more precise delineation of historical factors. Studies of extinction, transition states, cumulative effects of certain variables, etc., all fall into this category. One of the chief advantages of lower animals as experimental subjects has been the relative ease of controlling their behavioral history and of providing them experimentally with whatever history is pertinent to a given investigation.

Control Techniques (Continued)

As experimental psychologists have become more confident of their control techniques, they have begun to move up the phylogenetic scale, using more advanced species such as monkeys, chimpanzees, and humans in their experiments. These efforts have been highly successful in several research areas, but the experimental use of more advanced species has created new problems. The one pertinent to the present discussion is the increasing amount of intersubject variability observed in higher organisms. Much of the variability stems from the considerable and largely unknown behavioral history that higher organisms bring with them to the laboratory. Monkeys and chimpanzees have usually spent a number of years in their natural habitat before coming under experimental study. Humans not only arrive in the laboratory with an unknown history but continue adding to that history if the experiment is of a long-term nature. They do not usually remain in a controlled laboratory environment for the duration of a lengthy study.

There are two factors which are largely responsible for the successful technical and systematic extensions that have been made from lower to higher organisms, in spite of the increasing variability in behavioral history. The first of these is the use of experimental variables which are sufficiently powerful to override the effects of uncontrolled historical factors. For example, values of baseline parameters are selected which are known to produce maximal resistance to interference by extraneous variables; reinforcers for which there is a history of deprivation are used; frequency of reinforcement is kept as high as possible consistent with a desired length of observation period; types and values of reinforcement schedules are such as to minimize the occurrence of behavioral forms other than those under observation.

Sometimes it is possible, in selecting a reinforcer, to make use of the subject's history and to let it work for, instead of against, the application of laboratory control. One can take advantage of idiosyncrasies in a subject's history; or there may be culturally determined reinforcers which possess considerable generality from subject to subject. Lindsley, in working with psychotic adults, has found it possible to determine empirically the type of reinforcer which is most effective for his individual subjects (53). For some subjects cigarettes prove most effective; for others it is money; and in other cases nude pictures are the most effective reinforcer and, depending upon the individual, either male or female nudes may prove most useful; other subjects have been found to respond best when their behavior has the consequence of providing food for a hungry kitten. Although the factors in a subject's history which determine the relative effectiveness of different reinforcers offer a fascinating problem, the experimenter can, even without a full understanding of these factors, make use of them in gaining experimental control.

Some investigators make use of reinforcers which probably have gained their effectiveness from a background of experience which is relatively consistent in the culture from which the subjects are drawn. Such backgrounds often go, in common parlance, under such names as competitiveness, self-respect, level of aspiration, desire to please, etc. These names, of course, have no explanatory value, but the phenomena which they are intended to cover can be put to good use in gaining laboratory control over the behavior of higher organisms. Obviously, direct investigation of these phenomena will increase the degree of rigor with which we can extend our control techniques to higher organisms. Effective though such techniques may be, we cannot rest entirely content if they contain elements which are not thoroughly understood.

In addition to the use of powerful baseline variables, careful design of the experimental situation can help to minimize the effects of differential behavioral histories. Historical factors will intrude into an investigation to the extent that the stimuli in the experimental situation resemble those of past experience. The investigator must be ingenious enough to design his experimental environment and procedures so that the physical stimuli are as different as possible from anything the subject is likely to have encountered before, and yet provide enough latitude to permit the operation of the same behavioral principles that govern behavior outside the laboratory. Stimulus control within the experimental situation must minimize the degree of stimulus generalization with the outside world and still permit general principles to be observed.

This is the old problem of laboratory restriction versus generality of principles, and to solve it the experimenter must walk a narrow path. With adult human subjects it is, of course, not possible to place behavior completely and solely under the control of current variables. By the time adulthood has been reached, behavior has come under the control of variables too complex to be wiped out by any methods permissible in the psychological laboratory. But consistent and generalizable data can be obtained by means of combined stimulus control and the selection of powerful baseline parameters. The experimental situations have thus far been relatively simple. They have, however, at the least performed the useful technical function of demonstrating methods for gaining laboratory control over the behavior of higher organisms even in the face of existing behavioral backgrounds. By building upon the simpler situations it becomes possible to encompass more complex phenomena.

While techniques for eliminating the effects of uncontrolled behavioral history are an important advance, these are not the final answer to the control problem. Like many of the variables I have discussed, behavioral history cannot be eliminated from systematic consideration. Because of its inevitable presence it is a factor which requires study in its own right. At a given stage of systematic progress it may be convenient to eliminate historical factors from our story, but we must eventually evaluate these factors and take them into account in our systematic description of behavior. Thorough evaluation will also provide the most effective control. For then, even when it proves impossible to eliminate the effects of behavioral history, we will be able to specify what those effects are. Control by evaluation is always more effective and more satisfying than is control by exclusion.

LONG-TERM PROCESSES

There are some variables which, by their very nature, require a relatively long period of time before their full effects upon behavior can be observed. I do not refer here simply to a gradual learning process which may be involved in the behavioral adaptation to a new variable, but rather to the fact that a long period of time may have to elapse before the subject can even be said to have been exposed to the variable. Reinforcement rate, for example, is, by definition, a variable of this sort. The subject must receive a large number of reinforcements before their rate of occurrence can have an effect over and above the influence of any individual inter-reinforcement interval. Anger, for example, has shown that long interresponse times are rare in certain variable-interval reinforcement schedules because such interresponse times lower the reinforcement rate (1). A factor such as this intrinsically requires a long period of time before it can impinge upon behavior. Shock frequency is a similar type of variable. Any event must occur a large number of times before its rate of occurrence can become a controlling factor, not because the subject may require a long time to *learn* the rate, but because a rate cannot even be specified except over a period of time.

At what point can we say that the subject has been exposed to a rate of reinforcement, for example? There is no pat answer to this question in terms of currently available techniques. Our best solution at present is a circular one. We can only watch the behavior to determine whether it is being affected by reinforcement rate, and whether the effect has stabilized. The type of behavioral observation we make will depend upon the particular procedure we are employing in any given experiment. It may be possible to make our decision by simple inspection of cumulative response curves, of relative frequencies, or other common behavioral measures. Or it may be necessary, as in Anger's investigation, to carry out some relatively sophisticated control and measurement operations.

Reinforcement rate and other variables of this class may be of concern in either of two ways. We may be interested simply in specifying and stabilizing the effects of reinforcement rate; or we may wish to manipulate reinforcement rate as an experimental variable. In the first case we have no alternative but to let time take its course, and wait till our behavioral observations tell us that the variable has taken hold. But to repeat this waiting period each time we manipulate reinforcement rate as an experimental variable would be a tedious and expensive affair. This, then, is our second problem. Is there any way to shorten the time required to study the effects of variations in long-term variables such as reinforcement rate?

Techniques of stimulus control may hold the answer to this problem. If we can place reinforcement frequency under exteroceptive stimulus control, then we need only change a stimulus to observe immediately the effects of different reinforcement frequencies.

Pretraining would involve exposing the subject to the desired range of reinforcement rates, or any other long-term variable of interest. Each value of the variable, however, would be correlated with a distinctive stimulus. In the presence of one color, for example, there might be an average of one reinforcement per minute; in the presence of another color, frequency might be two per minute; and so on, through the whole range of values to which the subject is to be exposed.

Once stimulus control is well developed, the behavior will change appropriately as soon as the prevailing stimulus color, along with its correlated reinforcement frequency, is altered. We will then have available as a tool a multi-element baseline by means of which we can study the effects of reinforcement frequency in combination with other variables.

The acquisition of immediate control by the various stimuli can be hastened, during the pretraining phase, by making each change in reinforcement frequency a radical one, so that the behavior will feel the effects of the change without delay. Nevertheless, the establishment of such a multi-element baseline may still take a considerable period of time, depending upon how long the subject must be exposed to a reinforcement frequency before it takes control of his behavior. But the subsequent usefulness of this tool may well be great enough to justify the initial expenditure. So little is known of the action of long-term variables, and so much is suspected, that intensive investigative efforts along these lines are likely to prove both interesting and useful.

There is a second type of long-term process which is closely related to our previous discussions of adventitious contingencies and their involvement in learning. Because of adventitious correlations, any contingency which we set up experimentally may continue to shape itself over a long period of time. The shaping process will not necessarily reveal itself in our baseline measurements, but may manifest itself as a cause of variability when the baseline is manipulated experimentally.

When we set up a contingency between a response and an environmental consequence, there is usually a large class of variations on the response side that will satisfy the contingency. This class defines an operant. But the range of response variation within the operant is itself subject to modification by a number of factors. Those variations which require an unnecessarily large energy expenditure will tend to drop out. This process, however, will take time, since the high-energy responses do satisfy the contingency and produce the reinforcement. The topography of the behavior will also tend to approach a form which permits the most rapid procurement of the reinforcement after completion of the response. The process is again a slow one because relatively inefficient forms are nonetheless reinforced, and because the first instance of the most efficient response may not even occur until a late stage of the experiment. Detailed response features which are not necessary to satisfy the contingency may also persist for a long period of time simply because they accompany the reinforced behavior. The behavior may not shed these unnecessary features until several instances of reinforcement in their absence have occurred.

An automatic shaping process may, then, extend over a considerable period of time. The behavior gradually becomes channeled toward the most efficient form that will satisfy the reinforcement contingency. Small uncontrolled variations in response topography all contribute toward this stable end point. The process becomes beautifully visible when the reinforcement contingency is a spurious one. The initial behavior, adventitiously conditioned, gradually becomes modified as small variations cumulate, and the prevailing response at a late stage may bear no resemblance at all to the original form (82). The process remains open-ended, with no necessary final state, because the adventitious contingency provides no consistent relation between behavior and reinforcement through which a stable response form can be selected out.

The long-term automatic shaping process raises a control problem because it blurs our definition of the behavior sample with which we are working. If this sample is changing in time, we may not always be applying our experimental operations to the same material. The problem involves us in the larger question of the definition of a response. We have become accustomed to answering this question in terms of Skinner's concept of the operant, which assumes the equivalence of all behavior that produces the same consequences under the same stimulus control (80). The utility of this concept cannot be questioned, for it has made possible the observation of an unprecedented degree of orderliness in behavior. Identification of the operant as the unit of response has been the most powerful unifying conception in the study of behavior.

But we are now reaching the stage, made possible by our greatly increased technical and systematic sophistication, where subtle and complex phenomena heretofore untouchable in the laboratory are becoming available for experimental examination. Increasing subtlety in the behavioral phenomena under investigation must be matched by increasing subtlety and rigor of experimental control. It is unlikely that we can continue to ignore variations in response topography within an operant class, particularly when the phenomena under investigation require quantitative evaluation. If we adhere too rigidly to the assumption that the components of an operant unit are equivalent in all respects, we are not likely to appreciate and subsequently control major sources of variability in studies of subtle behavioral phenomena.

One approach to this problem is to specify the operant in terms of the behavioral property being measured. Whereas we have been accustomed to calling lever pressing an operant, the suggestion is to classify certain measurable aspects of lever pressing as separate operants, for example, rate of occurrence, latency, energy, etc. A lever-pressing rate of five responses per minute may be one operant, and a rate of ten per minute another. It is possible to make reinforcement contingent upon a specified value of some aspect of behavior, and to treat that value as a response in its own right.

Such a restriction of the operant class may indeed help to minimize the problems arising from long-term self-shaping processes. But it can only do so if the conceptual specificity is matched by an equal specificity of experimental control. If the operant classification is to be restricted to a response which occurs at a given rate, or with a given latency, etc., then the reinforcement contingency must also be so restricted, as must the stimulus control. Then, to the extent that such restriction limits the size of the behavioral class which can enter into the contingencies, we will have reduced the time required for automatic shaping to become complete.

This is not likely to be a permanent solution to the control problem. In addition to a possible decrease in lawfulness, there is at least one other compensatory disadvantage to excessive restriction of the behavior sample with which we work. The greater its restriction the less likely the operant is to exist at high strength initially, and the more difficult it will be to establish its participation in an experimentally controlled contingency. Unless the behavior occurs with an appreciable frequency to start with, we will have no opportunity to place it under experimental control without embarking upon a deliberate shaping program. To determine when this program is complete will be just as uncertain a task as to specify the end of a self-shaping process. The long-term problem will, in most cases, still be with us.

But perhaps this is the road to travel, for unforeseen results may destroy the relevance of my criticism. Perhaps if we wish to employ a fixed-ratio schedule of, say, 50:1, we should reinforce not just every fiftieth lever press, but every fiftieth lever press which has a force of 20 grams and a duration of 0.1 second. New kinds of lawfulness may well emerge from such restriction, bringing with them their own problems of data evaluation.

Appendix

A Terminological Note

THE MAJORITY OF WRITERS on scientific methodology have taken their examples from the physical sciences or from areas of biology other than psychology. For that reason, the references in this book to behavioral problems, techniques, and data involve terms that will be unfamiliar to many readers. The purpose of this note is to clarify enough of the terms that the reader may then use the illustrations to advantage and follow the discussion without undue distraction. I have not attempted to include all psychological terms, but only those I have used in this book.

Appendix

APPARATUS

When the psychologist brings an organism into the laboratory to study its behavior, he is immediately faced with a number of practical problems. If the subject is nonhuman, there must be living space available in which to house it, both before the experiment begins and during the periods between experimental treatments. Most animal subjects, then, have a *home cage*.

Food and water may or may not be available to the animal in its home cage, depending upon the particular investigation in which it is participating; or it may be available only at specific times. The availability of food and water is specified as the *deprivation schedule*. A 23-hour schedule of food deprivation, for example, indicates that, for each hour that the animal has access to food in its home cage, there are 23 intervening hours during which it has nothing to eat.

The problem then arises of selecting an *experimental space* in which to house the subject while the experiment is being performed. Laboratory experimentation automatically implies a certain degree of restriction upon both the activity of the subject and the types of observation open to the experimenter. By placing the subject in an enclosed chamber the experimenter restricts the subject's area of activity, but not his freedom of activity within that area. The size of the space, of course, depends on the size of the subject—relatively large to accommodate a chimpanzee or a human, and smaller for a mouse.

Ordinarily, subjects remain in the experimental space for a limited period of time, termed an experimental *session*. The experiment itself may extend over a large number of sessions, with the subject returning to its home cage or, if human, to his normal environment, between sessions.

The investigator restricts his observations by recording the effects his experimental operations produce on some selected aspect of the subject's behavior. In certain types of studies, the behavior selected for observation may be of interest for its own sake, as when the object of the investigation is to study copulatory behavior. In most of the investigations I have used as illustrative examples the specific *response* whose characteristics are being recorded is of no intrinsic interest. It is selected simply as an example of the organism's behavior, and presumably follows the same laws as any other example we might have selected. This assumption has been sufficiently verified so that any exceptions to it deserve further study, simply because they are exceptions.

The problem of which response of the organism to select for observation is usually solved on the basis of convenience, both to the experimental organism and to the experimenter. It should be a response which does not require excessive effort, and whose repetition does not fatigue the organism—unless, of course, effort and fatigue are the problems under investigation. It should be a response whose relevant characteristics are easily recordable, with minimal interference from the process of observation itself. For reasons to be noted shortly, there should be minimal constraint upon the subject's rate of responding.

With an organism such as the pigeon, the *pecking response* has been found to meet these requirements. On one wall of the experimental space is mounted a translucent disk, or *key*. When the bird pecks at the key the pressure operates a switch, which then sends an electrical pulse to the recording equipment and to other apparatus used for programing the experimental procedure. The pigeon is, of course, well adapted for the pecking response; it pecks easily and rapidly, and once it has pecked at the key it is in a position to repeat the response immediately. Attaching the key to a sensitive switch provides a simple solution to the recording problem. An additional feature of the key is its translucence; it can be illuminated by lights of various colors, the *key lights*, and visual patterns such as dots of various sizes, geometric figures, brightness patterns, etc., can be projected upon it. An example may be seen in Figure 22, page 221. The key lights serve the functions of stimuli in the various experimental procedures.

Not to be confused with the key light is the *house light*, which is simply a general source of illumination for the experimental space. It, too, may be used as a stimulus. Usually, turning on the house light signals the subject that the experimental session has started; turning it off marks the end of the session.

Pigeon keys have also been used successfully with the rat, which pushes against the key with its nose. But until recently it has been more usual, in experimenting with rats and other small mammals, to use a *lever* which the animal can depress. Basically, the lever is simply a metal rod projecting into the experimental space through one wall; when the subject presses the lever downward for a sufficient distance and with a sufficient force, a switch operates and sends a signal to the recording and programing apparatus. Any behavior by means of which the subject succeeds in operating the switch is counted as a *lever-pressing response.*

Lever pressing is actually a somewhat more congenial response for monkeys, chimpanzees, and humans, who are more accustomed to manipulating objects manually. Sometimes, instead of, or in addition to, a lever, the monkey's experimental space may have in it a chain hanging from the ceiling. Whenever the monkey pulls the chain it operates a switch and, in this instance, the animal's *chain-pulling response* is recorded.

Subjects in an experimental chamber press levers, peck keys, pull chains, etc., because their responses produce certain consequences. For example, the monkey's lever press may bring it some food. If the animal has been on a deprivation schedule, and is hungry during the experimental session, lever-pressing behavior will then predominate. The appearance of food as a consequence of the animal's lever press increases the probability that the animal will press the lever again. Any event, contingent upon a response of the organism, that alters the future likelihood of that response, is called a *reinforcement.*

Food is probably the most commonly used type of reinforcement in the behavior laboratory. It is not that the psychologist is interested in food-procuring behavior or in eating as such, although in specific instances that may indeed be his concern. He uses food reinforcement as a practical technique for generating and maintaining a sample of the organism's behavior so that he can then study it. In the section on procedures, I shall describe some of the ways reinforcement can be used to generate and maintain behavior in an experimental organism.

There is usually an automatic food dispenser, the *magazine,* located on one wall of the experimental space. If the food reinforcement takes the form of solid food pellets, the magazine, when activated, releases a pellet through a tube and into the *food tray,* where it is accessible to the animal. For pigeons, the reinforcement is usually grain; a solenoid mechanism makes the grain available to the bird for a fixed number of seconds at each reinforcement. If the reinforcement is water, or food in a liquid form, the magazine consists of a reservoir and a motor- or solenoid-driven cup. Each reinforcement consists of a period of seconds during which the filled cup is made available to the subject. The *amount of reinforcement* can be controlled by the size of the pellet, by the period of time the grain or liquid is available to the animal, or by the concentration of nutrients in the reinforcing substance.

Other types of reinforcement are also used to control behavior experimentally. The experimental space often has a floor made of metal rods—a *grid* or *grill*—through which electric shocks can be administered to the subject. Any response which permits the organism to escape from, or to prevent the occurrence of, the electric shock, will thereby be reinforced. Behavior which permits a subject to turn off the shock is called *escape behavior*. Behavior which allows a subject to keep the shock from coming on is called *avoidance behavior*.

An interesting and unusual type of reinforcement is *intracranial electrical stimulation*. Using appropriate surgical procedures, the experimenter inserts metal electrodes through an animal's skull into certain areas of its brain. These are *implanted electrodes*. When the animal is in the experimental space, wires are attached to the electrodes and connected, via the switch which is operated by the subject's response, to a source of electric current. Then, whenever the subject responds—for example, presses the lever—an electric current flows through that portion of its brain in which the electrodes are located. Thus the animal stimulates its own brain tissue. If the electrodes are properly placed, this *self-stimulation* will reinforce the animal's behavior; its probability of response will increase, and the characteristics of its self-stimulation behavior can be modified by the same operations as those I shall describe below for food reinforcement.

In addition to the visual stimuli provided via the key and house lights, auditory stimuli may be presented to the subject through a speaker located in or near the experimental space. An auditory stimulus may take the form of a steady tone or of a series of clicks. In order to mask apparatus sounds that might interfere with the experimental procedure, the experimental space is usually exposed to a source of *white noise,* made up of a wide range of sound frequencies.

RECORDING TECHNIQUES

THE EXPERIMENTAL PSYCHOLOGIST is interested in the laws that describe the likelihood, or probability, that an organism will respond in a certain way. Before going on to describe the manipulations he performs to change the organism's response probability, let us first look at his methods of recording the behavior.

THE CUMULATIVE RECORD. One index of the probability of a response is its rate of occurrence. How many times does the subject respond, for example, each minute? The *cumulative recorder* gives us a continuous visual picture of the subject's rate of response. The recorder is essentially a kymograph-like device, with a strip of paper driven by a motor at a constant speed, and with a pen riding on the paper. As long as the subject does not respond, the pen draws a line parallel to the direction in which the paper is moving. When the subject responds—presses a lever, pecks a key, or does whatever is being recorded—the pen moves a short distance perpendicular to the direction in which the paper is being driven. The result is a curve like that of Figure 6. The slope of the curve is proportional to the subject's response rate. When the curve is flat, it indicates that the subject did not respond at all during that period of time. When the slope is steep, it means that the subject was responding rapidly. The height of the curve at any point tells us the total number of times the subject has responded up to that time.

The curve is cumulative in that responses move the pen in only one direction. If the subject responds often enough to bring the pen to the top of the paper, the pen then automatically resets to the bottom and begins its climb anew, as may be seen in Figure 5. When the experiment covers a long period of time these separate excursions of the pen may be cut and placed closer together, or "telescoped," for more compact presentation in a report, as in Figure 26.

There are certain accessories on the cumulative recorder that provide other information than a measure of response rate. For example, an appropriate electrical signal will cause the pen to be displaced slightly, in an oblique direction from its normal path of movement. If the pen is displaced only momentarily, it may indicate the point at which the subject received a reinforcement, as in Figure 7, or a shock, as in Figure 16. In Figure 5, the pen is held in its displaced position for several minutes, and indicates the period during which a stimulus was being presented to the subject. The horizontal line during this period tells us that the subject did not respond while the stimulus was on.

In addition to its normal reset when it reaches the top of the paper, the pen may also be reset by an electrical signal at any other point in its excursion. This is sometimes done, as in Figure 29, to separate the data that arise from different stages of an experimental procedure.

When an experimental procedure involves two responses, two separate cumulative recorders may be used. The separate records can then be placed together and photographed on the same coordinates for convenient comparison. Figure 24 shows an example.

It should be noted that the cumulative record is, in a very real sense, drawn directly by the subject. Except in his choice of coordinates, determined by the paper speed and by the distance traveled in each movement of the pen, the experimenter performs no transformation upon the data. It is a direct record of the subject's behavior; furthermore, it is an immediate record, which permits the investigator to evaluate the moment-to-moment course of his experiment as it develops.

INTERRESPONSE TIMES. The reciprocal of the average response rate tells us the average amount of time elapsing between successive responses, or the average *interresponse time.* Once the subject has responded, how long will it take for him to respond again? There are measuring instruments that give us a statistical answer to this ques tion in the form of a frequency distribution of the subject's interresponse times during a given experimental session, or portion of a session. At the end of such a period the recorder will indicate, for example, how many times the subject paused for two to four seconds between responses, how many times he paused for four to six seconds, six to eight seconds, etc. This too is a measure of response probability. Given a response at a certain time, we can estimate when the next response is likely to occur.

OTHER RESPONSE CHARACTERISTICS. Response rates and interresponse times by no means exhaust the measures of response probability, but in the interest of simplicity I have not mentioned others in the text. Behavior, however, also possesses other measurable characteristics. Each response, for example, occupies a finite period of time, known as the *response duration*. It may also bear a temporal relation to a prior stimulus; the time between stimulus and response is the *response latency*. A response such as lever pressing or key pecking requires the organism to exert a certain amount of force, and this *response force* is also measurable with suitable instrumentation. Sometimes the behavior is recorded only indirectly, in terms of its effects upon the environment. For example, the experimenter may record the number of reinforcements the subject received; or the number he actually received relative to the total number he could have received if he had behaved in a perfectly efficient fashion. Similarly, he may record the number of shocks the subject succeeded in avoiding.

EXPERIMENTAL PROCEDURES

MAGAZINE TRAINING. It is a well-established principle of behavior that a reinforcement is most effective if it immediately follows a response. To state the principle somewhat differently, a reinforcement exerts its greatest effect upon the response that has occurred immediately prior to its delivery. In building a response into a subject's repertoire of behavior it is essential, therefore, to make sure that the reinforcement is received by the subject as soon as it responds appropriately. *Magazine training* is directed toward this end.

Suppose the experimental organism is a monkey; the response, lever pressing; and the reinforcement, food pellets. If the animal has received no magazine training, the first delivery of a food pellet after a lever press is likely not to have its desired effect. The noise of the food magazine and the sudden appearance of the pellet in the food tray—if, indeed, the animal sees it at all—are likely to frighten the monkey so that it leaps to the other side of the experimental space. After some adaptation to this initial experience, the monkey will eventually approach the pellet, or find it accidentally, and will pick it up. It may simply throw the pellet away, or it may play with it for a while and then eat it. This occurs a long time after it has pressed the lever. From the monkey's point of view, the consequence of pressing the lever was a frightening noise; lever pressing and pellet remain unrelated.

During magazine training, the lever is not available to the animal. Pellets are simply delivered gratis, independently of the monkey's behavior. The initial disturbance eventually adapts out, without ever having been associated with the lever-pressing response. The monkey's behavior comes under the control of the magazine sound; whenever the sound occurs, the animal stops whatever it is doing, picks the pellet out of the food tray, and ingests it. Then the lever is made available. The first time the animal presses the lever the magazine sound occurs, the pellet is immediately taken, and the connection between lever-pressing and food reinforcement is made. A few more reinforcements and the response is firmly established in the animal's behavioral repertoire, and is available for further study.

SHAPING. When the lever is finally made available to the animal, after magazine training, the experimenter can simply wait until the animal presses it, depending either upon a chance contact or upon the animal's tendency to explore and to manipulate its environment. In that case the experimenter will have no control over the precise form of the lever-pressing response; the animal may press the lever with either hand, with its mouth, or may jump into the air and land upon it. And, depending upon the location, size, force requirement, and other features of the lever, the first response may not be forthcoming for some time. To bring the response in more quickly, and to control its precise form, or *topography*, the experimenter deliberately *shapes* the desired response out of the mass of undifferentiated behavior being displayed by the animal.

Shaping is accomplished by a process of *successive approximation.*

If the animal starts out by remaining nearly motionless, the experimenter will first deliver a pellet each time the animal moves, regardless of the particular movement. Once the reinforcements have increased the probability of movement, the experimenter begins to restrict the type of movement that he will reinforce. He gradually requires the animal to move closer to the lever, to face the lever, to raise its hand higher and higher up to the lever, to rest its hand upon the lever, and finally to press it. Thus the animal gradually approximates the desired form of response, and once it responds appropriately no other behavior can produce the reinforcement.

REINFORCEMENT SCHEDULES. Once the experimenter has shaped the desired response, he continues to deliver a reinforcement to the subject each time the response occurs. This procedure of reinforcing every response is termed *continuous reinforcement*. The whole initial process by which the organism learns the response is often called *acquisition*. If the experimenter then disconnects the magazine, so that the subject can no longer produce the reinforcement, the frequency of the previously reinforced response will decline to a low value, eventually to disappear. The operation of nonreinforcement is termed *extinction*, and a response whose frequency has been decreased by nonreinforcement is said to have been *extinguished*.

There is a vast middle ground between continuous reinforcement and extinction. Once the behavior has been well established through continuous reinforcement it is no longer necessary to reinforce each occurrence of the response. A generic name for the procedure of reinforcing only some occurrences of the response is *intermittent reinforcement*. The system, or program, according to which reinforcement is delivered is called the *reinforcement schedule*.

The reinforcement schedules I shall now describe not only are effective in maintaining the organism's behavior but also are responsible for certain characteristics of the behavior. Each schedule generates its characteristic form of behavior, and it is often possible, by examining the cumulative record, to identify the reinforcement schedule in effect at the time.

FIXED INTERVAL. The availability of reinforcement can be programed by a timer. Let us say the timer has been set for five minutes.

The session begins, the timer starts to run, and no responses are reinforced for five minutes. Responses during this period have no effect; the experimenter simply records them. At the end of five minutes the timer stops and a switch closes. The next response sends a signal through the closed switch to the food magazine, and a reinforcement is delivered. The switch immediately opens, the timer starts running again, and for the next five minutes the organism cannot produce a reinforcement. The first response following the lapse of five minutes is again reinforced. The cycles continue, with reinforcement available to the organism only when five minutes have passed since the last reinforced response. This is a *fixed-interval schedule* of five minutes.

If the organism is sufficiently deprived of food; if the amount of reinforcement is great enough; and if the type of food is maximally effective as a reinforcer, an animal's behavior can be maintained on fixed-interval schedules as long as several hours. The animal's behavior will pass through several stages, but will eventually take on certain stable characteristics, an example of which may be seen in Figure 18. Following each reinforcement the animal does not respond at all, and the cumulative record is flat during this *post-reinforcement pause.* Following the pause, the animal begins to respond, slowly at first and then with increasing rapidity. The period during which the response rate is accelerating gives the record of fixed-interval behavior its characteristic *curvature.* The high steady rate that emerges from the curvature and continues until reinforcement is known as the *terminal rate.*

The fixed interval does not have to begin with a reinforcement. It can start at any point arbitrarily designated by the experimenter. Following a reinforcement, for example, the next interval may not begin until a certain stimulus comes on. In that case, of course, the pause at the beginning of the interval is not a post-reinforcement pause, and may simply be referred to as a *fixed-interval pause.*

VARIABLE INTERVAL. Reinforcements can be made available to the subject at irregular, rather than fixed, intervals of time. A common method of doing this is by means of a punched tape, driven by a constant-speed motor. As each hole in the tape passes beneath a sensing device, a switch closes and allows the next response of the subject to produce a reinforcement. The amount of space between successive holes in the *programing tape* determines the amount of time that must elapse between successive reinforcements. *Variable-interval schedules* are specified by the average amount of time between reinforcements and by the distribution of time intervals between reinforcements as they are scheduled by the tape.

If the variable-interval programing tape is efficiently constructed, the subject will respond at a relatively consistent rate at all times. There will be none of the cyclicity that characterizes fixed-interval behavior.

DIFFERENTIAL REINFORCEMENT OF LOW RATES. Reinforcement availability can be programed simultaneously by a fixed-interval timer and by the subject's own behavior. For example, the timer may make reinforcement available every 20 seconds, but only if the subject has not responded for 20 seconds. Each response of the subject resets the timer and starts the 20-second period all over again. Every time the subject waits for 20 seconds without responding, the next response will produce a reinforcement. Since this schedule has the effect of extinguishing responses that occur at a rate higher than one per 20 seconds, the schedule is characterized as the *differential reinforcement of low rates*, sometimes abbreviated *DRL*. When the organism's behavior comes to respect the schedule, it is characterized by *spaced responding*, which yields a low, steady response rate. The behavior is sometimes called *timing behavior*, or *delayed response*, for the subject must be able to delay its response for a specified period of time if it is to procure reinforcements.

FIXED RATIO. It is possible to make reinforcement availability depend solely upon certain properties of the subject's behavior. A common way of doing this is to require the organism to respond a fixed number of times for each reinforcement. An animal may, for example, produce a food pellet only with every fiftieth lever press, regardless of how long it takes to press the lever 50 times. This is called a *fixed-ratio schedule* of reinforcement, since the ratio of responses to reinforcements is constant. The schedule is analogous to the piecework method of payment sometimes to be found in industry.

Examples of the behavior generated by the fixed-ratio schedule are to be found in Figure 19. As in fixed-interval behavior, there is a post-reinforcement pause. Once the subject begins to respond, however, it almost immediately assumes a high, near maximal rate, which continues until reinforcement. The schedule typically produces a biphasic performance, with a response rate of zero immediately after each reinforcement, and an extremely high response rate at all other times. A number of conditions can influence the duration of the post-reinforcement pause; the size of the required ratio (longer pauses with higher ratios); the amount of reinforcement (for example, shorter pauses with larger pellets); the amount of deprivation (longer pauses when the subject is satiated); etc. When the conditions are such as to produce excessively long pauses, the behavior is picturesquely considered to be in a state of strain, and is labeled a *strained ratio* performance.

AVOIDANCE. As noted previously, an organism's behavior can be reinforced not only by the production of things such as food but also by the prevention of noxious stimuli such as electric shocks. A common procedure for generating avoidance behavior is to administer brief shocks to an organism at regular intervals—for example, five seconds—as long as it does not press a lever. When the subject does not respond, the interval between shocks is five seconds, and is known as the *shock-shock interval.* When the subject does press the lever, it postpones the next shock for a given period of time—for example, 20 seconds. Once the organism has responded, the next shock cannot come for 20 seconds, and every subsequent response starts the 20-second delay over again. The interval by which each lever press delays the shock is the *response-shock interval.* This procedure typically generates a stable rate of lever pressing (see Figure 35), with the rate itself being determined by the values of the shock-shock and response-shock intervals, among other factors.

STIMULUS CONTROL. Organisms, whether rats, monkeys, or people, do not normally go around responding in all possible ways at all times. A given type of behavior is usually appropriate to a given situation. By appropriate, we mean that reinforcement will be forthcoming only under certain conditions; it is under those conditions that the behavior appears. Reinforcement does not merely increase the probability of a response; it makes the response more probable upon the recurrence of conditions the same as, or similar to, those that prevailed during previous reinforcements.

A simple experimental technique for specifying at least one of the conditions appropriate for reinforcement of a given response is to provide the subject with a distinctive environmental stimulus on those occasions when reinforcement will be available. For example, when a tone is sounding a monkey may procure food pellets by pressing a lever; when the tone is off, the lever-pressing response is extinguished. Since the animal is never reinforced in the absence of the tone it will press the lever only when the tone is on. The subject is then said to discriminate the tone, and the process by which this comes about is called *stimulus discrimination.* Since the term, discrimination, has sometimes been given a certain explanatory status, beyond its operational definition, many experimenters prefer not to use it at all and refer instead to *stimulus control.* The lever-pressing response has come under the control of the tone, as indicated by the fact that the organism presses the lever only when the tone is sounding.

MULTIPLE SCHEDULES. An environmental stimulus may not only control the occurrence or nonoccurrence of a given response but may also control specific characteristics of the behavior that is reinforced in its presence. It may, in a sense, tell the organism something about other variables that are operative in the situation. For example, when the key is red we may reinforce a pigeon's pecking behavior according to a fixed-interval schedule of five minutes; when the key is green the reinforcement schedule may be a fixed ratio which requires 100 responses per reinforcement. Eventually, the bird's pecking behavior when the key is red will be typical of the fixed-interval schedule; when the key is green the cyclic pauses and high fixed-ratio rates will prevail. The investigator refers to this differential performance in the presence of the two stimuli by saying that the reinforcement schedules have come under stimulus control. This simply means that the subject behaves in each stimulus in a manner appropriate to the prevailing reinforcement schedule. Since there is more than one schedule, and more than one stimulus, the procedure is called a *multiple schedule of reinforcement.*

CHAINING. Up to now I have used as examples of reinforcement such biological necessities as food or avoidance of pain. Many other types of reinforcers have been found useful in the laboratory, and many of them, like food and avoidance of shock, seem to be natural reinforcers. An infant's behavior can be reinforced by a flashing light; a rat's behavior can be reinforced by allowing it to run in an activity wheel; a monkey's behavior can be reinforced by allowing it to manipulate certain movable objects. Those reinforcers which seem to be reinforcing in their own right, and do not require any special procedures to make them reinforcers, are called primary reinforcers, and their effect upon behavior is called *primary reinforcement.*

Even the most casual observation indicates that many, if not most, of the reinforcements that operate upon human behavior are in a different class than the primary reinforcements. Money, for example, is not a primary reinforcer. The signs of prestige, of social standing, the avoidance of parental disapproval—these are all types of reinforcement, but there is nothing inherently reinforcing about them. Special techniques are required to impart a reinforcing function to stimuli that were not originally reinforcing, and such stimuli are therefore called *conditioned reinforcements*, or *secondary reinforcements.*

To illustrate the basic procedure for establishing a stimulus as a conditioned reinforcement, let us make a slight modification in a multiple schedule. When a green light is on, a monkey can procure a food pellet by pressing a lever 50 times, *i.e.*, a fixed-ratio schedule of 50. After the animal receives a pellet, the color of the light changes to green. It will not change back to red until five minutes pass and then the monkey presses the lever again. In the green light, then, there is a fixed-interval schedule of five minutes, but the reinforcement at the end of five minutes is not a food pellet; it is simply a change in the color of the light from green to red. Food pellets are available only when the light is red, but the light can only become red by virtue of the subject's own behavior.

To recapitulate the sequence: Green light, fixed interval of five minutes; the first lever press after the light has been green for five minutes will change the color to red; when the red light is on, the fiftieth lever press will produce a food pellet; upon delivery of the pellet, the light becomes green and the cycle starts again.

In spite of the fact that there is no food reinforcement in the green light, the animal's behavior in the green light will be typical of a fixed-interval schedule of food reinforcement. The red light is sufficiently reinforcing to generate and maintain the fixed-interval behavior. The red light has acquired its reinforcing function, *i.e.*, become a conditioned reinforcer, because it is only in the presence of the red light that the animal is reinforced with food.

Because the red light, and its associated schedule of food reinforcement, can appear only through the mediation of the subject's behavior, this procedure is called *chaining*. The fixed-ratio schedule in the red light is chained to the fixed-interval schedule in the green light, and the connecting link in the chain is the subject's lever-pressing response. In this particular chain, there are two *members*, though there need be no such limitation. The red light acts as a conditioned reinforcement for the initial member of the chain, the fixed-interval behavior in the green light. The food pellet, which reinforces the second and final member of the chain, is called the *terminal reinforcement*. In this example, the terminal reinforcement is also a primary reinforcement, but that need not be the case. It, too, may have been conditioned.

Because a conditioned reinforcement derives its function from association with a stimulus that is already reinforcing, it is possible for a conditioned reinforcer to become much more powerful than any primary reinforcer. For a conditioned reinforcer can be associated with a wide variety of primary as well as secondary reinforcements. We can extend our example of chaining so that the subject, when hungry, will receive food in the red light; when thirsty it will receive water; when sexually aroused it will gain access to a partner; after a period of confinement it can gain access to a play area; when a tone is sounding along with the red light, a threatened shock can be avoided. The list can be stretched indefinitely. The red light will then be associated with a wide variety of reinforcements and it, in turn, will function as a conditioned reinforcer in a wide variety of situations. It will have become a *generalized reinforcement*. Money is a conspicuous example of a generalized reinforcement.

A Terminological Note

SOME GENERAL CONCEPTS

THE EXPERIMENTAL SITUATIONS I have used for illustration all share at least one important feature: the experimental organism is free to respond at any time. There are no harnesses to restrain the animal forcibly; the lever is never withdrawn from the experimental space to prevent the subject from responding at times that would be inconvenient for the investigator's theory. The only restrictions placed upon the subject's recorded behavior are those inherent in the laws of behavior. This is called a *free-responding situation.*

Those experimenters who use the free-responding situation, along with the continuous picture of the subject's performance that is available in the cumulative curve, develop a feeling for behavior as a process that goes on continuously in time. The conception of behavior as a temporal process gives rise to the term *ongoing behavior,* which expresses the temporal continuity of the subject's responses even though the individual responses themselves may be discrete and well defined. If the reinforcement for a subject in a free-responding situation is the avoidance of shock, the relevant variables in the situation will generate a certain level of *ongoing avoidance behavior;* other variables will give rise to *ongoing food-reinforced behavior,* etc.

Ongoing behavior gives the experimenter an important tactical advantage: he can manipulate it directly. He can introduce a new variable, or change the value of one that is already relevant, and he can observe any alterations that take place in the subject's ongoing behavior. The ongoing behavior can serve as a *baseline* from which to measure the effects of the experimental operations. A *behavioral baseline* is not some idealized state of behavior inferred from the performance of a group of individuals by means of a statistical averaging process. It is the continuous, and continuing, performance of a single individual.

Once the experimenter has established some level of *baseline behavior,* he is ready to change the experimental conditions. If the baseline behavior is maintained by a fixed-interval reinforcement schedule, he may alter the length of the fixed interval. Or he may change the size of the food pellet. A most useful type of baseline for measuring the effect of the experimenter's operations consists of behavior that is maintained in the *steady state;* that is to say, behavior whose characteristics do not change for long periods of time; behavior which remains steady, or stable. For example, the avoidance schedule that I described above will keep the subject's rate of response at a stable value over long periods of time, many hours or even days. Any changes that take place in such steady-state behavior can with confidence be attributed to the experimenter's manipulations.

Steady-state behavior is even more useful to the experimenter if it is *reversible.* Once the experimenter has changed the experimental conditions, thereby altering the behavior, can he then return to the original conditions and expect the behavior to return to its original steady state? If the original behavior can be recovered, it is said to be reversible. Reversibility makes it possible to replicate an experiment many times over in a single organism, and eliminates the troublesome, though interesting, problem of taking the subject's *behavioral history* into account. When the behavior is *irreversible,* i.e., not returnable to its original state, then the investigator must look into variables to which the subject is not currently being exposed but to which it has been exposed in the past, and which constitute the organism's behavioral history.

References

1. ANGER, D. The dependence of interresponse times upon the relative reinforcement of different interresponse times. *J. exper. Psychol.*, 52: 145–161, 1956.
2. ANTONITIS, J. J. Response variability in the white rat during conditioning, extinction, and reconditioning. *J. exper. Psychol.*, 42: 273–281, 1951.
3. AZRIN, N. H. Some effects of two intermittent schedules of immediate and non-immediate punishment. *J. Psychol.*, 42: 3–21, 1956.
4. BACHRACH, A. J. The psychodiagnostic test battery: test selection. In *Progress in Clinical Psychology*, Vol. III. New York: Grune & Stratton, 1958, pp. 40–49.

5. Bakan, D. A generalization of Sidman's results on group and individual functions, and a criterion. *Psychol. Bull.*, *51:* 63–64, 1954.
6. Békésy, G. V. A new audiometer. *Acta oto-laryngol.*, *35:* 411–422, 1947.
7. Bersh, P. J. The influence of two variables upon the establishment of a secondary reinforcer for operant responses. *J. exper. Psychol.*, *41:* 62–73, 1951.
8. Blough, D. S. Technique for studying the effects of drugs on discrimination in the pigeon. *Ann. N.Y. Acad. Sci.*, *65:* 334–356, 1956.
9. Blough, D. S. A method for obtaining psychophysical thresholds from the pigeon. *J. exper. anal. Behav.*, *1:* 31–43, 1958.
10. Boren, J. J. (Personal communication.)
11. Boren, J. J. Response rate and resistance to extinction as functions of the fixed ratio. Unpublished Ph.D. dissertation, Columbia University, 1953.
12. Boren, J. J., and Sidman, M. A discrimination based upon repeated conditioning and extinction of avoidance behavior. *J. comp. physiol. Psychol.*, *50:* 18–22, 1957.
13. Boren, J. J. and Sidman, M. Maintenance of avoidance behavior with intermittent shocks. *Canad. J. Psychol.*, *11:* 185–192, 1957.
14. Boring, E. G. Statistical frequencies as dynamic equilibria. *Psychol. Rev.*, *48:* 279–301, 1941.
15. Brady, J. V. (Personal communication.)
16. Brady, J. V. Ulcers in "executive" monkeys. *Scient. Am.*, *199:* 95–100, 1958.
17. Brady, J. V., Boren, J. J., Conrad, D., and Sidman, M. The effect of food and water deprivation upon intracranial self-stimulation. *J. comp. physiol. Psychol.*, *50:* 134–137, 1957.
18. Brady, J. V., and Hunt, H. F. An experimental approach to the analysis of emotional behavior. *J. Psychol.*, *40:* 313–324, 1955.
19. Brush, F. R., Brush, E. S., and Solomon, R. L. Traumatic avoidance learning: the effects of CS-US interval with a delayed-conditioning procedure. *J. comp. physiol. Psychol.*, *48:* 285–293, 1955.
20. Bullock, D. H., and Smith, W. C. An effect of repeated conditioning-extinction upon operant strength. *J. exper. Psychol.*, *46:* 349–352, 1953.
21. Cannon, W. B. *The Way of an Investigator.* New York: Norton, 1945.
22. Cronbach, L. J. The two disciplines of scientific psychology. *Am. Psychol.*, *12:* 671–684, 1957.
23. Cumming, W. W., and Schoenfeld, W. N. Behavior under ex-

tended exposure to a high-value fixed interval reinforcement schedule. *J. exper. anal. Behav.*, *1:* 245–263, 1958.
24. Dews, P. B. Modification by drugs of performance on simple schedules of positive reinforcement. *Ann. N.Y. Acad. Sci.*, *65:* 268–281, 1956.
25. Dinsmoor, J. A. Punishment: I. The avoidance hypothesis. *Psychol. Rev.*, *61:* 34–46, 1954.
26. Estes, W. K. An experimental study of punishment. *Psychol. Monogr.*, *57:* 1–40, 1944. Whole No. 263.
27. Estes, W. K. The problem of inference from curves based on group data. *Psychol. Bull.*, *53:* 134–140, 1956.
28. Estes, W. K., Koch, S., MacCorquodale, K., Meehl, P. E., Mueller, C. G., Schoenfeld, W. N., and Verplanck, W. S. *Modern learning theory.* New York: Appleton-Century-Crofts, 1954.
29. Estes, W. K., and Skinner, B. F. Some quantitative properties of anxiety. *J. exper. Psychol.*, *29:* 390–400, 1941.
30. Ferster, C. B. Sustained behavior under delayed reinforcement. *J. exper. Psychol.*, *45:* 218–224, 1953.
31. Ferster, C. B. The use of the free operant in the analysis of behavior. *Psychol. Bull.*, *50:* 263–274, 1953.
32. Ferster, C. B. Use of the blackout in the investigation of temporal discrimination in fixed-interval reinforcement. *J. exper. Psychol.*, *47:* 69–74, 1954.
33. Ferster, C. B. Control of behavior in chimpanzees and pigeons by time out from positive reinforcement. *Psychol. Monogr.*, *72:* 1–38, 1958. Whole No. 461.
34. Ferster, C. B., and Skinner, B. F. *Schedules of reinforcement.* New York: Appleton-Century-Crofts, 1957.
35. Findley, J. D. (Personal communication.)
36. Findley, J. D. Preference and switching under concurrent scheduling. *J. exper. anal. Behav.*, *1:* 123–144, 1958.
37. Frick, F. C., and Miller, G. A. A statistical description of operant conditioning. *Am. J. Pyschol.*, *64:* 20–36, 1951.
38. Guttman, N., and Kalish, H. I. Discriminability and stimulus generalization. *J. exper. Psychol.*, *51:* 79–88, 1956.
39. Guttman, N., and Kalish, H. I. Experiments on discrimination. *Scient. Am.*, *198:* 77–82, 1958.
40. Harlow, H. F. Primate learning. In C. P. Stone (Ed.), *Comparative Psychology*, 3rd. ed. New York: Prentice-Hall, 1951, pp. 183–238.
41. Hayes, K. J. The backward curve: a method for the study of learning. *Psychol. Rev.*, *60:* 269–275, 1953.

42. Herrnstein, R. J. Behavioral consequences of the removal of a discriminative stimulus associated with variable-interval reinforcement. Unpublished Ph.D. dissertation, Harvard University, 1955.
43. Herrnstein, R. J., and Brady, J. V. Interaction among components of a multiple schedule. *J. exper. anal. Behav., 1:* 293–300, 1958.
44. Herrnstein, R. J., and Morse, W. H. Effects of pentobarbital on intermittently reinforced behavior. *Science, 125:* 929–931, 1957.
45. Herrnstein, R. J., and Sidman, M. Avoidance conditioning as a factor in the effects of unavoidable shocks on food-reinforced behavior. *J. comp. physiol. Psychol., 51:* 380–385, 1958.
46. Holland, J. G. Human vigilance. *Science, 128:* 61–67, 1958.
47. Hull, C. L. *Principles of Behavior.* New York: Appleton-Century-Crofts, 1943.
48. Hunter, W. S. The delayed reaction in animals and children. *Behav. Monogr., 2:* 1913.
49. Huxley, T. H. *Science and Hebrew Tradition.* New York: D. Appleton & Co., 1897.
50. Kamin, L. J. Traumatic avoidance learning: the effects of CS-US interval with a trace-conditioning procedure. *J. comp. physiol. Psychol., 47:* 65–72, 1954.
51. Keller, F. S., and Schoenfeld, W. N. *Principles of Psychology.* New York: Appleton-Century-Crofts, 1950.
52. Libby, A. Two variables in the acquisition of depressant properties by a stimulus. *J. exper. Psychol., 42:* 100–107, 1951.
53. Lindsley, O. R., Skinner, B. F., and Solomon, H. C. "Periodic Project Reports," *Metropolitan State Hospital,* Waltham, Mass. June 1953–August 1956. Microcard No. FO–57–524–527, L. C. No. MicP 57–30.
54. Mechner, F. Probability relations within response sequences under ratio reinforcement. *J. exper. anal. Behav., 1:* 109–121, 1958.
55. Merrill, M. The relationship of individual growth to average growth. *Hum. Biol., 3:* 37–70, 1931.
56. Miller, G. A., and Frick, F. C. Statistical behavioristics and sequences of responses. *Psychol. Rev., 56:* 311–324, 1949.
57. Morse, W. H. An analysis of responding in the presence of a stimulus correlated with periods of nonreinforcement. Unpublished Ph.D. dissertation, Harvard University, 1955.
58. Morse, W. H., and Herrnstein, R. J. (Personal communication.)
59. Morse, W. H., and Herrnstein, R. J. Effects of drugs on characteristics of behavior maintained by complex schedules of intermittent positive reinforcement. *Ann. N. Y. Acad. Sci., 65:* 303–317, 1956.

60. Morse, W. H., and Herrnstein, R. J. The maintenance of avoidance behavior using the removal of a conditioned positive reinforcer as the aversive stimulus. *Am. Psychol., 11:* 430, 1956 (abstract).
61. Morse, W. H. and Skinner, B. F. A second type of superstition in the pigeon. *Am. J. Psychol., 70:* 308–311, 1957.
62. Perkins, C. C., Jr., and Cacioppo, A. J. The effect of intermittent reinforcement on the change in extinction rate following successive reconditionings. *J. exper. Psychol., 40:* 794–801, 1950.
63. Polya, G. *Mathematics and Plausible Reasoning.* Vol. I: *Induction and Analogy in Mathematics.* Princeton, N.J.: Princeton University Press, 1954.
64. Schoenfeld, W. N. On the difference in resistance to extinction following regular and periodic reinforcement. *Conference on the experimental analysis of behavior-notes.,* No. 20: (Mimeographed), 1950.
65. Schoenfeld, W. N., Antonitis, J. J., and Bersh, P. J. A preliminary study of training conditions necessary for secondary reinforcement. *J. exper. Psychol., 40:* 40–45, 1950.
66. Schoenfeld, W. N., and Cumming, W. W. Some effects of alternation rate in a time-correlated reinforcement contingency. *Proc. Nat. Acad. Sci., 43:* 349–354, 1957.
67. Schoenfeld, W. N., Cumming, W. W., and Hearst, E. On the classification of reinforcement schedules. *Proc. Nat. Acad. Sci., 42:* 563–570, 1956.
68. Sidman, M. A note on functional relations obtained from group data. *Psychol. Bull., 49:* 263–269, 1952.
69. Sidman, M. Avoidance conditioning with brief shock and no exteroceptive warning signal. *Science, 118:* 157–158, 1953.
70. Sidman, M. Two temporal parameters of the maintenance of avoidance behavior by the white rat. *J. comp. physiol. Psychol., 46:* 253–261, 1953.
71. Sidman, M. Some properties of the warning stimulus in avoidance behavior. *J. comp. physiol. Psychol., 48:* 444–450, 1955.
72. Sidman, M. Time discrimination and behavioral interaction in a free operant situation. *J. comp. physiol. Psychol., 49:* 469–473, 1956.
73. Sidman, M. Conditioned reinforcing and aversive stimuli in an avoidance situation. *Trans. N.Y. Acad. Sci., 19:* 534–544, 1957.
74. Sidman, M. By-products of aversive control. *J. exper. anal. Behav., 1:* 265–280, 1958.
75. Sidman, M. Some notes on "bursts" in free-operant avoidance experiments. *J. exper. anal. Behav., 1:* 167–172, 1958.

76. Sidman, M. Normal sources of pathological behavior, *Science, 132:* 61–68, 1960.
77. Sidman, M. The aversive control of behavior. (In preparation.)
78. Sidman, M., Herrnstein, R. J., and Conrad, D. G. Maintenance of avoidance behavior by unavoidable shocks. *J. comp. physiol. Psychol., 50:* 553–557, 1957.
79. Sidman, M., and Stebbins, W. C. Satiation effects under fixed-ratio schedules of reinforcement. *J. comp. physiol. Psychol., 47:* 114–116, 1954.
80. Skinner, B. F. The generic nature of the concepts of stimulus and response. *J. gen. Psychol., 12:* 40–65, 1935.
81. Skinner, B. F. *The Behavior of Organisms.* New York: Appleton-Century-Crofts, 1938.
82. Skinner, B. F. "Superstition" in the pigeon. *J. exper. Psychol., 38:* 168–172, 1948.
83. Skinner, B. F. Are theories of learning necessary? *Psychol. Rev., 57:* 193–216, 1950.
84. Skinner, B. F. Some contributions of an experimental analysis of behavior to psychology as a whole. *Am. Psychol., 8:* 69–78, 1953.
85. Skinner, B. F. A case history in scientific method. *Am. Psychol., 11:* 221–233, 1956.
86. Skinner, B. F. The experimental analysis of behavior. *Am. Sci., 45:* 343–371, 1957.
87. Skinner, B. F., and Morse, W. H. Sustained performance during very long experimental sessions. *J. exper. anal. Behav., 1:* 235–244, 1958.
88. Spence, K. W. The differential response in animals to stimuli varying within a single dimension. *Psychol. Rev., 44:* 430–444, 1937.
89. Stein, L. (Personal communication.)
90. Stein, L., Sidman, M., and Brady, J. V. Some effects of two temporal variables on conditioned suppression. *J. exper. anal. Behav., 1:* 153–162, 1958.
91. Underwood, B. J. *Experimental Psychology.* New York: Appleton-Century-Crofts, 1949.
92. Warner, L. H. The association span of the white rat. *J. genet. Psychol., 41:* 57–90, 1932.
93. Wickens, D. D., and Miles, R. C. Extinction changes during a series of reinforcement-extinction sessions. *J. comp. physiol. Psychol., 47:* 315–317, 1954.
94. Wilson, M. P., and Keller, F. S. On the selective reinforcement of spaced responding. *J. comp. physiol. Psychol., 46:* 190–193, 1953.

Permissions

The author extends grateful thanks to the following publishers and individuals for permission to quote from the indicated materials:

The American Journal of Psychology: W. H. Morse and B. F. Skinner, "A Second Type of Superstition in the Pigeon," Vol. 70, pp. 308–309, 1957.

American Psychological Association. From *American Psychologist:* L. J. Cronbach, "The Two Disciplines of Scientific Psychology," Vol. 12, p. 672, 1957. From *The Journal of Comparative and Physiological Psychology:* J. V. Brady, J. J. Boren, D. Conrad, and M. Sidman, "The Effect of Food and Water Deprivation Upon Intracranial Self-stimulation," Vol. 50, pp. 134–137, 1957; M. Sidman, "Two Temporal Parameters of the Maintenance of Avoidance Behavior by the White Rat," Vol. 46, pp. 253–261, 1953; M. Sidman, R. J. Herrnstein, and D. G. Conrad, "Maintenance of Avoidance Behavior by Unavoidable Shocks," Vol. 50, pp. 553–557, 1957; M. Sidman and W. C. Stebbins, "Satiation Effects Under Fixed-ratio Schedules of Reinforcement," Vol. 47, pp. 114–116, 1954. From *Journal of Experimental Psychology:* C. B. Ferster, "Sustained Behavior Under Delayed Reinforcement," Vol. 45, pp. 223–224, 1953; B. F. Skinner, "Superstition in the Pigeon," Vol. 38, pp. 168–172, 1948 (reproduced in *Cumulative Record,* Appleton-Century-Crofts, 1959). From *Psychological Review:* B. F. Skinner, "Are Theories of Learning Necessary?" Vol. 57, p. 211, 1950.

Appleton-Century-Crofts, Inc.: C. B. Ferster and B. F. Skinner, *Schedules of Reinforcement,* 1957; C. L. Hull, *Principles of Behavior,* D. Appleton-Century Co., Inc., 1943; F. S. Keller and W. N. Schoenfeld, *Principles of Psychology,* 1950; B. F. Skinner, *The Behavior of Organisms,* D. Appleton-Century Co., Inc., 1938.

Canadian Journal of Psychology: J. J. Boren and M. Sidman, "Maintenance of Avoidance Behavior with Intermittent Shocks," Vol. 11, pp. 185–192, 1957.

R. J. Herrnstein: "Behavioral Consequences of the Removal of a Discriminative Stimulus Associated with Variable Interval Reinforcement," unpublished Ph.D. dissertation, Harvard University, 1955.

Journal of the Experimental Analysis of Behavior: J. D. Findley, "Preference and Switching Under Concurrent Scheduling," Vol. 1, pp. 123–144, 1958; M. Sidman, "Some Notes on 'Bursts' in Free-operant Avoidance Experiments," Vol. 1, pp. 167–172, 1958, "By-products of Aversive Control," Vol. 1, pp. 265–280, 1958.

National Academy of Sciences. From *Proceedings of the National Academy of Sciences:* W. N. Schoenfeld and W. W. Cumming, "Some Effects of Alternation Rate in a Time-correlated Reinforcement Contingency," Vol. 43, p. 352, 1957; W. N. Schoenfeld, W. W. Cumming, and E. Hearst, "On the Classification of Reinforcement Schedules," Vol. 42, p. 567, 1956.

The New York Academy of Sciences. From *Annals of The New York Academy of Sciences:* D. S. Blough, "Technique for Studying the Effects of Drugs on Discrimination in the Pigeon," Vol. 65, pp. 334–344, 1956; P. B. Dews, "Modification by Drugs of Performance on Simple Schedules of Positive Reinforcement," Vol. 65, pp. 268–281, 1956.

Prentice-Hall, Inc.: Harry Harlow, "Primate Learning," in C. P. Stone (Ed.), *Comparative Psychology*, 3rd ed., 1951.

Princeton University Press: G. Polya, *Induction and Analogy in Mathematics*, 1954.

Scientific American: N. Guttman and H. I. Kalish, "Experiments in Discrimination," Vol. 198, pp. 77–82, 1958.

Index

Boldface type indicates that definitions can be found in the Terminological Note.

F

G

H

I

S